NINE ESSAYS

CAMBRIDGE
UNIVERSITY PRESS
LONDON: Fetter Lane

NEW YORK
The Macmillan Co.

BOMBAY, CALCUTTA and MADRAS
Macmillan and Co., Ltd.

TORONTO
The Macmillan Co. of Canada, Ltd.

TOKYO
Maruzen-Kabushiki-Kaisha

ARTHUR PLATT

NINE ESSAYS

by

ARTHUR PLATT

With a Preface by

A. E. HOUSMAN

CAMBRIDGE
AT THE UNIVERSITY PRESS

1927

PRINTED IN GREAT BRITAIN

E & G L Ind

PREFACE

THE author of the papers collected in this volume was one
whose published writings, though they show the rare
quality of his mind, do not portray the range of his studies
and the variety of his accomplishments. Nor do these
papers themselves complete the picture; but they have
been recovered and put together that the world may know
a little more of an uncommonly gifted man who was not
much before its eye, and whose reputation was highest
within the narrower circle which knew him well enough to
admire him rightly.

It is not certain that he would have consented to their
publication, for he must have felt that they bear some
traces of the circumstances which called them forth.
University College London, like many other colleges, is
the abode of a Minotaur. This monster does not devour
youths and maidens: it consists of them, and it preys for
choice on the Professors within its reach. It is called a
Literary Society, and in hopes of deserving the name it
exacts a periodical tribute from those whom it supposes
to be literate. Studious men who might be settling *Hoti*'s
business and properly basing *Oun* are expected to provide
amusing discourses on subjects of which they have no
official knowledge and upon which they may not be entitled
even to open their mouths. Platt, whose temper made him
accessible, whose pen ran easily, and whose mind was richly
stored, paid more of this blackmail than most of his
colleagues, and grudged it less; but the fact is not to be con-

cealed that these unconstrained and even exuberant essays
were written to order. The only one which he allowed to be
printed, and that only in a college magazine, is *Aristophanes*.
Two however have a different origin and were composed
with more deliberation. *Science and Arts among the Ancients*
is an address delivered before the Faculties of Arts and
Science in University College on a ceremonial occasion,
the opening of the Session in October 1899; and the Pre-
lection is one of those read in public by the candidates for
the Cambridge Chair of Greek when it fell vacant in 1921.

John Arthur, eldest of the fourteen children of Thomas
Francis Platt, was born in London on the 11th of July 1860
and died at Bournemouth on the 16th of March 1925. He
was sent to school at Harrow, whence he went up to Cambridge in 1879, winning a scholarship at Trinity College. In
the first part of the Classical Tripos of 1882 he was placed
in the second division of the first class, a position which
may have disappointed himself but did not surprise those
friends who, whenever they went into his rooms, had found
him deep in books which had no bearing on the examination.
In the second part a year later he obtained a first class in
Literature and Criticism and also in Ancient Philosophy.
In 1884, like his father and grandfather before him, he was
elected a Fellow of Trinity. This Fellowship he lost under
the old statutes by his marriage in 1885 with Mildred
Barham, daughter of Sir Edward Bond, K.C.B., sometime
Librarian of the British Museum, and granddaughter of
R. H. Barham, the author of the *Ingoldsby Legends*. Their
children were one son and one daughter. For the next
eight years he taught at the coaching establishment of

Wren and Gurney in Bayswater; in 1894 he was chosen to succeed his friend William Wyse as Professor of Greek in University College London, and soon after took up his residence about a mile away on the edge of Regent's Park. He held his Professorship more than 30 years. In 1921, when Henry Jackson died, he was persuaded to become a candidate for the Chair of Greek at Cambridge, to which few or none of the competitors had a juster claim; but he was relieved when he was not elected, and it is certain that Cambridge would have been less to his taste than London as a place to live in. He would have vacated his office at University College by reason of age in July 1925, but in 1924 he was attacked by illness, and did not live to complete his term.

At the time of his appointment some feared that they were yoking a racehorse to the plough and that his duties might be irksome to him because they could hardly be interesting. Much of the teaching which he was required to give was elementary, and he seldom had pupils who possessed a native aptitude for classical studies or intended to pursue them far. But he proved assiduous, patient, and effective: only an oaf could help learning from him and liking him; and with his best students he formed enduring ties, and would inveigle them into reading Dante or Cervantes with him at his house of an evening after they had taken their degrees. Outside his own class-room he was a centre and fount of the general life of the College, most of all in the Musical Society and among his colleagues in the smoking-room after luncheon. Nearer to his house he made another circle of friends. He was a Fellow of the Zoological Society, frequented its Gardens, and inspired

a romantic passion in their resident population. There was
a leopard which at Platt's approach would almost ooze
through the bars of its cage to establish contact with the
beloved object; the gnu, if it saw him on the opposite side
of its broad enclosure, would walk all the way across to
have its forelock pulled; and a credible witness reports
the following scene.

I remember going to the giraffe-house and seeing a
crowd of children watching a man who had removed his
hat while the giraffe, its neck stretched to the fullest
capacity, was rubbing its head backwards and forwards
upon the bald crown. When the object of this somewhat
embarrassing affection turned his head, Platt's features
were revealed.

In youth he had poetical ambitions, and his first book
was a volume of verse; a smaller one on a personal theme
was printed privately, and so was a collection, made after
his death, of sonnets, very personal indeed, with which
he had entertained and striven to ameliorate his colleagues.
He early produced recensions of the *Odyssey* and the *Iliad*,
in which it was his aim to restore, so far as might be, the
original language of the poet or poets, and thus to pursue
further that special line of Homeric study which began
with Bentley and his digamma, engaged the acute but
undisciplined minds of Payne Knight and Brandreth, and
has left as memorials of its progress the editions of Bekker
and of Nauck. Nothing could be more different, or could
better display his versatility, than his other chief work,
the translation of Aristotle's *De generatione animalium* with
its multifarious notes on matters zoological. A slighter
performance was a free rendering of the *Agamemnon* of
Aeschylus into the prose of King James's Bible.

Among the Greek scholars of his country Platt belonged
to that company of explorers whose leading figures, after
the universal genius of Bentley, are Dawes, Porson, and
Elmsley. Minute and refined observation for the ascertain-
ment of grammatical and metrical usage was his chosen
province; and his early investigations of Homeric practice
were his most characteristic work, and probably surpass
in value his later and more various contributions to interpretation and textual criticism. Metrical science, upon the
death of Elmsley, had deserted its native isle and taken
flight to the Continent: Platt was one of the very few
Englishmen who in the last hundred years have advanced
the study, and among those few he was the foremost. In
conjectural emendation, like Dawes and Elmsley, he was
shrewd and dexterous enough, but not, like Bentley and
Porson, eminent. In literary comment he did not ex-
patiate, although, or rather because, he was the most
lettered scholar of his time. He stuck to business, as a
scholar should, and preferred, as a man of letters will, the
dry to the watery. He knew better than to conceive himself that rarest of all the great works of God, a literary
critic; but such remarks on literature as he did let fall
were very different stuff from the usual flummery of the
cobbler who is ambitious to go beyond his last.

If his contemporaries rated him, both comparatively
and absolutely, below his true position in the world of
learning, the loss was chiefly theirs, but the blame was
partly his. He had much of the boy in his composition,
and something even of the schoolboy. His conversation
in mixed company was apt to be flighty, and his writing,
though it was not so, carried jauntiness of manner to some

little excess. Those who judge weight by heaviness were
perplexed and deceived by a colloquial gaiety, much less
unseemly indeed than the frolic sallies of Dawes, but
striking more sharply on the sense because not draped like
them in the Latin toga; and it was disturbing to meet with
a scholar who carried his levity, where others carry their
gravity, on the surface, and was austere, where he might
without offence or detection have been frivolous, in con-
ducting the operations of his mind.

That he wrote little was the direct and natural consequence of his extraordinary capacity and the variety of
his interests and attainments. He would rather improve
himself than instruct others. He wrote on subjects where
he could make definite and original contributions to the
advancement of learning: otherwise he preferred to read.
Greek was his trade, but the home in which he dwelt was
great literature, whether its language were Greek, Latin,
English, French, Italian, Spanish, German, or Persian.
The best authors were his study, but his reading ran far
beyond them; his curiosity invaded holes and corners, and
his taste ranged from the *Divine Comedy* to *Jorrocks's
Jaunts*. He followed his inclinations and read for his own
delight, with a keen and natural relish, not a dutiful and
obedient admiration of the things which are admired by
the wise and good. Nor were his studies warped and
narrowed by ambition. A scholar who means to build himself a monument must spend much of his life in acquiring
knowledge which for its own sake is not worth having and
in reading books which do not in themselves deserve to be
read; *at illa iacent multa et praeclara relicta.*

Music was a rival of literature in his affections, and his

knowledge of the art and its history was almost an expert's. He followed with interest and understanding the progress of discovery in the natural sciences, and his acquaintance with zoology in particular was such as few laymen can boast. In conclusion it is proper to mention his vices. He was addicted to tobacco and indifferent to wine, and he would squander long summer days on watching the game of cricket.

His happy and useful life is over, and now begins the steady encroachment of oblivion, as those who remember him are in their turn summoned away. This record will not preserve, perhaps none could preserve, more than an indistinct and lifeless image of the friend who is lost to us: good, kind, bright, unselfish, and as honest as the day; versatile without shallowness, accomplished without ostentation, a treasury of hidden knowledge which only accident brought to light, but which accident brought to light perpetually, and which astonished us so often that astonishment lost its nature and we should have wondered more if wonders had failed. Yet what most eludes description is not the excellence of his gifts but the singularity of his essential being, his utter unlikeness to any other creature in the world.

A. E. HOUSMAN

CONTENTS

Frontispiece
ARTHUR PLATT

Theognidea. *C.R.* xxvi, 73.
Thucydidea. *J.P.* xxxiii, 270.
Thucydides, ii, 48. *C.R.* xxxiii, 63.
Virgil, Aen. vi, 567 and iii, 702. *C.R.* v, 337.
On a Virgilian idiom. *J.P.* xxiv, 46.
Xenophon, Oeconomicus. *C.R.* x, 382.
Emendations of Xenophon's Hellenica. *C.R.* xxxv, 100.
On Oxy. pap. vol. ii. *C.R.* xiii, 439, xiv, 18.
ἐγώ. *C.R.* x, 381.
On τε etc. with vocatives. *C.R.* xxiii, 105.
On the iambic trimeter. *J.P.* xviii, 161, xix, 146.
On the Indian dog. *C.Q.* iii, 241.
The Lyrceian water. *C.Q.* x, 83.
Split totems. *C.R.* v, 339.
Rendering into Greek elegiacs. *C.R.* xi, 70.

Reviews in *C.R.*:

Van Leeuwen and Da Costa's Iliad. ii, 174.
Edwards' Iliad, xxiii. v, 476.
Van Leeuwen and Da Costa's Odyssey. vii, 31.
Butler's Trapanese origin of the Odyssey. vii, 254.
Lang's Homer and the Epic. vii, 318.
Van Leeuwen's Enchiridium. vii, 359.
Butler on the Odyssey. ix, 56.
Way's translation of the Odyssey. xx, 60.
Herkenrath's Der Enoplios. xxi, 155.
Walker's Ἀντὶ μιᾶς. xxv, 16.
Meillet's Origines indo-européennes des mètres grecs.
    xxxviii, 20.

SCIENCE AND ARTS AMONG THE ANCIENTS

*(Opening of Session of the Faculties of Arts
and Science in University College,
London, October 1899)*

Science and Arts among the Ancients

In addressing the Faculties of arts and sciences a person who is not even supposed to know anything but Greek cannot, as it seems to me, do much better than by giving a sketch of the relative position of arts and sciences among the Greeks, as regards their education. To discuss that question at all completely would be a matter of much time and would require an immense amount of explanation. A mere definition of the words arts and sciences as understood by the Greeks would occupy all the time available to-day. Still one may contemplate the lines of a mountain from a distance, and draw the simple outline on a sheet of paper with some profit, though knowing that on a nearer view those lines would assume different forms, be broken up into ravines and projections, and sometimes even run into one another without the sharp boundaries which appear from afar off. All sorts of qualifications and innumerable links of transition must be simply omitted by me.

Some years ago the representatives of science, waking up after a long period during which they had been ignored in education altogether, made very startling demands. They said that science was the one thing needful, that arts had had an unconscionably long innings and it was time they declared[1], that everybody ought in childhood to learn exactly what happens when a wax candle is burnt, because it was more useful than learning the accentuation of the genitive plural of παῖς. The representatives of arts and what

[1] Terms borrowed from the game of cricket.

is called a liberal education were equally fierce on their side—they said they had no notion of declaring before they were all given out, and in particular Matthew Arnold said that the chemistry of a candle and the accentuation of παίδων were both facts of equal value for education, but he would like to know what science could put in the place of literature. The noise of that controversy has, I think, pretty well died away—both parties have cooled down— Science in particular has largely withdrawn her claims to anything like an exclusive education—and the teaching thereof in public schools remains a farce—both sides recognise that they have no business to dictate to everybody, that what is one man's meat is another man's poison, and on the whole you *must* let people follow their own bent. In fact the question is really between two types of mind, into which the human race naturally divides itself—the artistic and imaginative and poetic which wants to enjoy, the scientific and analytic which wants to know. It is easy to call both bad names, but it is better not. In this College at any rate they dwell in perfect peace, and their language is unimpeachable.

The conflict, as I have said, is really one between two types of mind—only secondarily between different subjects. If we all had the same type of mind, the conflict of subjects would vanish. The history therefore of the conflict in ancient times is concerned *apparently*, but only *apparently*, with different matter from that with which it has been concerned in recent times. It assumes at first the form of a battle between poetry and philosophy. Later on philosophy splits into two main parts, science and what we now call philosophy in a more restricted sense, or mental and moral science and logic. This latter branch, what we now call philosophy, has got ranged on the side of arts somehow —and indeed philosophy proper is a somewhat ambiguous kind of creature, a species of *Volvox*, and stands somewhat between the two, the prey of both. As for mathematics, though they may now be included in an arts course, they are obviously purely scientific in reality, but as Aristotle has invented logic as an alternative for them we may look upon them from a distance with great respect and say no more about them.

Faculties can exist only in Universities, Colleges or some bodies of that kind which undertake to educate people, not Correspondence Colleges nor Imperial Institutes. The Greeks can hardly be said to have possessed anything which could be called a College, though the philosophical schools of Plato and Aristotle and others approximate thereto. And our third Faculty of Medicine was never brought into any connexion with the other subjects by them.

The Faculty of Medicine, indeed, has *always*, so to say, dwelt on the other side of the street[1]. In primitive times no doubt there was no such thing—I have sometimes speculated whether that is why Methuselah lived so long. Herodotus informs us that in Babylon if anyone was ill he was taken out and laid on the ground or propped against the wall in front of his house, and everyone who passed that way stopped to ask what ailed him and recommended him anything that he thought useful. How long any sick man ever survived this course is a question which Herodotus

[1] University College and its Hospital are on opposite sides of Gower Street.

does not raise. Nor does he state that anyone ever went back into his house.

In Homer also we are told that a physician is better than any other man at cutting out arrows and applying healing herbs. He is only *better*, but there is as yet no separate Faculty. But in Greece, at any rate in very early times, physicians wrote great text-books and killed men according to rule, and already by the time of Plato and even earlier the philosophers had marked off this profession as the only one with which they would not meddle. It is possible they did not know when a doctor might not be called in to them. The encyclopaedic Aristotle left them to themselves, and I believe that even Mr Herbert Spencer has done the same. Leaving this then aside, the first germs of the division of knowledge and education into two Faculties of arts and science appear at the time of the great awakening of thought in the fifth century before Christ, 2400 years before this lecture. The antithesis began between two classes of men who typified the two great aspects of the human mind, the creative or imaginative or artistic on the one hand, the inquiring or understanding or scientific on the other. The poets were the voice of the former, the philosophers of the latter. Philosophy in those days did not mean what it does now: to put it briefly it included all literature or written matter which was not art or history, and an enormous quantity of talk; but it also included rhetoric, which is generally counted to be an art. The name applied to the first philosophers was "sophist," a word of no bad signification at first—it meant simply a man who was notable for wisdom or learning, a man who, like Browning's Grammarian, decided not to live but know, not to enjoy but to think and analyse. Professor Ker told you a story in his Oration last Foundation Day about a certain unprincipled person who being asked what the sophists were like referred the inquirer to the Professors of University College. I have always thought myself that this was rather hard on the sophists, who were after all a body of very remarkable men. However that may be, at first the philosophers devoted their energies simply to speculating about natural sciences. They had no method for the most part—they simply sate down and made guesses, some good, some bad, a pleasant but ineffectual method of advancing human knowledge, still popular I understand among candidates. Then they began to turn their attention to the life of men; they taught rhetoric, they taught virtue, they examined and criticised the current ideas of mankind, and among other things they came across poetry.

Up till that time the poets had had everything their own way, they were monarchs of all they surveyed and their right there was none to dispute. The inspired verses of Homer were regarded as a Bible, appealed to as a final and sovereign settlement of every question. By a verse from Homer Solon is said to have disposed of an awkward political difficulty, just as the President of the Transvaal even now confounds Mr Chamberlain by a quotation from Isaiah or the Psalms—in Dutch.

In education also the poets were supreme. In those blessed days, a true age of gold, a young man was expected to learn nothing but what young women used to learn in England until recently. I have heard distinguished scholars wish that they had lived in those days. Music and poetry along with reading, writing and arithmetic—a *very* little arithmetic—these formed the whole intellectual education of the men who fought at Marathon and Salamis, who built the Parthenon and wrote the *Agamemnon*. Music and poetry always went hand in hand, and it is now quite impossible for us to understand the value the Greeks set upon music. To them it was not a mere amusement but the most powerful agent, or one of the most powerful, for forming character. It was of an excessively simple character, as we should now think; harmony in our sense of the word was unknown, counterpoint could still less be expected, and the instruments used were principally occupied with supporting the voice. Yet the effect wrought upon them by it was far beyond anything which we can now comprehend. Nothing perhaps can better make us realise the importance of music on moral training among them than a very remarkable passage of Polybius. Perhaps you will excuse my reading it to you in an English translation.

"Music," he says, "and I mean by that *true* music, which it is advantageous to everyone to practise, is obligatory with the Arcadians. Everyone is familiarly acquainted with the fact that the Arcadians are the only people among whom boys are by the law trained from infancy to sing hymns (and paeans), in which they celebrate the heroes and gods. They next learn the airs of Philoxenus and Timotheus, and dance with great spirit to the pipes at their festivals. Similarly it is their custom, at all festal gatherings, not to have strangers to make the music but to produce it themselves, calling on each other in turn for a song.... Their object in introducing these customs was not the gratification of luxury and extravagance. They saw that Arcadia was a nation of workers, that the life of the people was laborious and hard, and that in consequence of the coldness and gloom which were the prevailing features of a great part of the country the general character of the

people was austere. And it was with a view to softening
and tempering this natural ruggedness and rusticity that
they not only introduced the things I have mentioned, but
also the custom of holding assemblies and offering sacrifices
in both of which women took part equally with men, and
having mixed dances of girls and boys, and in fact did
everything they could to humanise their souls by the
civilising and softening influence of such culture.

"But the people of Cynaetha entirely neglected these
things, though they needed them far more than anybody
else, because their climate and country is by far the most
unfavourable in all Arcadia. They on the contrary gave
their whole minds to *mutual animosities and contentions*.
They in consequence became finally so brutalised, that no
Greek city has ever witnessed a longer series of the most
atrocious crimes.

"I have had three objects," concludes the historian, "in
saying thus much on this subject. First that the character
of the Arcadians should not suffer from the crimes of one
city. Secondly that other nations should not neglect music.
Lastly I speak for the sake of the Cynaethans themselves,
in order that, if God gives them better fortune, they may
humanise themselves by turning their attention to education and especially to music."

So far Polybius.

When I consider the coldness and gloom of the metro-
polis, and the melancholy results which followed upon the
Cynaethans' neglect of music, I feel inclined to hope that
the practice of pianoforte playing may not entirely be
dropped by *both* sexes in favour of the "mutual animosities
and contentions" of the fierce struggle for a University
degree. Heaven only knows how dreadful the results may
be. Perhaps there may be one or two among my hearers
who will be warned in time.

The decline and fall of music is indeed one of the most

remarkable phenomena in the history of education. It is a symptom of a great change, not entirely for the better. The reason why music was valued by the Greeks was its moral influence. *We* have made education purely intellectual and leave moral influence to come in how and where it can manage it. Briefly, all education began by being *moral*—and it has ended by becoming all intellectual. Hence when music is recognised at all by Universities and similar institutions (unless it is a mere accomplishment) it is studied as a branch of mathematics and nothing else. One is expected to know about thorough bass and the chord of the thirteenth and so on—as a part of general education it holds no place, and the practice of it is contemptuously relegated to the realms of deportment and dancing.

Aristotle himself, while considering music a most important branch of education in youth, actually forbade the practice of it in later life—he declares that "no well-bred gentleman ever sings or plays unless it be over his wine or for a jest." But the consideration of the ethics of music in advanced life must be left to my amiable colleague Professor Roberts[1]. It is time to go back to the fifth century before Christ.

Homer was backed up in a more philosophical style by a number of poets who wrote doubtful ethics in verse, chief among whom were Simonides and Pindar. These bards were quite happy to hitch the ordinary ethical ideas of the period into verses, to make with an air of profound thought generalisations not unworthy of Mr Tupper, and to contradict themselves and one another with the careless felicity

[1] Who had a fine voice, and was always called upon for a song after a College dinner.

of didactic poets or occasionally with the acrimonious politenesses of modern philosophers. But nobody at first cared to ask exactly how their various maxims were expected to square with the rude possibilities of actual life or even the airy fabric of a complete system. If one of them said "Money, money makes the man," and another said virtue alone can make one happy and keep him so— if a third extolled knowledge or genius—the public were quite content to quote them all indifferently as all of them equally infallible—they were poets—servants and prophets of the sacred muse—they *must* know all about it like Mr Kipling. To criticise them was as if one were to criticise the papers on general science set in the Matriculation Examination.

Great was the outcry, as may be well supposed, when the daring and impious sophist laid his hand upon the ark. Heraclitus of Ephesus, a man of unquestionable sagacity and depth of mind, and one of the proudest and haughtiest of men, declared that Homer ought to be flogged out of Greece. Such blasphemy must have struck the rest of the world with something of the same horror as Voltaire's *Écrasez l'Infâme* struck Catholics of France in the last century. Plato followed up the attack by another of a very elaborate kind. His assault was made from two distinct points of view, the one ethical and the other metaphysical. The stories told by Homer about the gods are immoral and disgusting, he said; therefore they cannot be true, because the gods are good. But if we should grant for the sake of argument that they were true, they ought even then to be buried in silence, the minds of the young especially should not be contaminated by such doctrines and by such examples, just as the University of London cannot allow Lamb's *Specimens of the Dramatic Poets* to be set for a B.A. In a well-regulated state therefore the poems of Homer will not be admitted at all; we shall confess his greatness as a poet, and it will be with the deepest regret—but—we shall inexorably exclude him from our gates. Moreover all poetry and all art of every kind is, when looked upon from a metaphysician's point of view, essentially a thing of a low and inferior kind. This world is a fleeting show, it is full of error and deception, a sea of perpetual change whose billows are never constant—if we desire *truth* we must rise entirely above it into a region of philosophic abstraction and pure thought, where there is no change, no storms, but truth abides unchanging—and one would think just a little dull. The phenomena of *this* world are but a bad imitation of the world of truth. But what does the artist do? He comes and imitates the things we see about us—the people we know in this life—his art is an imitation of an imitation and thereby is at once degraded. (I say nothing of the value of this argument.) How strange then it is to find the poets giving themselves such airs! How strange to find them talking as the lawgivers of mankind, posing as men who are somehow of a superior rank to ordinary mortals!

Plato himself speaks of the quarrel as one of long standing. If the philosophers proved by ethic, metaphysic and logic that the poets were no great matter after all, the poets retorted in their own way. They have always been noted for vanity and irritability, they are *not* noted for logic, and their method of defence is apt to degenerate into abuse and sarcasm and reiteration of their superior claims. They made sarcastic observations on the "rabble of over-clever heads," they wrote comedies on the philosophers and their ideal states and raised inextinguishable laughter at their expense—nay, they go on doing it still. Tennyson entreats other people not to vex the poet's mind with their shallow wit and assures them they will never be able to fathom *him,* and after over 2000 years Mr Swinburne takes up the cudgels for Aristophanes against Plato and defends the poet in language which really cannot be here repeated.

Education however has always remained in the hands not of poets but of—pedants and.... It was not Aristophanes but Plato who drew up the first scheme for a University course, and, as may be well supposed, the arts did not make much of a figure in it. Poetry was confined to the service of the gods—Sternhold and Hopkins were to replace Homer.

Music too was to have her wings clipped—all further progress was forbidden. Only certain kinds of music were to be allowed and those only the simpler and more archaic. One may illustrate his proposed legislation in this matter by supposing ourselves to be now forbidden to play any music except in the keys of A minor and C major, or to perform any work composed since 1759—I sometimes wish we were.

Philosophy in Plato's scheme was the final subject to which everything else was subordinate, and (as was natural considering his contempt for this world) he really makes education the preparation for another and a better life. Sciences, so far as he condescends to recognise them at all, are nothing but a preparation for philosophy and are destined to withdraw our thoughts from the transitory to the eternal. This being so it naturally followed that he took serious objection to the sciences as studied in his own

In Plato everything, to use a chemical metaphor, is held in solution; by his greatest pupil and antagonist all the different elements were precipitated. What had formerly jostled together and interfered with one another, were now separated apart. A great deal of Aristotle's activity in ethics, politics, metaphysics, consisted in little but sifting and arranging what is to be found already in Plato. He had the genius of pigeon-holing, and he carries out the process remorselessly. At the same time he added much of his own, and especially he corrected or cut down the errors and superfluities into which Plato's luxuriant imagination had led him, and he created logic. Thus philosophy, as we now understand it, in him becomes an ordered system and a very dry one, but he can in no way be considered its creator except in logic—but the other part of philosophy as then understood, that is to say, aesthetics and the sciences apart from mathematics, were absolutely created by him.

Before speaking of Aristotle's achievements in this connexion one must make a distinction to be carefully kept in view. Aristotle may be reasonably taken to be the true patron of all University education in this respect—the Master of those who know, as Dante calls him—that he first disentangled and made plain the relative value of the sciences, art and philosophy. But he did not claim that all these should be represented in the actual education of the young—or of anybody. It is a great misfortune that most of his scheme of education is lost—perhaps it was never entirely completed. But we know enough of it to know that it was very like that of Plato in many ways. He was even stricter than Plato in his regulations about the sort of music which the young should study. He does not appear to have gone very much further in the allowance of poetry which he doled out. What he would have proposed about science and philosophy we simply do not know. A general education to be applied to all his free citizens was in fact still a comparatively small affair, and the notion of anything resembling a modern University never entered his head.

If he had resembled modern writers on the subject, he would have insisted that whatever interested *him* personally should be crammed down the throat of everybody else. But he was far from saying any such thing. And indeed when a man is interested, as *he* was, in every conceivable branch of knowledge, he is naturally preserved from such a desire. Of course, however, he never could, any more than any reasonable man, have contemplated any sort of education without Greek.

Nevertheless one may well admire in him that feature also, that in laying down a scheme of education he was absolutely devoid of any partiality or predilection for his own pursuits. Here again he went far beyond Plato—far beyond any other educationist with whom I am acquainted.

Secondly if he and Plato were practically agreed about education for the young, for people up to about eighteen or twenty, they differ *toto caelo* about what studies may be pursued in more advanced years. Plato, being first and foremost a metaphysician with a sort of religious system, would not have us study anything but metaphysics and a kind of mystic religion. But Aristotle, though his statements if he ever made any on this point are lost, plainly had no narrow views of that sort. He spent his life in research and teaching in almost every realm of knowledge then open, or then first conquered by him. He carried on, we may say, all by himself the whole business of both the Faculties of arts and science, creating many of his own subjects. Compared with him indeed what are any of us?

ἐπάμεροι· τί δέ τις; τί δ' οὔτις;

He was the greatest teacher and researcher of his time in aesthetics, ethics, logic, psychology, metaphysics, rhetoric, political science, political economy, constitutional history, theology, botany, zoology, embryology, anatomy, physiology, physics—I hope I have omitted none but am by no means sure—and in several of these his is the greatest name on record. Certainly here we have our two Faculties pretty well represented. The worst of it was that when he died no Committee under Heaven could have elected a Professor to succeed him.

To discuss Aristotle's scientific greatness in the very flimsiest manner, to narrate his achievements and estimate his position in science, would require a whole series of lectures—and it may be added that it would require somebody who knew something about it to deliver them. I must here content myself with quoting a testimony or two from those who are competent to speak. The late Dr Romanes, after reviewing Aristotle's work on biology, declares at the end that considered simply as a scientific man, to say nothing of his other writings, Aristotle is the greatest intellect the world has ever seen. When Ogle sent to Darwin his translation of Aristotle *On the Parts of Animals*, Darwin replied in these words in the course of his letter of acknowledgment:

From quotations which I had seen, I had a high notion

of Aristotle's merits, but I had not the most remote notion what a wonderful man he was. Linnaeus and Cuvier have been my two gods, though in very different ways, but they were mere schoolboys to old Aristotle.

George Henry Lewes wrote a book upon Aristotle, with the express purpose of denying and running down his scientific work. Martin Luther was fond of talking about devils and a great authority upon them (we all know how he once threw a bottle of ink) and he ought to know, if anybody ought to know, and *he* said that Aristotle was unquestionably a devil of the most malignant type; something of the same spirit animates Lewes' amiable book. Yet when he comes to the treatise *On the Generation of Animals*, by which embryology was founded, Lewes himself is melted, his hard heart is like the rock struck by Moses and gushes forth thus:

It is an extraordinary production. No ancient and few modern books equal it in comprehensiveness of detail and profound speculative insight. We there find some of the obscurest problems of Biology treated with a mastery which, when we consider the condition of science at that day, is truly astounding.... I should not be candid were I to conceal the impression which the study of this work left on my mind, that the labours of the last two centuries have furnished the data to confirm many of the views of this prescient genius. Indeed I know no better eulogy to pass on Aristotle than to compare his work with the *Exercitations Concerning Generation* of our immortal Harvey. The founder of modern physiology was a man of keen insight, of patient research, of eminently scientific mind. His work is superior to that of Aristotle in some few anatomical details; but *it is so inferior to it in philosophy that at the present day it is much more antiquated, much less accordant with our views.*

That is pretty well, I think, for a hostile witness.

Such is the position Aristotle holds in science, and the Faculty of science should inscribe his name in letters of gold over their doors—what then did *he* think of the Faculty of arts? Did he, like his master, reject art and poetry and cast it forth into outer darkness? On the contrary, he appears as mediator between the two. Even as he stripped philosophy and science of the poetic glamour with which Plato had clothed them, and thereby put them into the right track, so he also stripped poetry of the false claims put forward by her admirers and cut away the ground of the objections taken by her opponents. It is not the business of poetry, he proclaimed, to teach ethics or politics. It is not the business of her critics to examine Homer's morality; let them neither exalt it into a rule of life, nor imagine it to be mischievous, for rightly understood it is neither the one nor the other. Poetry is concerned with the emotions, philosophy and science with the intellect. Both are needed to cultivate fully the double nature of man.

His treatise on poetry is the first and to this day the greatest on the subject. Dry indeed it is, but yet what else can such a work be? It is not the business of education to be amusing. Lessing declared it to be as infallible as Euclid, and Euclid seldom smiles.

Aristotle says himself: "Education ought certainly not to be turned into a means of amusement; for young people are not playing when they are learning, since all learning is accompanied with pain."

The study of literature, if it is to be of any good to us, must be serious. Reading *bad* novels is a pursuit precisely on a level with fancy needlework—both serve to fill up time—novels indeed have one advantage, they cannot be hung upon the backs of chairs. Since Aristotle's time the study of literature, considered as *mental* education and not only moral, has become of vastly more importance—it has become the study of foreign languages, dead or alive. It has itself become to a certain extent a sort of science, and it is in a scientific way that it must be treated in Colleges and Universities.

So science has gradually laid her hands upon everything, as far as teaching goes, and it was Aristotle who really began the process. It was he who made philosophy scientific by the introduction of a strict logic, and it was he who made the arts scientific by applying as scientific a method as possible to poetry. Education began by being nothing but art—Plato rejected art almost altogether and wanted to substitute a fanciful philosophy—Aristotle brought back art but made the treatment of it scientific.

The Middle Ages indeed reverted without knowing it to Platonism to a large extent. They thought themselves Aristotelians, but their new Faculty of Theology, the only important one with them, was the recrudescence in another form of the spirit of Platonic philosophy oddly bound and fettered by Aristotelian logic. Science could not move an inch, and arts were made the handmaid of the dominant theology. But with the great reformation of thought which made a new world in the sixteenth century the Aristotelian principles again got the upper hand in time. Yet the great revolt against the Middle Ages, which includes Protestantism and the Renaissance of Art and Science everywhere, made a dead set against Aristotle. His thought and doctrine held such sway over the mind of the whole world of Christendom that when it struggled to get out of its prison it thought Aristotle was its jailor. As Luther reckoned *him* along with the Pope to be the great enemy of religion and denounced him in that sweet language characteristic of him, so Galileo and Bacon took him for the great enemy of science! The foolish people whom Galileo had to vanquish were the blind followers of Aristotle, which is a very different story. Galileo was once present when a Venetian anatomist demonstrated that the origin of the nerves was the brain and not the heart and then asked an Aristotelian what he had to say. The philosopher after a pause replied: "You have made this appear so openly to my senses that I must needs confess it to be true *if it were not opposed by the text of Aristotle*, which says distinctly that the nerves spring from the heart." (As a matter of fact Aristotle never did say anything of the kind—but that is what comes of neglecting Greek.) But after these blind followers had been disposed of, the more that every branch of knowledge has advanced, the more has Aristotle been regarded as truly great and the more deeply has he been studied.

The great danger indeed of arts in Universities is nowadays that they are likely to be *too* scientific. The mere teaching of languages especially, continually tends to devour the enjoyment of them. It is pitiable to see people engaged in learning one grammar after another and cramming one set of idioms after another, and leaving the masterpieces of literature, to which these are the keys, unentered and untrod. A German philologist, being asked at the end of his life what he saw in Homer, answered scornfully *Roots*. And in truth philology is the curse of all our modern teaching of languages. The student of languages who neglects the literature is like the man Bunyan saw in the *Pilgrim's Progress*, occupied with a muck-rake, toiling in the dirt while all heaven opened its beauties above him and he saw them not. The wisest of the moderns bids us live in the Whole, the True, the Beautiful. The natural man is too prone to seek only the Beautiful, education is too prone to make us seek only the True in too limited a sense; let all so far as in us lies seek the Whole.

But a verse of Wordsworth even now occurs to me:

Enough of science and of art—
               close up these barren leaves.

EDWARD FITZGERALD

(Literary Society, University College, 1896)

Edward FitzGerald

Mr President, Ladies and Gentlemen,

When I was enticed into promising to read a paper before this learned Society, I pondered a good deal the question what subject or author to bring before you. And I concluded that if I could bring some of you acquainted with an author you might not know and who was very much worth knowing, I should be doing a greater service to you than by any amount of talking about people you know already.

No author seemed to me so fit for the purpose from this point of view as Edward FitzGerald. Though his great work has been before the world nearly forty years, and though he numbers more admirers every year, he is yet not generally known in the way that Tennyson, and Browning, and Swinburne are. At least, I think not. There is no reasonably cheap edition of him to be had, which is at once proof of this, and partly the cause of it, and several persons of my acquaintance have enrolled themselves my debtors for life for introducing him to them.

FitzGerald was born in 1809—an easy date to remember, for nearly everybody was born in 1809—I need only mention Tennyson and Darwin. His great work was published in 1859, the year of the *Origin of Species*. He died in 1883. Really, that is about all that anyone need want to know about his life until they know the man, and then they may want to know everything—*everything*. For the greater part of those seventy-four years he lived like

a recluse in Suffolk, on the coast of the North Sea, dreaming
his life away among dreams and shadows, except for his
love of sailing—in *that* he was a true Briton. All the summer
he used to be sailing about the east coast. Once he even
went as far as Holland—to see Paul Potter's *Bull*, said
a story about him, but, finding a fair wind back to England
when he got there, he thought it a pity to lose it, and
promptly sailed back without seeing Paul Potter or anything else. For the fishermen and sailors he had a great
affection—in particular for one of them whom he made
captain of his crew, and whom he called by the euphonious
title of *Posh*. His real name is unrecorded. This Posh, said
he, is one of the three greatest *Men* I have known—the
other two being Tennyson and Thackeray—and Posh was
superior to *them* in being less self-conscious. His morality,
he says again, was that of Carlyle's heroes, the Norse sea-
kings and people, not ours but different, and none the
worse for that. Unluckily, one feature of Posh's morality
was an ill-regulated thirst, and, after many remonstrances
and broken vows, FitzGerald had to part company with
him.

But it is not with the yachtsman but with the dreamer
of dreams that we have to do here. For he dreamed *one*
dream that is more lasting than we ourselves, or he, or the
roses he planted, or the very Suffolk coast he lived on,
which the sea is devouring by square miles every winter.
Let us come to his great work. O, do not be afraid, I am
not going to
inflict again
More books of blank upon the sons of men.
It is not an epic nor an essay on the character of Hamlet—

it is just 404 lines long, and very likely some of you know
it all by heart already. And not only is it lamentably short,
but it is only a translation. Yes, but what a translation!
"a planet equal to the sun which cast it," says Tennyson
of it.

There was born in Persia, in the latter half of the
eleventh century, a certain Omar. He was a great man
among the Persians, famous for learning, especially astro-
nomy, and poetry and heterodoxy. He was one of the
eight wise men who reformed the calendar, he was author
of astronomical tables, and of a treatise on the extraction
of cubic roots, and another on algebra, which he wrote in
Arabic, as if it was not bad enough without. Probably no
other man ever made the rebellious muse of mathematics
(mad Mathesis, as Pope calls her) run so well in harness
with her sister of verse. His poems consist simply of
quatrains, little epigrams of four lines long a-piece; they
are arranged in alphabetical order, and to read them in the
original must be almost as festive as reading through a
dictionary. Their subjects are—he was a Persian, and so,
of course, his subjects are "praise of love and wine," and
speculation in religious metaphysics. That is what *all* Persian
poetry is, at least all the poetry of the great Persian poets,
as far as I know, with one great exception. The passion
of that nation for the nebulous, hazy region, which is not
exactly philosophy because it is not logical, nor exactly
religion because it is not practical, nor ethics because it is
not dull—this passion of theirs, I say, is truly remarkable.
Read Mr E. G. Browne's *A Year amongst the Persians*, and
you will find them still at it to this day—they will not talk
of anything else. They look at this world through a rosy

haze of mysticism, in which all things flow into one another
and nothing is plain, in which everything is a symbol of
something else, and, in the end, all things are absorbed in
the Divinity. More especially is it the great end of man to
get rid of his own individuality, and be mystically united
with God. This world is a mere illusion and a miserable
fraud—we must get rid of all desire, all passion, we must
remorselessly crush our own individuality—just as with the
Buddhists on the East and Stoics on the West. For until
we lose ourselves and *become* God, we cannot find ourselves.
This theory is most beautifully illustrated by a saying of
Jelaluddin: "One came to the Beloved's door (i.e. God),
and knocked. And a voice from within said: 'Who is there?'
And he said, 'It is I.' Then the voice said: 'This House will
not hold Me and Thee'; and the door was not opened unto
him. And the lover (the soul of man) departed into the
wilderness, and fasted and prayed in solitude. And after
a year he came again to the Beloved's door, and knocked.
And a voice from within said: 'Who is there?' and he said,
'It is THYSELF.' And the door was opened unto him."

Such is the region in which the Persian mind loves to
dwell, such the order of ideas amid which Omar grew up.
But there *he* could not stay. As he says himself:

> Myself when young did eagerly frequent
> Doctor and Saint, and heard great argument
> About it and about; but evermore
> Came out by the same door where in I went.
>
> With them the seed of Wisdom did I sow,
> And with mine own hand wrought to make it grow;
> And this was all the Harvest that I reaped—
> "I came like Water, and like Wind I go."

And he goes on, alluding to his astronomical studies:

Up from Earth's Centre, through the Seventh Gate,
I rose, and on the Throne of Saturn sate,
    And many a Knot unravelled by the Road,
But not the Master-knot of Human Fate.

There was the Door to which I found no Key,
There was the Veil through which I might not see:
    Some little talk awhile of ME and THEE,
There was—and then no more of THEE and ME.

So, failing to find any world but this, and any providence
but destiny, he set about making the best of this world—
in fact, he is not a romantic Stoic masquerading in a
peacock's plumage, like his poetic brethren, but an Epicurean. The way in which he enforces the Epicurean view
is, of course, principally by praising wine; for he is a
Persian poet and a Mohammedan, to whom wine is
forbidden by his religion. So it adds a piquancy to it,
because it is naughty as well as nice. And, of course,
the orthodox looked upon him with horror, though he
was protected by the Sultan. So he says:

Indeed, the Idols I have loved so long
Have done my credit in this World much wrong;
    Have drowned my Glory in a shallow Cup,
And sold my Reputation for a Song.

Indeed, indeed, Repentance oft before,
I swore—but was I sober when I swore?
    And then and then came Spring, and Rose-in-hand
My threadbare Penitence apieces tore.

And much as Wine has played the Infidel,
And robbed me of my Robe of Honour—well,
    I wonder often what the Vintners buy
One half so precious as the stuff they sell.

And, in particular, he rebels against the doctrine of self-denial, which was universally preached by the Sufis, and which was inculcated in respect to wine by the Mohammedan religion—so wine with Omar is a type of the enjoyment of this world in general. Like Faust, he revolts against the command: "Entbehren sollst du, sollst entbehren—Das ist der ewige Gesang."—"What will you get?" asks the old sceptic; "The future life and all your mysticism are dreams—take what you can get *here*."

> I must abjure the Balm of Life, I must,
> Scared by some After-reckoning ta'en on trust,
>   Or lured with Hope of some Diviner Drink,
> To fill the Cup—when crumbled into Dust!

> Oh threats of Hell and Hopes of Paradise!
> One thing at least is certain—*This* life flies;
>   One thing is certain and the rest is Lies;
> The Flower that once has blown for ever dies.

Well, this old heathen remained very much in the shade for some eight hundred years, because of his unorthodoxy, and his alphabetical arrangement, and one thing or another, until he fell into the hands of FitzGerald, who, says Mr Swinburne, has made Omar one of the greatest of English poets. FitzGerald began studying Persian in 1853, under the guidance of Professor Cowell. He presently began turning odd stanzas of Omar into English—many into rhymed monkish Latin, too. And after a while he strung them together into a kind of chain with some connexion, and so made a sort of soliloquy in a garden out of the scattered jewels of Omar.

Persian scholars will tell one that FitzGerald palmed off a very inferior article on the English market; that he dressed up his Omar out of all recognition, making him appear taller than he really was, as Xenophon says of those Athenian ladies who had a strange custom of wearing high-heeled shoes. And they are quite indignant about it, looking upon us admirers of Omar just as we look on the benighted inhabitants of Continental Europe who persist in admiring Lord Byron long after *we* have exploded him. But, for all that, it appears that Omar really did strike FitzGerald as the most interesting of the Persian poets. It was just because he felt a certain kinship with him that he was able to make such a success out of him. For Fitz-Gerald wandered in the same valley of darkness himself. He, too, was naturally of a religious turn of mind; on his tomb are inscribed, by his own wish, the words: "It is He that has made us, and not we ourselves," and yet he, too, failed to find any world but this. In Omar he could find that same idea of resignation to that which "has made us and not we ourselves," just as in Aeschylus or Marcus Aurelius, or the greatest of all poems that deal with these mysteries—the Book of *Job*. For has not Omar said:

We are no other than a moving row
Of Magic Shadow-shapes that come and go—
Round with the Sun-illumined Lantern held
In Midnight by the Master of the show;

But helpless Pieces of the Game He plays
Upon this Chequer-board of Nights and Days;
Hither and thither moves, and checks, and slays,
And one by one back in the Closet lays.

The Ball no question makes of Ayes and Noes,
But Here or There as strikes the Player goes;
And He that tossed you down into the Field,
He knows about it all—HE knows—HE knows!

The Moving Finger writes; and, having writ,
Moves on: nor all your Piety nor Wit
  Shall lure it back to cancel half a Line,
Nor all your Tears wash out a Word of it.

Ah, make the most of what we yet may spend,
Before we too into the Dust descend;
  Dust into Dust, and under Dust to lie
Sans Wine, sans Song, sans Singer, and—sans End!

It is not a lofty or heroic strain, no doubt; many persons
are sure always to be shocked by it, and to say that it is
nothing but the despairing cry: "Let us eat and drink, for
to-morrow we die." "I know you will thank me," writes
FitzGerald to a friend, when sending him a copy, "and I
think you will feel a sort of 'triste Plaisir' in it, as others
besides myself have felt. It is a desperate sort of thing,
unfortunately at the bottom of all thinking men's minds;
but made music of." In those words he exhausts all
criticism of his own poem. Never, surely, did any poet
more justly weigh his own work in a single sentence.

But FitzGerald's way of making the best of this world
was very different from the easy Epicurean philosophy
which Omar professed, and which he appears to have, to
some extent, practised. Assuredly Omar was no vulgar
Epicurean himself—he, who was qualified to be a professor
of mathematics—but, for all that, the burden of his song
is simply:

Drink!—for, once dead, you never shall return.

Strange, indeed, that such a doctrine should be popu-
larised in England by the man whose motto was Plain
Living and High Thinking, the man who would give his
friends of the best when they came to see him, while he

himself would walk up and down the room, munching an apple or a turnip. I am not inventing; his biographer *says* a *turnip*. For he was a vegetarian—indeed, he once nearly killed Tennyson, by persuading him, too, to turn vegetarian for six weeks.

Well, you have a pretty good idea by this time of the contents and of the style of the poem. Now for a word on FitzGerald's principles of translation. The unhappy translator is always being impaled on the horns of a dilemma. If he translates literally, he produces stuff no mortal can read. "I am sure," says FitzGerald elsewhere of another poem, "I am sure a complete translation, even in prose, would not have been a *readable* one, which, after all, is a useful property of most books, *even of poetry*." If, on the other hand, he makes a good and readable thing of it, then arise all the people who know the original, and begin to peck at it like domestic fowl. If one steers a middle course, one pleases nobody. FitzGerald boldly adopted the principle that what is wanted in a translation is *this*: To give people who don't know the original a sort of idea of the effect it produces on people who do. For this end we must throw all attempt at a *literal* translation to the wind. We must soak ourselves in the spirit of an author, and reproduce that spirit in as good poetic style as we may be master of. So, not only with Omar, but with his other translations too, he omits whole passages, puts in bits of his own, modifies and arranges everything, and makes— a poem. It is interesting to compare Paley's translation of the *Agamemnon* of Aeschylus with FitzGerald's from this point of view. Paley assures us himself, in his preface (and I suppose he ought to know), that *his* is readable and

tolerably literal, and then offers us such gems as: "You are
some crazy-headed person, or possessed by some god"; or,
again, "And my inward parts do not vainly bode—the
heart that whirls in eddies against the midriff, while it
justly looks for a fulfilment of its fears." Really, if Aeschylus
is that sort of thing, why do we rise up early and so late
take rest that we may proceed B.A. in Arts? Now listen
to another bit from FitzGerald, about Helen's flight from
Menelaus:

> Not beside thee in the chamber,
> Menelaus, any more;
> But with him she fled with, pillow'd,
> On the summer softly-billow'd
> Ocean, into dimple wreathing
> Underneath a breeze of amber
> Air that, as from Eros breathing,
> Fill'd the sail and flew before;
> Floating on the summer seas,
> Like some sweet Effigies
> Of Eirène's self, or sweeter
> Aphrodite, sweeter still:
> With the Shepherd, from whose luckless
> Hand upon the Phrygian hill
> Of the three Immortals, She
> The fatal prize of Beauty bore,
> Floating with him o'er the foam
> She rose from, to the shepherd's home
> On the Ionian shore.

There is hardly a word, hardly a single word of all that in
Aeschylus. But which of the two gives one the impression
that Aeschylus gives—Paley or FitzGerald?

But, of course, FitzGerald could not escape the domestic
fowl. Just listen to one of them cackling. The most

P   3

splendid stanzas of the whole poem are those which end
the first long soliloquy:

> O Thou, who didst with Pitfall and with Gin
> Beset the Road I was to wander in,
>   Thou wilt not with Predestination round
> Enmesh, and then impute my Fall to Sin!
>
> O Thou, who Man of baser Earth didst make,
> And even with Paradise devise the Snake;
>   For all the Sin wherewith the Face of Man
> Is blackened, Man's forgiveness give—and take!

By the addition of the last two words, FitzGerald has
turned a commonplace idea enough into the most fearful
indictment ever uttered by Man against his Maker. One
would have thought that any comment on it could only take
the form of admiration. But Professor Cowell—well, Professor Cowell is a Professor, and I do not like to hear
persons of dignity lightly spoken of, and, moreover, he was
a good friend to FitzGerald as ever man had, and it is
thanks to him that he ever learnt any Persian at all, and
that we are talking about him here to-day—*but*, I say,
Cowell writes: "There is no original for the line about the
snake" (as if anybody cared); "I have looked for it in vain
in Nicholas; but I have always supposed that the last line
is FitzGerald's *mistaken version* of Quatrain 236. Fitz-
Gerald mistook the meaning of *giving* and *accepting* as used
here, and so invented his last line *out of his own mistake*.
I wrote to him about it when I was in Calcutta, but he
never cared to alter it." He never cared to alter it! The
unconscious irony in those last words is simply delicious.
And how characteristic of FitzGerald is the story. Any
other man, one would think, would have written back to

consign the Professor to a hotter climate than Calcutta, and to observe that, if there was any one line in the English language a man might be proud of, it was just that. But FitzGerald was the most modest of men, "one who as persistently avoided fame as others seek it." I can fancy him smiling over that remonstrance, and putting off his corrector, giving him the impression that he (Cowell) was quite right, but that his poor verses were really not worth troubling about.

Well, let us thank the gods that _we_ know no Persian, and try to estimate the position of this Omar purely as _English_ literature. I always think of Gray's _Elegy_ in connexion with it. "And Gray," says FitzGerald, in one of his letters, "ah, to think of that little Elegy inscribed among the stars, while —— & Co. are blazing away with their fireworks here on earth." Even so did he himself inscribe that little elegy of his among the stars, while nobody heard or thought about him, and while all the literary papers were full of those other noisy people. Not that I fail myself to like them, but it certainly is my opinion that FitzGerald may very likely outlast the whole gang of them, just as Gray's _Elegy_ has beaten all the works of his contemporaries, who were so much more brilliant than he. Each of the two lived more or less in seclusion, buried with their books— the world forgetting, by the world forgot—each polished his little elegy for years. The subject of each is very much the same—quite commonplace—nothing out of the way, just such reflections as every man makes about life and death, and, therefore, as immortal in essence as man himself. Whatever creeds may rise and fall, whatever mutabilities of empire and science and manners there may be, so long as we are, in the end of it all these reflections must strike home.

> The boast of heraldry, the pomp of power,
> And all that beauty, all that wealth e'er gave,
> Awaits alike the inevitable hour....

Each of the two was so fastidious that he rejected at least one of the most beautiful stanzas, now to be found only in the notes.

On a close comparison, I think—I am afraid—the palm must be yielded to Gray. His *Elegy* is better arranged as a whole—naturally, when one thinks how the other was pieced together out of the chaotic heap of the original Omar. And taking stanza for stanza, line for line, there are better stanzas and better lines in Gray. He has not the same natural easy flow as FitzGerald, whether melancholy or humorous or whimsical, but he has more weight and dignity and power. He took himself more seriously. Modesty is a good thing, or so they say who understand about it, but FitzGerald was perhaps *too* modest; if he had been more ambitious he might have taken even more pains than he did, and insisted deliberately on making a treasure for ever, as Gray did. Yet, perhaps he would have spoilt it, so we had better be content. Then, too, when we compare the two, we must allow for the lapse of time. Time has laid a decaying finger here and there upon Gray. There are bits of the *Elegy* which are written in the poetic slang of the day; "Froze the genial current of the soul," for example, is as detestable a piece of eighteenth-century poetic slang as you can find; such things pass muster well enough in their own time, when everybody is used to expressions of the sort, but after a while they turn out to be colours which will not last. And how do we know how much poetic slang of the *nineteenth* century there may not be in Fitz-Gerald? At any rate, as Omar has it, "One thing is certain, and the rest is Lies"—the Persian allusions in FitzGerald are a nuisance. One is always liable to an incursion of Oriental tinsel in European poetry. Goethe, Hugo, Leconte de Lisle, Byron, Bodenstedt, have all amused themselves with it and irritated us. And then there was Moore. When I was young, some forty years ago, people used still to read *Lalla Rookh,* and used to like to talk about Bendemeer's stream, and the Green Sea, and yataghans, and such a deal of skimble-skamble stuff. You could not read ten lines without looking at a note to find out what was meant by a *zel* or a *chibouk* or a *talipot tree*; things about which Moore knew no more than I do; but which he had laboriously crammed up in Oriental dictionaries. These things, too, are of the nature of fireworks, and, though they may take the fancy for a time, they soon lose all their lustre. "I do not like the fashion of your garments," said King Lear to a person whose only "apparatus" was a blanket; "you will say, they are Persian, but let them be changed." That is a very appropriate motto for poetry of the kind.

> "Well, let it take them," says FitzGerald,
> "what have we to do
> With Kaikobád the Great or Kaikhosrú?"

A sentiment one often echoes. Only he did not deliberately drag them in. On the contrary, he cut quantities out. Still, in the long run, it must be a great advantage to Gray that he is purely English—or, rather, purely human, for even to England there is hardly an allusion in his *Elegy*.

Yet, surely, when all allowance is made for the effects of time, and the weariness of Persian allusion, such lines as these must be as "immortal," as we are pleased to call it, as Gray himself:

> They say the Lion and the Lizard keep
> The Courts where Jamshýd gloried and drank deep:
>   And Bahrám, that great Hunter—the Wild Ass
> Stamps o'er his Head, but cannot break his Sleep.
>
> I sometimes think that never blows so red
> The Rose as where some buried Cæsar bled;
>   That every Hyacinth the Garden wears
> Dropt in her Lap from some once lovely Head.
>
> And this reviving Herb whose tender Green
> Fledges the River-Lip on which we lean—
>   Ah lean upon it lightly! for who knows
> From what once lovely Lip it springs unseen!
>
> Ah, my Belovéd, fill the Cup that clears
> To-DAY of past Regrets and future Fears:
>   *To-morrow*!—Why, To-morrow I may be
> Myself with Yesterday's Sev'n thousand Years.
>
> For some we loved, the loveliest and the best
> That from his Vintage rolling Time hath prest,
>   Have drunk their Cup a Round or two before,
> And one by one crept silently to rest.

"But time goes on, and shorter paths I know," says Pindar. FitzGerald made many other translations: *Salaman and Absal*, from Jami; *Bird-Parliament*, from Attar—Persians both. Both poems deal, of course, with the eternal mysticism, the abnegation of the body and

union of the soul with God. I will read an extract from the
Bird-Parliament, which is a fable to satirise those who
hesitate between this world and the other:

There was a Queen of Egypt like the Bride
Of Night, Full-moon-faced and Canopus-eyed,
Whom one among the meanest of her Crowd
Loved—and she knew it, (for he loved aloud)
And sent for him, and said "Thou lov'st thy Queen:
Now therefore Thou hast this to choose between:
Fly for thy Life: or for this one night Wed
Thy Queen, and with the Sunrise lose thy Head."
He paused—he turned to fly—she struck him dead.
"For had he truly loved his Queen," said She,
"He would at once have given his Life for me,
And Life and Wife had carried: but he lied;
And loving only Life, has justly died."

He also translated the *Agamemnon* and both the
Oedipuses, and eight plays of Calderon. But the British
public *will not* swallow Calderon in any shape; I suppose
he must be read in the original, and I daresay it would turn
out that he is not worth the trouble. I should advise anyone who may be tempted to look at them to begin with
the *Mighty Magician*. Then he made a boiled-down version
of Crabbe's *Tales of the Hall*, which, I think, has never
been published. Crabbe was a great passion of his, he was
always trying to cram him down other people's throats.
"Positively, I am at my eternal Crabbe again," he says, in
a letter to Mrs Kemble. But it is no use; in the race for
oblivion Crabbe has easily distanced even Hazlitt[1].

Then there is a prose dialogue called *Euphranor*, which, to
my taste, seemed scarce worth reading, though Tennyson

---

[1] A paper in praise of Hazlitt had lately been read to the Society.
Platt afterwards came to a better judgment of Crabbe.

called the end of it the finest piece of English prose he knew! So do tastes differ.

But what seems like to live best after Omar is the *Letters*—one series to different friends and another to Fanny Kemble. Which of the two is the more delightful I do not know; but I think there are no other letters like them in English. Pieces of delightful literary criticism— often fearfully unorthodox; but what a joy it is to meet a man who says what he thinks, and does not feel bound to admire what he doesn't admire. He deplores his own taste in the most simple manner, how he could not like Goethe, for instance, and how he could not read ten lines of *Paradise Lost* because of some pedantic classical allusion or construction, which "sends one from Hell or Heaven to the school-room, worse than either." "Well, but I believe in the Vox Populi of two hundred years; still more of two thousand," he writes; *he* would not set up his own private taste above the world's, as most of us are so fond of doing. Then there are most unexpected and capricious ideas always turning up. Thus of a sonata of Beethoven's he writes: "It is meant to express the discord and gradual atonement of two lovers, and Beethoven was disgusted that every one did not see what was meant; *in truth*, it expresses *any* resistance gradually overcome—Dobson shaving with a blunt razor, for instance." What other mortal would ever have compared a Beethoven sonata to a man shaving? Then his banter about Spedding, the editor and biographer of Bacon, and his own dearest friend. Spedding had an immense forehead, and was bald, like all truly great men, and FitzGerald tells us of drawings of Swiss lakes, with Spedding's forehead rising over the mountains; and, again, when Spedding went to America, we are gravely told of the confusion caused to the shipping in the Channel, because the sailors would mistake his forehead for Beachy Head.

But I hear two objections taken to the Letters—they are too feminine, and the Capital Letters are used in a chaotic way at the beginning of words. Well, the Capitals can be left alone. He always had a Fancy for Them; but, as to the other charge, is it not just that feminine quality which gives the Letters their charm? In a general of division or an anatomist or a New Woman to be feminine may be a mistake; but here what have we to do with that? One does not want a man to write letters in the spirit in which he would lead a charge of cavalry! It is just that feminine quality in his nature which makes the man himself and his letters so lovable. "One loves Virgil somehow," he says, after quoting him in one of them, and is it not just the same with Virgil, whom the Neapolitans nicknamed the Maid? It is that gentle melancholy temperament which gives its charm to the verse of both. The letters of Horace Walpole may be infinitely more brilliant and sparkling, they may have more amusing stories in them, but one does not love Walpole—not a bit.

It has been said of FitzGerald that he writes to his friends rather as a lover than as a friend. And he says himself in a letter of 1834:

Your letter has indeed been a long time coming, but it is all the more delicious. Perhaps you can't imagine how wistfully I have looked for it; how, after a walk, my eyes have turned to the table, on coming into the room, to see it. Sometimes I have been tempted to be angry with you; but then I thought that I was sure you would come a hundred miles to serve me, though you were too lazy to sit down to a letter. I suppose that people who are engaged in serious ways of life, and are of well-filled minds, don't think much about the interchange of letters with any anxiety; but I am an idle fellow, of a very ladylike turn of sentiment, and my friendships are more like loves, I think.

Therefore perhaps it was that he was so much beloved by those who knew. Tennyson and Thackeray both counted him the dearest of all their friends, and so, no doubt, did the Third Great Man, Posh. Even Carlyle, who had a good word for nobody, could find nothing to say against him worse than to call him "the ultra-modest man, with his peaceable, far-niente life." Of course, Carlyle would have no sympathy with his pursuits; to translate Persian and Greek and Calderon was, in the language of the philosopher, to occupy one's self with dead dogs. "Unser Zeitalter bedarf kräftiger Geister," said a greater than Carlyle, and yet at odd times, despite Presidents and Kaisers, one may still dream with a melancholy pleasure over that eternal lamentation, old as the song of Linus among the cornfields, or the wailing of the Syrian maidens over their wounded Thammuz:

Yet Ah, that Spring should vanish with the Rose!
That Youth's sweet-scented Manuscript should close!
    The Nightingale that in the branches sang,
Ah whence, and whither flown again, who knows!

But, to borrow a phrase from an Alexandrine poet, the Nightingales of FitzGerald yet live, and shall sing to generations yet unborn when we are all with Kaikobád and Kaikhosrú.

ARISTOPHANES

(*The Quarto*, vol. IV, 1898)

IT is one of those things which are generally known that
Plato declared a truceless war upon the poets, and not only
ejected Homer with the greatest respect indeed, but with
stern decision, from his ideal polity, but also said that
tragedy and comedy did a great deal more harm than good;
and these opinions of his have been a good deal talked about
because Plato is the chosen philosopher of all those who
are by nature hopelessly unphilosophical, like you and me.

His objection to tragedy is briefly that it encourages you
to weep and carry on about the misfortunes of imaginary
characters in a way of which you would be ashamed in real
life if a misfortune happened to yourself. The tendency of
the natural man is to give way to his grief, but the philosopher ought to be stoical, and tragedy feeds the natural
tendency and is therefore bad. Aristotle, who conceived
his mission to be principally to set Plato right, and who
did it with great energy and success, turned this very
objection of Plato's with extraordinary skill into the justification of tragedy. The tendency to give way to misfortune,
he answered, is a tendency which will grow in us if we do
not get rid of it, just like a malignant humour in the body,
and there is nothing better to be done than to purge it out
of us. Tragedy enables us to get rid of it periodically, and
the more we do so by a good cry occasionally over fictitious
evils, the more shall we be able to resist real evils with the
dignity befitting a student of moral science. It is an interesting circumstance that the Aristotelian view was first

correctly understood by the great Milton, as may be seen from his preface to *Samson Agonistes*.

Plato's objection to comedy was of a similar nature. Comedy encourages you to laugh at things of which you would be ashamed in private life. And remember that the comedy of those days was a comedy of a licence and indecency and virulent personal abuse of living men to which no parallel has ever been seen since upon the stage[1]. Why, the old comedy shocked even the public, for it was put a stop to by the authorities in course of time. It is true that what shocked *them* was not the immorality and indecency, it was the free political criticism and the personal abuse, abuse which naturally fell principally on the authorities themselves. But when once its wings had been clipped, the old comedy languished like a bird in a cage, and soon died.

What did Aristotle answer here? or what would he have answered? It is not certain that he tried to justify the old comedy at all; he appears to have thought Menander, not Aristophanes, the true type of comedy. But we may at least answer on his own lines that just as tragedy was valuable as purging us of the natural tendency to lamentation, so the old comedy was valuable as purging us of the natural tendency to laugh at what we ought not, as civilised and rational beings, to laugh at at all. An occasional giving up of ourselves to the instinct of the unregenerate savage to rejoice in all manner of abominations will make us all the better able to play the part of members of a civilised, cultivated and polite society as a rule.

[1] By Plato's time the old comedy was already dead and buried, but if he objected so strongly to the middle comedy, *à fortiori* would he have objected to Aristophanes. (Author's note.)

But I daresay you are asking all this time why comedy or art of any kind should have *any* moral effect on people. Well, all I can say is that the Greek persistently looked upon it from that point of view. Art must be useful according to them, or it is nothing. And as they are the only people in the history of the world who ever had a genuine and natural feeling for art, and as they created every form of art in existence, they have some right to be heard. No doubt to say art must be useful is the most Philistine thing one well *can* say, but what is one to say of the modern doctrine which had such vogue in France in 1830 and onwards, the cry of "art for art," which has ended in Zola? If art exists for art, what has it to do with me? "Art for man" is the only rational doctrine for an artist who is a man himself. And that means that it must be useful? Well, I don't know; what do you mean by useful? Some people talk as if nothing were useful which one cannot eat or drink or run to death over a ploughed field in a scarlet coat. "The beautiful is as useful as the useful, even more useful," said Hugo, and I think he was right, and that the Greeks were right too.

But let us go back to the old comedy, to what is summed up for us in the one name Aristophanes, and apply some of all this "bald disjointed chat" to him. First of all let us look at the way Bergk opens his chapter on Attic comedy. It is, says he, a painting of manners, an imitation of ordinary life. At the same time he admits that Aristophanes is one of the greatest writers of comedy. Bless me, what a confusion of thought there stands revealed in the mere juxtaposition of these two sentences! If comedy is never anything but an imitation of life, Aristophanes is not only not a great writer of comedy, he is not a comic writer at all, he is the most incompetent and ridiculous of bunglers, and ought to be hissed off the stage. Why then is he a great writer of comedy? Because comedy, in its origin, was a literature of revolt against convention, and he has carried this revolt further than any other writer.

"Man," says The Philosopher, "is more gregarious than any beast of the field, yea, than any whatsoever of the social hymenoptera." But think what a price those poor hymenoptera pay for their society! The majority of them reduced to a neuter asexual condition, a swarm of males whose principal occupation is being massacred annually, a Royal Family exclusively employed in laying eggs! Happier surely the roving humble-bee, who lives like the Cyclops, "without society and without law, ruling over his wife and children, nor do they trouble themselves about one another." Imagine a hive-bee suddenly endowed with the speech, the insight, and the fun of an Aristophanes; what a new *Parliament of Bees* could he compose! Now in every man there is a humble-bee as well as a hive-bee; not only is he naturally gregarious, but he is also naturally an animal who seeks to gratify his passions as they come to him. And along with this he has developed moral, political, and social sentiments, which distinguish him from gorilla or tiger; nor only so, but "by policy and long process of time" he has agreed tacitly or avowedly to bind himself by a host of restrictions. There are laws engraved or engrossed on brass or iron or parchment, and there are laws innumerable not written anywhere, but practically recognised by everyone. The law "thou shalt not kill," or at least "thou shalt not kill a member of thy own tribe," is the most binding of all, for without it all society would fall to pieces. The law "thou shalt not tell thy neighbour what thou really thinkest of him" is equally binding in civilised society; whoso breaks it habitually will lose all his friends, unless he be as fortunate in them as I am. Then, again, it is a law that a man should wear a particular kind of dress (and what a dress!) in London, and hence the "Philosophy of Clothes" may be used to illustrate the true theory of the old comedy. For when we flee away for the summer we throw off this constraint with great joy, wear whatever seems comfortable, set all the dictates of decorum and etiquette at defiance. And a breach of custom of this kind does us all the good in the world; we return refreshed to the routine of London, and are able to keep it up without undue depression for another year. No doubt this is a very mild example, but it is on the same lines. As we revolt against many small conventionalities in our holidays, so the Athenians revolted in their comedies, at festivals like the Dionysia, in a far more thorough and energetic fashion. On these occasions all the instincts of the animal within us, which are repressed by society, were again wakened up.

And above the animal lies another stratum, that of the unthinking, unheroic, commonplace "homme sensuel moyen." He, too, is allowed his fling, when Strepsiades triumphs over Socrates, or Sganarelle over philosopher and physician. The virulent abuse of people we do not like finds here its vent; indeed, comedy is said to have arisen from the custom of merrymakers abusing one another in extempore Billingsgate on the Bank Holidays of those days, and abuse of this sort remained a prominent feature in the full-blown art. When Dante had got a very long way down in hell, he stopped listening to a very unedifying quarrel between Messer Adamo of Brescia and the Greek Sinon. Virgil, who represents the Reason, rebukes him for it, and tells him that if he listen any longer he will be angry with him, and Dante, with great shame, leaves them to their quarrel and passes on. This natural and low instinct in us which leads us to be amused at hearing two people abuse one another, whether in the street, in the pit of hell, or the pages of *Nature*, was indulged to the height. Especially in politics the abuse of prominent statesmen, which even now reaches a considerable pitch in the evening papers, was carried to prodigious lengths, and in the most vulgar style. The whole political system is part of our conventionality, it is irksome to the natural man, and he likes now and then to rise and declaim against it though he really knows it to be necessary. The unrestricted freedom of speech in its lower forms is one of the most prominent features of the old comedy; society makes us restrain our instinct to say what we think of people and things we do not like, and put things mildly, and comedy did away with this restraint.

Then there is the revolt against morality as a whole. In every respect the natural instinct prevails. To lie, to steal, to kill, if it suits your purpose, is the natural thing to do in the old comedy. If any danger threatens, you run away. Hence the typical hero is a coward and an immoral rascal, if you look at him seriously. The most prominent feature of this revolt against morality was the incredible indecency of these representations, to which there was absolutely no limit.

Moreover religion fettered the Greek continually, a splendid glittering pompous religion, all external without a scrap of genuine inward religious feeling. To connect it with morality was left to a few poets and philosophers; to the general public it was ritual, combined with a ridiculous mythology. But this ritual was a very serious matter, it came into everything one did. Sacrifices and libations, and an eternal round of religious festivals—even tragedy and comedy were religious ceremonies—hampered the Athenian at every turn. Hence naturally we find the revolt against religion along with the rest, and those gods who were worshipped by the state, and for disbelieving in whom (as his accusers said) the wisest and best of the Athenians was put to death, these very gods are brought on the stage under every circumstance of ridicule and buffoonery. And that too by the very man who attacked Socrates in another play for his alleged "atheism"! This shews pretty clearly how unsafe it is to argue from the plays of Aristophanes to his real sentiments.

Lastly—or at least the last thing I shall here remark on— the natural man rises up in all his glory as a punster. There is perhaps nothing more disgusting to his neighbours. The man who whistles, the man who is in love, the man who talks football shop, the man who runs college magazines— all of these pale their ineffectual fires before him. Yet there is nothing more natural to man than to make puns, children revel in the most idiotic, the stone age I conceive was worse plagued with them than with any other curse of primitive man, and *Pithecanthropus erectus*, if he was able to talk at all, punned like a Lamb. Only a long and severe course of civilisation has checked them, and even now they are not as extinct as might be wished. In Aristophanes they appear in all their native hideousness, "naked and not ashamed" like the rest of him. Nothing annoys one so much in him now as these silly puns; presumably they pleased at the time, but in that respect at any rate we may boast that our comic taste has improved since.

Yet all this revolt against constraint and civilisation has nothing bitter about it; it is always perfectly good-humoured in spite of the satire which pervades and permeates it, and finds vent not in sneers but in open gigantic laughter. Often enough has it been seen that a great man has been disgusted by the falsehoods and hypocrisy which are in some degree necessary to society—only lately a very little man named Nordau has been holding forth about them— or by the lower animal which is the substratum of the human creature. Neither the one nor the other can be helped; society cannot exist without shams, and man cannot become an angel all at once. The wise and healthy mind will recognise this and make the best of it. But certain minds fix themselves upon the wrong side of the tapestry; they become embittered in consequence, and find vent in a satire which is not good-humoured but savage, not Aristophanic but—who has not already thought of the dreadful name of Swift? To him all the disagreeable part of life which we keep dark became so prominent, and so tortured his sensitive spirit that he could think of nothing else; hence rose like a Fury from the pit that "saeva indignatio" which lacerated a heart surely by nature lovable and noble, till it turned him into the most tremendous satirist the world has ever seen. Whoever reads the last voyage of Gulliver may well feel unclean until the evening and for many days. Like the old comedy, Swift cuts off from man all his nobler growth, and displays the ghastly skeleton beneath him, but instead of being a wholesome draught his comedy has become as the waters of Marah. Neither representation of man is true, but Swift pretends that his is so, and the horror of it is that he makes his reader think so too.

In Rousseau the revolt takes a diametrically opposite form. He says that civilisation is a bad thing, and we ought to return to the happy state of things "when wild in woods the noble savage ran." If he had only known as much of savages as we do! But here we meet a philosophical theory, not literature. Such theories were familiar enough at Athens also.

A greater name by far than these will give us another example. There was a period in Shakespeare's life when that milk of human kindness which was so sweet in him, turned sour, when he wrote satire as bitter and almost as terrible as Swift's; *why*, we cannot tell, for no hand will lift the curtain that veils his inner life. It was the period of *Lear, Timon, Troilus*. But his divine nature righted itself again, and in his latest plays came back a serenity and sweetness all the more heavenly for the storm he had passed through.

If after every tempest come such calms
May the winds blow till they have wakened death;

but I know of no parallel in literature. Dante's bitterest satire is uttered in the heaven of heavens.

All general and wide satire thus springs from the same root in our nature as does the earliest comedy. But the professional satirists, hideous owls like Juvenal, who

screech in a night without moon or star, are a brood not to
be mentioned in connexion with such good company. They
are to comedy as vinegar to wine, and they are not even
sincere as Swift was. When satire informs and invigorates
the comedy of manners, the later comedy which really *is*
an imitation of life, then, indeed, we come to something
of the same kind and to the one writer of comic drama[1]
who is truly worthy to be set beside Aristophanes, "Molière,
ce moqueur grave comme un apôtre." Yet what a difference! that line of Hugo's is as admirable as a description
of Molière as it would be absurd if applied to the other. In
Molière the satire is indeed grave and serious; with all his
unsurpassed comic power his greatest works are almost
like tragedies in tone and impression; and then the revolt
in him is not against all society but only against court
follies and aristocratic manners[2]. Yet what he loses in
width, he makes up for again in other ways, in the magnificent characterisation, in the common sense which goes
beyond the flights of mere poetry as the common sense of
Socrates did beyond the flights of Plato, in that depth of
feeling and restrained passion which positively sometimes

[1] The romantic comedy is here excluded as being altogether of
a different type. *Twelfth Night* and *Amor Honor y Poder* and *La
Boba para los Otros*, Hugo's *Esca*, and Musset's *Fantasio* may be
a more delightful species of literature than anything else in existence,
but strictly speaking can hardly be ranked as "comedy" proper.
(Author's note.)

[2] Of course this is only a single detail in Molière among many
others. Revolt is not the essential principle with him. He is the
culmination of the later comedy, and hence it is that he draws upon
Plautus and Terence when he adapts a play from the ancients. What
could he have got from Aristophanes to suit his peculiar bent? It is
a curious thing that the only successful adaptation of Aristophanes
should have been made by, of all people, the sweet, tender and sublime Racine. (Author's note.)

reminds one of Sophocles, as in the great scene of Agnès and Arnolphe, in that warfare upon cant and hypocrisy in which he again resembles Socrates and which makes some people so angry with him, in that power of treating an ethical subject all round from every point of view which makes *Le Misanthrope* so great—and so difficult to appreciate. Look at what Mr Morley says about this same *Misanthrope* in his book on Voltaire, how he is puzzled with it, how angry he gets with this prodigious mind which is so wide in its view, that it cannot take up one side against the other. In truth he evidently has a well-grounded suspicion that if Molière had known him he would have laughed consumedly at *him*, the Right Honourable John Morley. And Schlegel had the same uneasy feeling too; Schlegel is of course one of the very silliest persons who ever undertook to criticise literature; he had immense knowledge and no judgment, he understood as much about poetry as comparative philologists usually do, he was "no true man" said Goethe. Such a person in the presence of Molière blinks like an owl in the sun, and of all his absurd criticism that upon Molière is probably, to use a celebrated phrase of his own, "the very vilest."

However, the only modern writer in whom the genuine Aristophanic genius reappears is a man who did not write comedies—he could not have done it had he tried—a man whom it is hardly respectable to mention, Rabelais. One cannot recommend anybody to read him as a whole, for a great deal of him is really very dull, but everybody ought to know Besant's delightful *Readings in Rabelais*. But after all the difference is very great. He has the same outrageous laughter, the same revolt against all constraint—and natural enough in him was this revolt, for at nine years of age he was put into a monastery and all the joy of life cut off from him, and when he came out the rebound might be expected to be violent enough—but he was no Greek in spirit and had no sense of form, so that he often becomes utterly amorphous, the common snare of the humourist, and he had no lyric capacity. The "climbing apes" were there, but not the "singing nightingales," to quote the phrase of Heine concerning Aristophanes. Panurge is the one modern example of the typical character of the old comedy, but where is the song of the *Clouds* or of the *Birds*? And, moreover, the whole thing is not worked out with the unity and thoroughness of the ancients. The great and wise Pantagruel is a noble figure in himself in the later books, but he is out of place in his surroundings.

As I have referred to Heine's famous description, I will take this opportunity of observing that this revolt against convention is what Heine must have meant by his obscure phrase "world-annihilation." It is out of a "world-annihilation," he says, that springs the fantastic tree of Aristophanic comedy, with its climbing apes and singing nightingales. It means that Aristophanes first annihilates the *social* world and order in which we live, and then builds up his fantasies on the ground which remains, that is on the lower nature of man. This, too, is what Hegel was groping after when he talked of the "subjectivity" of comedy, which Mahaffy makes such fun of, and quite fairly. But they say that Hegel generally meant something if only you could find out what. Anyhow, this "subjectivity" is the individual rising up against society and everything outside him, and asserting his own will for the moment as the only law to be obeyed.

So far we have considered Attic comedy in its general aspect; now consider the particular circumstances in which Aristophanes found himself. He was an Athenian, shut up in the city by the exigencies of the war with Sparta. He lived when the new learning of the Sophists—which was like the criticism of the French *philosophes* in the last century—was overrunning Greece, and all the old beliefs, religious, moral, and social, were crumbling into chaos under that dissolving acid. He lived under a democracy, guided or humoured by statesmen of a type we know only too well in England.

Now the ordinary constraints of civilisation are nothing to the constraint imposed by the war on the Athenians. They lived a free and easy life on their estates and farms, they hated being cooped up in the city and having all their vines and fruit-trees and crops destroyed. Of course therefore the spirit of revolt shows itself in violent attacks upon the war and everybody concerned with it. Aristophanes is for ever preaching peace; it is the natural instinct to avoid trouble and disagreeables; the higher policy, Pericles and the statesmen, may insist on the necessity and the advantages of war, but the natural man submits to it with grumbling, and his grumbling finds a furious voice in comedy. The *Peace* is entirely devoted to it, and there is hardly a play in which it does not turn up somewhere. Dicaeopolis triumphing over Lamachus is the blissful vision which fancy substitutes for the melancholy truth. But did Aristophanes *really* think the war was wrong? Goodness only knows.

In just the same way, comedy must always attack the prevailing party in politics. Whatever party is in power, the people must feel themselves to some extent constrained by it; they will always be to some extent "agin the Government." How could Aristophanes attack the oligarchs? There was no fun to be got out of them. Hence, his violent attacks upon Cleon (at least partly) and his perpetual girding against democracy. But how far was he in earnest? Goodness only knows.

Then again he attacks the new learning: the *Clouds* is entirely devoted to a satire upon Socrates, who is taken as the type of it. With the greatest recklessness for truth, Socrates is made out to be nothing but a Sophist of the worst kind, a teacher of immoral doctrines. The scientific theories of the Ionian "nature philosophers," for which we know that he had not the slightest sympathy, are thrust upon him. The promises of the rhetorician are put into his mouth. The very sophists upon whom he waged unrelenting war are all gathered up into a bundle and labelled Socrates, and combined with the personal peculiarities which marked him out as a natural butt for comedy. Was Aristophanes in earnest? He was a personal friend of Socrates, and on very good terms with him.

Euripides represented in literature the spirit of this new learning, which ruined the simplicity and grandeur of tragedy as it ruined everything else in the old order of things. And so he comes in for a copious rain of abuse. Was Aristophanes in earnest? He was a man of taste.

In these last instances you will say that this is not a revolt

against the constraint of the higher life at all. To revolt
in the name of Aeschylus against Euripides is certainly
not the revolt of the lower against the higher. No, but it
is the revolt of the plain "common sense" man within us against ideas, philosophy, new notions which are
difficult to grasp and comprehend unless we have been
brought up in them. It is the same sort of uprising as
we find among plain people against science, true or
false, against new ideas in politics, right or wrong,
against new schools of painting or music. And here,
indeed, Molière walks hand in hand with Aristophanes.
The indolent conservative within us is higher than the
animal, but he is below the philosopher, below the man
of ideas, as much as he is below the poet and creator.

But there is *one* thing against which a Greek will not
rebel—art and the laws and limitations of art. As much
waywardness and audacity as you please in the matter,
but no tampering with the form. Obviously for an artist
to rebel against the laws of his art is as suicidal as for a
philosopher to try and overthrow the reason, and one
might have hoped both to be impossible, but alas! experience shows that they are not. A better instance in the
case of art cannot be wished for than is afforded by many
of Browning's poems. No doubt it is a great nuisance and
trouble to have to find rhymes when you are bursting with
noble and profound thoughts; which of us has not felt
that? Browning felt it so keenly that he ruined *A Grammarian's Funeral* by such rhymes as *fabric* and *dab brick*,
just out of spite and as a protest against the bondage of his
art. It is largely because of his carelessness for form that
the stream of Rabelais wanders into desultory dull marshes,

and gets choked in noisome shallows. The same defect makes *Tristram Shandy* unreadable as a whole. This is indeed the natural besetting sin of humourists of this kind, and we may be thankful to the extraordinary conservatism of Athens in questions of artistic form, that their comedy escaped it as easily as their tragedy. For the wildest effusions of humour were confined within formal limits as strict as those of tragedy.

It is only consistent and reasonable that this immense topsy-turvydom, this annihilation of the world we live in, and substitution of an airy dream in which our un-sophisticated unmoral nature emerges naked and un-ashamed, it is only right that the whole vision should be logically carried out, and should end in a blaze of triumph, in the glorification of unrighteousness. In the *Birds* above all the wild schemer and dreamer Pisthetaerus, after building Cloudcuckootown in the air and reducing the gods to submission, marries Basileia the daughter of Zeus, and leaves the stage in a festal procession, burlesquing the attributes of Zeus himself. Modern critics have positively been offended by this climax; poetic justice, they conceive, demands that this audacious and impious rascal Pisthe-taerus should be punished, that at least we should be given to understand that his triumph is but apparent. Poetic justice indeed! what has any kind of justice to do in a state of things where we are in revolt against every law? The dream of a world in which we can give full play to all our unregenerate instincts must be carried out at all hazards, the charming wild vision must be consummated and crowned, and die out like a glorious day in all the colours of the sunset. Time enough afterwards to wake up and go back to our black coats and high hats; let us dream the dream out.

> Ah Love! could you and I with Him conspire
> To grasp this sorry Scheme of Things entire,
> Would not we shatter it to bits—and then
> Re-mould it nearer to the Heart's Desire!

So the finale of the *Clouds* is the triumph of the average unreflecting man over new ideas, just as that of the *Birds* is the triumph of the natural desire of man to do what he likes over the limitations of space and time and the laws of the physical universe.

So closely are tragedy and comedy united in the ideas which lie at their root. For it is precisely the enforcement of these limitations which is the lesson of tragedy. Antigone loses her life for a convention which a hero of the old comedy would have laughed to scorn[1]. Ajax dies for a trifling religious matter which Pisthetaerus would have ranked with burglary, lying, and studies from the nude. Agamemnon is shown to us for a moment in the height of all his glory, only that he may be struck down by a dreadful doom. That we are to remember we are but men, that the mightiest may not presume, that

> The glories of our blood and state
> Are shadows, not substantial things,

that we can by no means do as we like, these are the lessons of tragedy. And the old comedy turns it all inside out, and makes a world in which we can do exactly what we please without fear and without reproach.

To say much about the characters of the plays, after what has gone before, would be superfluous. The heroes,

---

[1] *Frogs*, 191. (Author's note.)

if heroes they can be called, are just what I have spoken
of throughout, as the unregenerate natural man, absolutely
selfish and unblushingly seeking to satisfy all his instincts,
except the moral, which he hasn't got. For honour and
reason, decorum and decency, he cares not a fig; he is
simply a very clever animal, without the moral sense yet
developed in him. From the intellectual point of view, he
is the average common-sense man, who will not be taken
in by any "bottled moonshine" of any philosopher or
sophist, who has a profound disbelief in and contempt for
science and everything that is at all above the run of his
own ideas[1]. Herein indeed he resembles the man of the
world whom we meet in the comedy of manners, the
elderly hero of Terence or Molière. But to speak of the
characters of Aristophanes as if they were on the same
ground altogether as those of ordinary comedy, as Lessing
and other critics do, is a great mistake. The aim of the old
comedy was no representation of manners with mild
sarcasm upon them, but a very different thing indeed, and
the characters differ accordingly. There is indeed only one
parallel to them with whom I am acquainted, Panurge.
Caliban also, whom I suspect of being the offspring of
Panurge by Sycorax, offers strong points of resemblance.

Yet even Strepsiades and his like profess a certain
morality whenever it suits them so to do. They affect,
perhaps they feel, the greatest indignation at certain

---

[1] Hence the fact that the hero of the old comedy is an old man.
The generosity and openness to impressions of youth unfit young
men for the post; we want a cynic who has "seen through all that
nonsense," who has "humé ses formules" as the old Marquis de
Mirabeau had it, who understands the meaning of the proverb "si
jeunesse savait, si vieillesse pouvait!" (Author's note.)

crimes and misdemeanours; for example, Pisthetaerus rebukes the youth who comes to him wishing to be a parricide, Strepsiades objects to the "worse reason," the personified representation of rhetoric on the wrong side, on the ground that it is immoral. Yes, but the truth is that parricide and the new sophistry are both contrary to our natural instinct. There really are certain elementary laws of morality which are now as much instincts with us as eating and drinking, and the parricide seems to us below the animal itself. Such laws as those do not interfere with our "subjectivity." And as to the "worse reason," it certainly is not its immorality that makes it a legitimate butt for the old comedy; this very Strepsiades is moving heaven and earth to escape payment of his debts. But also it must be admitted that Aristophanes is not consistent; his characters will, if it suit him, alter at a moment's notice just to raise a laugh; and in this broad farce it does not signify; there is no harm if they do. Compared with ordinary morality, one may say, the characters are immoral; as soon as they are confronted with any *new* immorality they become moral for the nonce, they at least assume the cloak of morality to defend themselves against the unfamiliar. For that is what men dislike in ethics, as in art, in medicine, in everything else—the unfamiliar.

There is one play of Aristophanes in which all this is changed—the *Plutus*. It does not belong to the old comedy at all, but to what is called the middle comedy. Plutus the god of wealth is blind, and therefore riches are unfairly distributed. The play shows how Plutus recovers his sight, and thereupon riches are divided properly—the good man gets more and the bad man gets less. What a change! This play is positively a sermon. The hero is not our old friend at all, he is virtue suffering under undeserved poverty and rewarded at the end. The dispute between poverty and wealth may remind us of the *Clouds*, but the whole air and sentiment is different. The people are ordinary people; we are approximating to the new theory of comedy, that it should be an imitation of real life. And, indeed, on *that* ground we should be justified in saying that *Plutus* is the best of all the extant plays of Aristophanes. We are called upon to sympathise with the honest Chremylus and rejoice in his good fortune, for all the world as if he were the Vicar of Wakefield.

But the new comedy has not yet found its legs. The abstract idea of Wealth personified is, as we can now see clearly, a mistake. He would have been all very well in the old comedy, but in his present surroundings he is a bore. *L'Avare* deals with a somewhat similar subject, but in how much more satisfactory a manner! How it would be spoilt if we had a blind god coming in to talk with Harpagon! The imitation of manners collapses at once in the presence of such a creature. In the wild fantastic world of the old comedy such allegories are quite in place. When we have Socrates swinging in a basket discussing how many times a flea can jump the length of its own foot, a chorus of clouds floating in airy raiment and singing lovely melodies, an old Athenian gravely trying to cheat his creditors by the most nonsensical expedients, when we have all this astounding fabric of absurdities jostling one another, we are not in the least put out by a couple of figures coming on the stage labelled Right and Wrong, and disputing against one another. Simply because here we are not concerned with the imitation of real life at all; if we were, it would be a prodigious failure. No, what *is* a failure is not the *Clouds* but *Plutus*. It is neither fish, flesh nor fowl; it has relics of the old garments still hanging about it, while it is partly dressed in the new. Then again it has not enough plot for the comedy of manners; and so it is altogether a disappointing work, as much below the *Acharnians* and the *Birds* on the one side, as it is below *Phormio* and the *Rudens*, *Tartufe* and *Le Joueur* on the other.

There is no end to what may be said further on this fascinating subject, which has here been only treated from one side, and that inadequately enough. But if you have got as far as this you are sufficiently bored, and I bethink me of another story.

Two respectable citizens, men of a dignified prosperity, were walking down Piccadilly and one of them holding forth to the other. Let him tell it in his own words, as he told it to somebody else, who told it to a friend of mine who told it to me. "I had got rather a nice point about Home Rule, and I had been explaining it with perspicacity and some degree of eloquence for about twenty minutes, and was wondering how he would answer it and what impression I had made upon him, when he looked up and said: 'What an extraordinary thing it is that two old men like Gunn and Shrewsbury[1] should go on making such a lot of runs.'"

[1] Cricketers of the day.

LA ROCHEFOUCAULD

(Literary Society, 1902)

La Rochefoucauld

It has been truly said by a great poet that the proper study of mankind is man. That is a fact one is apt to lose sight of in colleges and places where they make CO_2. We are rather inclined to think that the comparative value of the Medicean and other MSS of Aeschylus, the phylogenetic value of the blastoderm, or the wave length of the ultra-violet rays, is the really important thing for man to interest himself in. And *à propos* of this I am reminded of a saying of a man who was great alike in mathematics, science, religion and literature, the immortal Pascal. "I had passed much time," he says, "in the study of the abstract sciences; but I lost my taste for them because I could share it with so few. When I began the *study of man* I saw that these abstract studies are not *proper* to him; I saw that in throwing myself into them I wandered further from my true state than the rest of the world does in ignoring them; and so I forgave men for neglecting them. But I did think that at least I should find plenty of companions in the study of man, because it is that which is his proper study. I was mistaken. There are still fewer who study man than who study geometry." Everything in Pascal is great and astonishing; and how astonishingly true is this. In vain descended from heaven the maxim "seek to know thyself"; we do not know ourselves nor one another, and we do not seek the knowledge, for the world is too much with us, and we think the average of Mr Fry[1] or the colour of a riband to be more important to us.

[1] A cricketer of the day.

But a literary society can least of all afford to neglect that study, for literature is largely, if not entirely, the expression of man's nature. And of all those literary persons who have sought to penetrate into the recesses of the mind few have thrown a more piercing light into its secret places than the accomplished and amiable Frenchman whom we have to-day taken for our subject. Amiable I say deliberately, for amiable he was above most men, however much the world may have chosen (in its rough and ready fashion) to dub him "cynic."

Francis, Prince of Marsillac, Baron of Verteuil and Duke of La Rochefoucauld, was born 15th December 1613. At the age of sixteen he served in an Italian campaign, and thenceforward his life was divided for many years between the court and the camp. As for his military exploits, I think we will leave them on one side; he never was very greatly distinguished as a soldier, and the French wars of that century are profoundly uninteresting. But his career in politics, if politics is a word to be applied to the court intrigues of that period, was much more important. The years 1630 to 1642, during which La Rochefoucauld was between sixteen and twenty-eight, are the years of the rule of Cardinal Richelieu, the greatest ruler of France between Louis XI and Napoleon. But his rule was no easy matter. By the ascendancy of his character and the force of his will he had subdued the weak and obstinate King, Louis XIII, to himself, but to keep him in leading-strings was an incessant struggle. On the other side was the Queen, Anne of Austria, more celebrated for the beauty of her hands and arms than for any more solid qualities of head and heart, eternally intriguing in a senseless sort of way with the Spaniards or anybody else whose interests were opposed to those of France, surrounded by busybodies and bad counsellors such as Mme de Chevreuse, dabbling in love affairs with Dukes of Buckingham and the like, hating the King and hated by the King, and hated above all by Richelieu, who is said to have been in love with her himself once. All the more turbulent among the great nobles of France rallied round her naturally, for they all hated the Cardinal, unable to understand his greatness, refusing to see that he was making France a great power, but quite able to see that he had an awkward habit of cutting off their heads. La Rochefoucauld's own father was compromised in the enterprise which conducted the Duke of Montmorency to the scaffold, and was accordingly exiled to Blois; the young La Rochefoucauld (whom I will call by this title proleptically to save trouble) was allowed to remain at Paris, and naturally he joined the discontented party. He seems to have felt a genuine pity for the persecutions to which the Queen was exposed (not altogether undeservedly) and attached himself especially to her service, acting as a channel of communication between her and Mme de Chevreuse. In course of time he naturally found his way into the Bastille, but was released after only eight days, and departed to serve in the army again.

After the death of Richelieu (4th December 1642) and of Louis XIII (14th May 1643) things got worse and worse. The new King was a child, Anne of Austria was regent, and the nobles who had intrigued against Richelieu might expect to rule the roost. But if they did, they were disappointed. Richelieu had bequeathed a successor to chastise them, even Mazarin, and now the minister was in league with the Queen. Indeed there is evidence that Mazarin was actually secretly married to her. Richelieu had been hated and feared, Mazarin was hated and despised. A supple Italian, ever resorting to craft and falsehood, sometimes overreaching himself by his own tortuous methods, avaricious and cowardly, he did not seem the man marked out by destiny to rule an old and haughty nation proud in arms. Yet somehow or other he always emerged victorious in the end.

The civil wars which broke out under his ministry are known as the Fronde. Of all civil wars the Fronde is perhaps the most frivolous. It has been regarded as a forerunner of the great Revolution, and it is true that the people of Paris did rise because of excessive taxation, but the people were at this time only the tools of a few ambitious and unscrupulous leaders. The Duke of Beaufort, Madame de Chevreuse, who in the kaleidoscope of politics was now against her old friend the Queen, and the beautiful and fascinating Duchess of Longueville were the principal fomenters of the revolt. As for La Rochefoucauld, he had been the lover of the former lady and was now of the latter. Thus he was drawn into the discontented party, but never was of great importance in it. But these facts are significant of the whole story. A civil war raised by women in which all the actors are fighting for their own ends, in which there are no great principles involved, in which men, like Condé himself, changed over from one side to the other for some paltry motive, and which ended by the leaders all betraying the people when they could get some sop for themselves—such a war is a weariness to the flesh. To us now there are only four of the actors in it who are alive, the

immortal names of Athos, Porthos, Aramis and d'Artagnan
—four did I say? Could I forget for a moment their
devoted followers, Planchet, Bazin, Mousqueton and
Grimaud? But everybody has read the glorious series of
their exploits as set forth by the great Dumas (it may be
as well to observe that I do not mean the chemist, but the
novelist, Alexander the great as he is fondly called by us
that are his devotees). *Twenty Years After* is a sufficient
picture and a sufficient criticism of the Fronde, and on the
whole I would advise you to be content with it. *I* shall not
attempt to characterise it further, but shall simply call
attention to its natural effect on La Rochefoucauld.

To begin with, let us quote the portrait given of him by
the Cardinal de Retz. De Retz as we all know had a way
of etching in his portraits with biting acid, and he was a
personal enemy of La Rochefoucauld, yet the impression
I have got of the latter makes me think that de Retz is
pretty right in his account of him. "There has always been
something unintelligible in La Rochefoucauld," says the
Cardinal.

He has always wished to mingle in intrigues from his
childhood....He has never shown capacity for any sort
of affair, and I do not know why, for he had qualities which
would have supplied in anybody else those in which he was
wanting. His view was not wide enough and he did not
even see clearly the whole of what was within its range:
but his good sense, which was remarkable in theory, together with the sweetness of his character, his insinuating
manners and his admirable ease in intercourse with others,
ought to have made up for his lack of penetration better
than it did. He has always been a prey to irresolution, but
I do not know to what to attribute this irresolution; it
cannot come from the fruitfulness of his imagination, which

is anything but lively. I cannot attribute it to the sterility of his judgment; for though his judgment is not keen in action, he has a sound foundation of reason. We see the effects of this irresolution, without knowing the cause. He has never been apt for war, though very much a soldier; he has never been a good courtier by his own unaided efforts, though he has always had the good will to be so. He has never been a good party-man, though engaged in party all his life. The shamefaced and timid air, which marks him in society, turned in affairs into an apologetic air; he thought he had an eternal necessity for apologising, and this, taken with his maxims, which do not always show enough faith in virtue, and his practice, which has always been to back out of affairs as impatiently as he had entered into them, causes me to conclude that he had much better have discovered his own limitations and been content to pass, as he might have done, for the most polished courtier and the most honourable man in everyday life who had appeared in his time.

Such is the character of him drawn by an enemy indeed, but one of the most piercing judges of men who have ever written. Amiable, gentle, honourable, a prey to irresolution—put such a man into the surroundings in which he passed all the time of life which has most effect in forming a man's judgment of the world, mixed up with intrigues of every kind in which he was but the cat's-paw of others more practical and more unscrupulous than himself. He had seen the hollowness of all those pretenders to virtue and patriotism who sold their professions for a title or a bag of gold, he had been betrayed and befooled by those he trusted, he must have been conscious that he was himself a failure in practical life, at least of that kind, and he came out of it all a disappointed man, with a root of bitterness in him. Small wonder that his maxims are often cynical, small wonder that he who had seen the great Condé turn traitor and the contemptible Mazarin come out at the top, did not make sufficient allowance for virtue, as de Retz has it. When one considers de Retz himself, the complaint certainly seems rather impudent, and it is also worth remarking that on one occasion La Rochefoucauld spared de Retz's life. Perhaps that was what impressed de Retz so much with his irresolution. I don't think *he* would have hesitated if the advantage had been the other way.

And as the final drop in the cup of disenchantment the Duchess of Longueville, who to put it delicately was not a bit better than she should be, threw him over for some other fellow whose name is not worth remembering. La Rochefoucauld underwent all the torments of jealousy. It has been observed that of all the weaknesses of man he seeks to justify in his maxims none but jealousy—but it must be added that it is very faintly. Then in a battle he was wounded in the head and for a time lost his sight. He had now plenty of time for reflection, and this was a turning-point in his life. After a long sojourn in darkness he recovered his sight, and settled down to live in leisure and tranquillity after that stormy youth of his. He was still only forty-two, a very good age for a man, though I say it as shouldn't.

This last period of his life extends over twenty-five years, to 17th March 1680. We have come from the age of the Fronde to the age of Louis XIV, from barricades and street fighting to drawing-rooms and the interchange of compliments, from the bickerings of an aristocracy to the lifeless splendour of the Grand Monarch. Or, to put it in a word, from *Twenty Years After* to the *Vicomte de Bragelonne*.

Of La Rochefoucauld's own life in this period there is not much to say. You will find constant references to him in the letters of that divine creature Mme de Sévigné; every afternoon he and Madame de Lafayette used to sit and talk together; he in his later years crippled by gout and often suffering horribly, she also an invalid—and no wonder, for she had given birth to the modern novel—how amazed she would have been to behold the vast progeny which has sprung from her. The man who could count Mme de Sévigné and Mme de Lafayette among his devoted friends must indeed have been himself something better than a withered cynic.

The external life of La Rochefoucauld now becomes a blank, a matter of powdered wigs and shoe polish. The age of *salons* had begun, an institution peculiarly Parisian. There assembled in the drawing-rooms of the ladies who led society everyone with pretension to *esprit*, there they discussed ethical questions with avidity. Scandal and gossip no doubt had their share, but it is the eternal glory of those Parisian ladies that they at least to a large extent rose superior to their sex, and strove to make not persons but principles their theme.

Ethics were in the air; everybody was interested in ethics of some sort or other, from the frivolities of the gentleman who distinguished twelve distinct varieties of sighs to the deep earnestness of the two greatest of La Rochefoucauld's contemporaries, Pascal and Molière. Ethics in those days were really interesting, however little you who go to lectures on them may believe it. People investigated one another and themselves and wrote what they called portraits of one another and themselves. Here are some extracts from La Rochefoucauld's portrait of himself.

The conversation of people of breeding is one of the pleasures which touch me nearest. I like it to be serious and that moral questions should form the principal part of it.

I love reading in general; that which I love most is that in which something may be found to mould the intellect and fortify the soul. Above all I find extreme satisfaction in reading with a person of intelligence; for then one reflects at every moment on that which one is reading, and from the reflexions one makes on it arises the most useful and most agreeable conversation in the world.

I love my friends; and I love them in such a way that I should never hesitate a moment to sacrifice my interests to theirs. I can lower myself for them and suffer patiently their ill humours; only I do not bestow many caresses on them, and I have not any great inquietude in their absence.

That shows all the best side of the man; here is a paragraph which is more like the average view of him:

I am not very much affected by pity, and could wish I were not so at all. However, I would do anything to comfort a person in affliction, and I believe one *ought* to do anything, even to testify much compassion for his suffering, for the miserable are so foolish that this does them the greatest good in the world. But I hold also that we should be content with testifying it, and take good care not to feel it; it is a passion which serves no purpose in a well-ordered mind, which only enfeebles the heart, and which one ought to leave to the people. For the people do nothing for reason and need passions to make them do things.

There speaks the cynic, the courtier, the aristocrat, the irresolute reflecting man who puzzled de Retz because he failed in everything. What wonder? Such an one is not a leader of men, no philosopher ever was. But we find in him

that strange inconsistency which though ever strange is
ever so common; it is just these men who despise the
multitude, who pass hard judgments on men in general,
who are sceptical concerning human virtue and the truth
of friendship—it is just these men who are the most de-
votedly attached to their friends, perhaps who are most
loved by their friends. And I think that La Rochefoucauld
only spoke the truth when he said he would never hesitate
between his friends' interests and his own.

The principal literary occupation of that society was the
composition of Memoirs and of Maxims. La Rochefoucauld wrote both, though his *Maxims* have so overshadowed
his *Memoirs* that everybody knows the one and nobody
the other. Never was there such a host of Memoirs as was
produced about that time. Hardly an actor in the Fronde,
man or woman, maid or priest, could refrain from writing
his or her version of the troubles. Nobody reads them, for
how can anyone read about the Fronde, except in the pages
of Dumas? Certainly I would not recommend anybody to
read La Rochefoucauld's. It is true that Bayle, he who wrote
the great Dictionary, positively ranked them above Julius
Caesar's when they first appeared—to compare them with
Caesar is too ridiculous for words. In the one case the
supreme man of action of all the world, narrating in a
matchless style the simple record of his achievements with
not a sentence superfluous nor a sentence uninteresting, in
the other a meditative dreamer trying to narrate events
which he could not control nor even understand, which are
not interesting in themselves, and in whose account every
page is dull. It is hard to believe that the *Memoirs* are the
work of the author of the *Maxims* at all.

You would have expected such a man to write history like Tacitus, and instead he writes like one of our modern historians.

There is one passage however which is interesting to all readers of the *Three Musketeers*. You all remember the famous story of the diamond ornaments in that veracious chronicle; here is the original story as given by La Rochefoucauld, whether true or not, God knows:

The Duke of Buckingham, was, as I have said, a magnificent and showy person; he took great pains over his appearance in court assemblies. The Countess of Carlisle, who had a great interest in observing him, soon perceived that he made a point of wearing certain diamond ornaments which were strange to her; she had no doubt that the Queen of France had given them to him, but to make doubly sure she took the opportunity of a private conversation with the Duke at a ball in England and cut off these ornaments, intending to send them to Cardinal Richelieu. The Duke of Buckingham discovered his loss in the evening. He guessed at once that the Countess of Carlisle had taken the diamonds and feared the effects of her jealousy, thinking her quite capable of placing them in the hands of the Cardinal in order to ruin the Queen. In this extremity, he despatched that instant an order to close all the harbours of England, and forbade anyone to leave the island on any pretext whatever until a given time. Meanwhile he had a new set of diamond ornaments made like those he had lost, and sent them to the Queen, informing her of what had happened. By thus closing the harbours he stopped the Countess, and she saw that the Duke had had all the time required to countermine her plot. Thus the Queen escaped the vengeance of her angry rival, and the Cardinal lost a certain means of convicting the Queen and making certain the suspicions of the King. For it *was* the King who had given her the ornaments, which *she* had then given to Buckingham.

That is the simple story from which sprang one of the most enchanting adventures in fiction. I confess I do not believe the historian any more than the novelist—and it is a strange thing that M. d'Artagnan is never mentioned by La Rochefoucauld. I shall extract two other passages as of some interest. In the first the bitterness overflows for once from the author's heart, and we are reminded of the prevailing tone of the *Maxims*:

In the end I met with scarcely more gratitude from Mme de Chevreuse for thus ruining myself a second time to remain her friend, than I had found in the Queen. Madame de Chevreuse forgot in her exile all that I had done for her as easily as the Queen had forgotten my services when she was able to repay them.

That is what comes of putting your faith in peers and princes and such people; it is not a school for learning belief in human virtue.

My second extract throws a light on the failure of the *Memoirs* and on the character of the actors in the Fronde.

It is almost impossible to write a really exact account of the disturbances, because those who set them going, being influenced by bad motives, have taken care to prevent their being known. They feared that posterity would accuse them of devoting the happiness of their country to their own private interests. Besides this reason, it is difficult enough for anyone recounting the affairs of his own time to keep his passions so pure that he shall not abandon himself to hate or flattery, the reefs on which truth generally makes shipwreck. For myself, I propose to give a disinterested recital of all that has passed, that I may leave to the reader entire liberty to praise or blame.

That I believe is the theory of modern historians, and perhaps that is why it is impossible to read them.

But let us come to the *great* book, the *Maxims*. The popular opinion is that La Rochefoucauld is a cynic, and there is an end of him, that his book is a collection of sayings calculated to annoy, and there is an end of it, that his philosophy consists of tracing everything in us to *amour propre*, and there is an end of that. I will not deny that there is much truth in this view.

"You may be cleverer than another man," says La Rochefoucauld himself, "but you won't be more clever than *all* the others." And Goethe, who said the last word on nearly everything, has summed up this question also (I mean the question of the value of the world's opinion) in a nutshell: "there is no doubt this public, so much honoured and despised, is almost always wrong in particulars, hardly ever in its broad views."

The broad view then, we may take it, is correct; La Rochefoucauld is a cynic, his *Maxims* do annoy, and he is fond of setting down *amour propre* as the mainspring of our actions.

We will take the three points in order. And with regard to the first, it is natural to begin with asking what we mean by calling him a cynic. Historically, the Cynics were a sect of the followers of Socrates; why they were called Cynics nobody knows, but their chief peculiarities consisted in the exaggeration of certain of the salient points in the character of Socrates. That extraordinary man was in part an ascetic; he disdained appearances, never wore shoes even in the coldest winter, was content to live on bread and water, and considered a moral life alone sufficient for happiness. These sides of his manifold character the Cynics took up and exaggerated, neglecting all the rest. Diogenes in his tub, despising Alexander the Great (not Dumas this time but the Macedonian) in the height of his glory, is the extreme type of them. According to their name, they lived like dogs, and shut themselves off from all the highest life of man, representing that revolt against civilisation which crops up every now and then in so many times and places. Such a life necessarily leads to a low view of human nature. He who is content to live like an animal must needs look on man as an animal and nothing more, however much he may prate of virtue, which he does not understand. For the virtue of man is the virtue of a social being whose reason has raised him above the animals. And the Cynics were not even social animals. And as for *their* virtue, it was purely negative, being nothing but the avoidance of all those desires which bind us to enjoyments.

In modern times the meaning of the word has changed. The cynic is no longer the Indian fakir who dwells like a solitary animal in the woods absorbed in the contemplation of himself. But he is a person who looks on man from a low standpoint, who like Diogenes despises all glory and all the varnish of civilisation, who loves to draw out the animal nature or at any rate the selfishness of man. That he speaks the truth is true, but it is not the whole truth. That he speaks the truth is indeed just what people complain of, for if he did not he would be harmless, but he speaks truths which are unpleasant. People generally do not like either what is true or what is false, so far simply as it is true or false; they like what is pleasant to them. They like being flattered because then they hear what is pleasant but false, they like hearing a pleasant truth still better because it is pleasant and true.

When thus La Rochefoucauld is called a cynic I take it
that what it comes to is this, that he speaks unpleasant
truths, and that he does not speak the whole truth. And
if there is anything calculated to make one a cynic is it
not just this, that a man who forces you to contemplate
a truth you do not like should be called a cynic, that you
should therefore refuse to listen to him and should think
you have disposed of him and his arguments because you
have labelled him with a nickname? But I think better of
you who are here present, for I perceive that you are
listening to me.

But he does not speak the whole truth! No, I daresay
not, and should very much like to know how many writers
do. But it does not occur to people to complain of some
amiable writer who wears rose-coloured spectacles and sees
everything through a haze of benevolence and sentimen-
tality, a Dickens for example—it does not occur to them
to complain that "he does not speak the whole truth and
therefore we will not read him." What right have you to
expect the whole truth? Would it not be better to consider
first which sort of writer is more likely to do you good? If
indeed one were compelled to confine oneself to one or
other kind, I would say, "keep the benevolent gentleman
with his spectacles, and leave the teller of unpleasant
truths alone." But there is no such compulsion, and in
fact the case is very much the other way. Everywhere we
meet with the pleasant truths and the pleasant falsehoods,
whether in books or in life; and it spoils us. It is a good
thing to brace oneself a little with the tonic of a La Rochefoucauld now and then. It is a good thing to be reminded
that the agreeable illusions of youth, the ebullient en-

thusiasms of friendly conversation, the protestations which are truly meant at the time, will often fail to stand the test of time, that after all other people are more concerned with themselves than with you, that as La Rochefoucauld says "gratitude is often nothing but a lively sense of favours to come." Else if we persist in thinking too well of men we may find the day when our illusions shall be stripped from off us, and we see the world as it is and it will horrify us and we shall turn misanthropical and curse mankind and die. Are not these things written for our edification in the *Phaedo* of Plato and in Shakespeare's *Timon of Athens*?

Call then La Rochefoucauld a cynic if you like, but let that only be the greater reason for taking his bitter medicine, be it only as an antidote after the manner of Mithradates King of Pontus.

Besides I cannot help thinking that this charge of cynicism is somewhat exaggerated. I remember the golden saying, one of the shortest of all, "on pardonne tant que l'on aime." I remember those two beautiful sayings which better than any others illuminate the very heart of friendship: "It is more shameful to distrust one's friends than to be deceived by them." And again: "We cannot love anything except in its relation to us, and we only follow our own taste and our own pleasure when we prefer our friends to ourselves: nevertheless by this preference alone can friendship be true and perfect."

Those are not bad epigrams for a cynic to make, and not easily will you find anything more beautiful and more true.

But it is time to be getting on to the second objection, that the *Maxims* annoy. This is precisely the proof that they are true. When Swift tells us that we are Yahoos, in every respect inferior to his Houyhnhnms, we do not care; we only laugh at it because we know it is not true nor anywhere near it. But to read La Rochefoucauld is to be put to one perpetual blush. Do not mind it; it is a good thing and very becoming, especially if one has a fair complexion; blushing has always been held to be a mark of modesty and ingenuousness. It *is* annoying for an elderly person like me to read that the old are fond of giving good advice because they are no longer able to give bad examples. Or that we think we are leaving our vices when it is our vices that are leaving us. Or that the passions of youth are hardly more opposed to salvation than the lukewarmness of the old. Or that we come fresh to each distinct age of life and are apt to show a sad lack of experience in each despite the number of our years. But *you* shall not get off either. "Most young people think they are natural when they are only unpolished and rude." Women especially do not love him, for much the same reason that Byron asserts they did not like Don Juan, because he strips off the sentiment from love and laughs at that and everything else. I never yet met a woman who had read La Rochefoucauld or who could abide him. They do not like to hear that the intellect of most women serves rather to fortify their folly than their reason. Nor that there are few women whose merit outlasts their looks. Nor that it is with true love as with ghosts: everybody talks of it and nobody has seen it.

But I confess that it seems to me that when La Rochefoucauld talks of women he does not hit the mark as he does with men. He talks from the average male standpoint, which is absurd. And yet he spent all his life under the influence of women. Besides his early love affairs, in his sober autumn he was the devoted friend of Mme de Lafayette and Mme de Sablé. And then he talks of them like that! No, the reason women don't like him is not because of what he says of *them* in particular; it is because of those maxims which apply to men and women alike, and which are not absurd at all, unfortunately. Such as "whatever good we hear of ourselves, we never hear anything new to us." And "there is no man who believes himself inferior in *all* his qualities to that man of the world whom he thinks the most of." Yes, we all think *we* should have had the sense to clear out of Moscow before the cold weather began.

Then again there are some elderly gentlemen of my acquaintance who must feel uneasy when they read this question: "Why must we needs have memory enough to retain in its minutest details all that has happened to us, and *not* enough to remember how often we have related them to the same person?" And: "We can forgive those who bore us, but not those who are bored by us." And: "Gravity is a mystery of the body invented to hide the emptiness of the mind." I am reminded of—but never mind. And above all there is one question which made me wriggle like a worm the first time I read it: "Why is it that we all complain of our memory and none of us of our judgment?" Since then I have taken to giving myself airs on the strength of my memory and to professing that my judgment is no better than other people's. And yet here I am pronouncing confidently on La Rochefoucauld and there you all sit judging him and me and not having the slightest doubt that you are quite right.

Now for the third objection, which is thus stated by
Voltaire: "There is hardly more than one truth in the
book, that *amour propre* is the motive of everything."
It is true, adds Voltaire, that this idea is presented under
such varied aspects that it is almost always piquant. But
certainly, though many of the maxims I have already
quoted do *not* illustrate this theory, yet it is true that that
is the prevailing idea, that is the great impression we carry
away from the book.

I confess that it is difficult to come to any very clear
conclusion about this matter. It seems certain that if we
interpret the theory of *amour propre* to mean that we must
seek our own happiness in all we do, which indeed is the
foundation of utilitarianism, it is impossible to escape from
admitting that it is true. The martyr prefers the flame to
recantation because he would be unhappier if he recanted
than he is when he burns. The man who reads papers to
literary societies must, I suppose, think it would be worse
still for him if he backed out of it. In whatever choice we
make between alternative actions we must needs choose
that which appeals the more strongly to us ourselves.
We may say we sacrifice ourselves to our party, our family,
or even our college. But if any man plays cricket for his
college rather than for his county, it is after all because
his college appeals more to him personally. There *is* no
escape; we can only love things or people in their relation
to us, we can only act because this or that action appeals
to us. The very attempts his critics make to escape prove
only that there is no escape. M. Rébelliaud, for instance,
says that there are other motives for our actions, such as
custom, imitation, inconsistency. And how does that help

him? You *may* do a thing from custom, very true. But why do you want to keep up the custom? Because you feel it is easier for you to keep it up than to break it, because your self-love is interested in keeping it up. How many things we do through custom simply because our vanity is pleased by having a custom! Inconsistency is just the same turned inside out. And imitation; if you do a thing through imitation it is because it pleases you to imitate. Really, if M. Rébelliaud cannot find a better defence than that, he had better capitulate at once. The very reason why he and others protest against La Rochefoucauld is because to admit the truth of what he says hurts their self-love and their vanity. Their very protestations are signs that he speaks the truth. Lord Byron with all his faults was sincere and straightforward, and this is how he bursts out (*Journal*, 1st December 1813): "Curse on Rochefoucauld for being always right! In him a lie were virtue—or at least a comfort to his readers." And as Saintsbury observes, it is a great deal easier to abuse than to refute him.

But then if that is all La Rochefoucauld means, that we must be moved to everything by ourselves, it seems a truism, and nothing for respectable librarians of the Institute to get angry about.

Yet there must be something in the objections made; so much smoke would never rise without some fire beneath it. And I think the real difficulty all comes of lack of definition, as usual.

Amour propre may and does mean self-love in the sense already given to it, but of self-love there are divers kinds. It will be sufficient for the present purpose to divide it

into two by the method called by Platonists dichotomy.
To put it briefly, there is a good self-love and a bad self-
love. When your self-love leads you to sacrifice yourself
because you feel you cannot endure not to do so, that is
a good self-love, which is to say that it is praised by other
people. Such is the self-love of the martyr, the patriot,
the man who plays cricket for his college. But the other,
the bad self-love, is unfortunately much commoner; in fact
it is in plain English selfishness, and in La Rochefoucauld
more particularly that variety of selfishness which is called
vanity. After writing all this I find it all crystallised in one
of the maxims of Vauvenargues: "If there are two kinds
of self-love," says he, "one which makes us hard and selfish
and cruel and one which makes us compassionate and
obliging to others, is that any reason for confounding the
two?" By these few words Vauvenargues blows the whole
edifice of La Rochefoucauld to smithereens. I often wonder
that Vauvenargues is so little known in England. I fear
the reason is that he takes a steady view of life as a whole
and is not bitter and one-sided. Do you remember what
Samuel Rogers said? He was famous for his sarcastic and
malicious sayings (which indeed were much better than
his poetry) and in defence of this habit of his he once said
to somebody: "You see, my voice is very weak, and if I did
not say ill-natured things nobody would hear me." So it is
that people open their ears to La Rochefoucauld and close
them like a deaf adder to Vauvenargues.

The way, then, in which I conceive that the attack upon
La Rochefoucauld ought to be directed is this. It is quite
true that we must be guided by self-love in all we do, even
when we sacrifice self, but La Rochefoucauld lays too much

stress, lays we may say the *whole* stress of his criticism of
man upon the inferior kind of self-love, upon selfishness
and vanity. The better kind does appear in him once
or twice, but not often. Especially in that noble maxim
concerning friendship, which I have quoted once and will
quote again, for never can one repeat it too often. "We
cannot love anything except in its relation to us, and we
only follow our own taste and our own pleasure when we
prefer our friends to ourselves: nevertheless by this preference alone can friendship be true and perfect." Therein
lies already the whole of the distinction I have just striven
to elaborate a little. Therein shine out the human eyes for
once from behind the mask in which he chose to shroud
himself.

Was he conscious himself or not of what he was doing?
Did he deliberately confound the two meanings of self-
love? I think not; I think he got into the way of seeking
after the motives of men, and saw that all must needs come
of self-love in some sense, and was misled into too low
a view of man's nature in consequence, partly by the
ruinous education he had gone through, partly by an
ambiguity and the *generally* bad meaning of the term
amour propre, partly by the mere fact that grubbing
after motives necessarily leads men to take such a
view.

In this connexion I remember an interesting story which
Mme de Rémusat tells of Napoleon. Never, she says, did
any man carry the habit of seeking for motives in men to
such a pitch as he. Shortly before his Egyptian expedition,
he went to visit Talleyrand who was lying ill. He talked
with such enthusiasm of his plans that he quite carried

away the cautious and hard and selfish diplomat, who in a moment of generosity said: "There is a large sum of money lying in that drawer, take it if it will help you and I will chance your repaying it." Napoleon took it, went to Egypt, lost his army, came back, became First Consul, and repaid the money. But he said when he repaid it: "I have been puzzling ever since you lent me this money to find out what conceivable motive you can have had for doing it, and I cannot imagine what it can have been." Talleyrand answered that there wasn't any, that it was in an access of generous enthusiasm. "Then," said Napoleon, "you were a dupe."

That is what comes of carrying to an extreme the habit of seeking after motives. And this brings me to another way of putting it. One may divide self-love into conscious and unconscious; the unconscious lies at the root of all that we praise and call virtue, the conscious we blame. And La Rochefoucauld's mistake may be said to come of representing all our actions as coming from conscious self-love and neglecting the unconscious. That is what it comes to when de Retz complains that he does not allow enough to virtue. And that of course is the natural pit for a man to fall into who thinks about these things. He who thinks about motives must be conscious of them, and will easily give too much weight to conscious springs of action. But that sort of self-love which produces what we call unselfishness is unconscious, and here it is that La Rochefoucauld's analysis fails. Most men are not conscious of their motives, because, as Pascal found, there are even fewer men interested in the study of man than in the study of geometry.

Moreover unluckily, for this same reason, a great deal of the worse self-love is also unconscious. We do not know how vain we are. Pascal himself lays as much stress on this as ever did any cynic. "Those who write against glory," he says, "wish to have the glory of having written well, and those who read wish to have the glory of having read it; and I myself who write this have perhaps this desire, and perhaps those who read it will have it too." It is in this unveiling of the unconscious vanity and selfishness of the mind that the true and terrible force of La Rochefoucauld lies. No other ever laid bare with such sagacity all those secret nerves, which ache under his scalpel. "That which renders the pain of shame and of jealousy so keen, is that vanity cannot be called in to support them." "What makes the vanity of others intolerable, is the fact that it wounds our own." "What we call liberality is most often only the vanity of giving, which we love better than what we give." "We easily forget our faults when they are only known to ourselves." How horribly true and undeniable all these things are, and yet to which of us do they not come like flashes of light to reveal our own deformity? That is why Byron cursed La Rochefoucauld in his vehement way, why so many will not endure him and why some are drawn to him by a dreadful fascination.

Yes, it is indeed quite true that this is the principal impression which we get from the maxims, as the innumerable facets on the eye of an insect unite in an impression on the insect's brain. The more astonishing is it that he has contrived to present this idea in so many forms and with such perpetual freshness. Every time it seems to be new. But then it is interspersed with many other ideas which do not come under the same head at all. For of order and arrangement in the book there seems to be none. Here and there you get little groups of maxims which are connected, but generally speaking they seem thrown together at random. But if there is no particular form about the book as a whole, the form of each separate maxim is perfection, and a deal of polishing it took to bring them to it, as you may see by comparing the earlier versions with the final.

But it is not a book to be continually with one after all. The squirrel gyrates wonderfully in his cage, but it is a cage, and now and then a breath from the outside world comes upon one and one longs to escape from cages and drawing-rooms. After reading twenty or thirty of these perfect epigrams, what a change it is to recall some of those great sayings of the truly inspired men who never were corrupted as La Rochefoucauld was by evil communications. Think of that hard saying of Spinoza, which indeed should be treasured up and fed upon in our hearts, "He who truly loves God must not expect to be loved in return," or that which Goethe drew from it, as he confesses, "If I love thee, what is that to thee?" Or take that question so beautifully treated by Aristotle, Why is it that he who confers benefits loves more than he who receives them? La Rochefoucauld would have said (I do not know that he actually does) that the recipient loves less because his vanity or self-love is hurt by being in an inferior position, whereas the self-love of him who confers the benefit is flattered. And much truth there may be in that, but how much more noble is Aristotle's answer. He who confers the benefit stands to him who receives in some sort as the artist to his own work or the parent to his own child, and therefore loves the more of the two, just as the poet loves exceedingly his own poems, rejoicing in them as if they were his children. More noble and beautiful is that and surely not less true in the case of all those unsophisticated and uncorrupted who have kept themselves unspotted from the world. And it is better on the whole to cling to those nobler views; little enough we may all be, and good it may be to realise that now and then, but if we cannot be good for very much, let us at least like children play at being good, for it is of such, and not of La Rochefoucauld, that is the kingdom of heaven.

LUCIAN

(Literary Society, 1905)

Lucian

I⊤ is written in the *Life of Lord Macaulay* that he was as well acquainted with his Lucian as most literary men are with Voltaire. The statement is made with uplifted eyebrows, an air of surprise. It wakes in turn surprise in the mind of the classical scholar. It is very remarkable, he thinks to himself, that the chosen youth of England, all the boys in all the schools who are not too stupid to do anything but Science and Modern Languages, should spend many years in the acquisition of the Classics and should make so little use of them, when they have got them, that they positively know their Voltaire and do not know their Lucian. They pick up a little French in an odd hour or two under the supervision of an amiable and incompetent Frenchman who has been a failure in his own country. They spend many hours every week in studying the Classics under the guidance of men who have distinguished themselves at the Universities in cricket, football and athletic sports. And the end of it is that they do not know their Lucian and probably imagine that he was a Latin poet put to death by Nero for writing one of the most tedious epics upon record.

After spending much valuable time in considering this problem, I believe I have at length arrived at a satisfactory solution. The classical student becomes so highly trained in the pure idioms of Attic Greek that he is shocked by the occasional lapses from it in the pages of this delightful Syrian. It is true—it must be admitted with regret—that Lucian *is* shaky in his uses of μή and οὐ. Yet I beseech you

not to be too much influenced by this. The correct use of
μὴ and οὐ is after all not absolutely everything in literature.
There are excellent authors who do not attempt to write
Attic Greek at all, there are authors of repute who do not
even know any—for example Mr George Moore and St
Paul. Lay aside for once this literary purism, and condescend to take a glance at a man who is much more amusing
and delightful reading than most of the people you toil
through in pursuit of a degree.

Lucian was born somewhere about A.D. 120 at a place
called Samosata, in Syria, on the banks of the Euphrates.
Of his early years little enough is known. His parents
thought a liberal education too expensive, so he was sent
to a school of art, poor boy. His uncle was a sculptor of
some sort, and the nephew was taken into his shop. One
day was enough for Lucian, he broke a slab of marble, his
uncle thrashed him, he came home in tears and, of course,
his mother took his part. That night, if we may believe
Lucian's own account (though it is generally better *not* to
believe what he says) he dreamed a dream. Two women,
whom in modern language we may interpret as the genius
of the Slade and the genius of the Faculty of arts, laid hold
of him and struggled for him so that he was nearly rent
in twain; Lucian chose wisely, deserted the Slade for ever
and went in for arts. In those days that meant that he
became a rhetorician. He wandered about the world from
Syria to Gaul lecturing on rhetoric and the art of public
speaking. Somewhere about 160 he gave up rhetoric also, because he judged it to be little better than flat lying (and men
were not made prime ministers in those days for their skill
in "lying in state at Westminster," as a late acquaintance

of ours did both before and after death). So he went and settled at Athens, where he perfected that beautiful Attic style which is so remarkable in a man brought up on the banks of the Euphrates. For though he never did get some little details right, which are now taught to mere beginners, he yet wrote a Platonic Greek which on the whole is most beautiful and admirable. Late in life he was appointed to some sort of Government office, but it was a sinecure and only intended to keep him comfortable in worldly goods, probably the War Office. Much plagued with gout in his age (a subject on which he wrote an amusing mock tragedy) he finally died, it is said a hundred years old.

The time at which he lived was very interesting. The old order was changing, yielding place to new, nor was it yet clear in which particular way the change would come in the thought of men. The beautiful and withal absurd old Paganism, the religion of Artemis crowned with the crescent moon hunting in the woodlands, of golden Aphrodite rising from the salt sea, of Zeus shaking Olympus with his nod and kicking his son out of heaven and beating his wife, of Dionysus reeling ripe among a rout of Silenuses and Bacchantes—all this had long become incredible and ridiculous. It is true that in the lifetime of Lucian a desperate attempt was made to make the dry bones live, as yet later it was to be again under Julian. But it was a galvanic business at the best. And as those venerable oak trees gradually mouldered into dust, there sprang up about them a whole wilderness of new and fantastic growths, men believed everything and nothing, Apollonius of Tyana worked miracles and founded a sort of sect, that incredible impostor Alexander of Abonutichus did the like,

a monstrous rout of Oriental religions invaded the vacant
ground, the dog-headed Anubis, Isis with her sistrum and
Mithra with his bull—in Tiberim defluxit Orontes—all the
ghosts came out in the twilight after their fashion, even
as we now see in the decay of faith people, presumably
sane, resorting to palmistry and table-turning, dwelling
uncomfortably for a week together in haunted houses to
study spiritual manifestations, and speculating seriously
on the question whether hobgoblins do or do not wear
clothes. Among the other innumerable sects was one called
Christians, generally supposed to be exceedingly mischievous, to be principally occupied with the worship of
an ass's head and to be a mere variety of Judaism on just
the same footing as the rest. It was by no means yet clear
that Christianity would beat the rest—those learned in
such matters declare positively that about the end of the
second century it seemed to be a turn of the scale whether
Christ or Mithra should prevail—Mithra was worshipped
by countless thousands throughout the Empire; for instance, along the line of the Roman occupation in the north
of Britain the legionaries have left innumerable relics of
his cult. To Lucian all of these things were on the same
footing, and he laughed at all with equal impartiality and
equal wit. Perhaps the best specimen of his attacks upon
the established religion is the dialogue called—let us say
Jupiter-Irving. Jupiter is shown in a great state of mind,
ranting in high-flown iambic verses:

O man's first disobedience and the fire
That wretch Prometheus stole from heavenly hearths!
To be a god or not—that is the question—
Ye quivers with three-bolted thunder stored—
With ever burning sulphur unconsumed—

Athena entreats him to condescend to explain—"*we*
haven't swallowed Euripides wholesale," she says, "and
can't keep it up in that strain." Juno says sarcastically
she knows what's the matter—it's some new love affair of
Jupiter's, but he says it's much more serious—it's just
a toss-up whether the gods are to be honoured any longer.
Two philosophers—let us say Professor Huxley and the
Archbishop of Canterbury—have been disputing about
Providence in the nineteenth century—Huxley says there
are no gods and that the world is a matter of chance and
natural selection—the excellent Archbishop did his best
to keep his end up—but they agreed to put it off till to-day.
"So," says Jupiter, "you see what a fix *we're* in." They
decide to hold an assembly of all the gods—proclamation
is made and the gods assemble, but there is a great dispute
about precedence—some of them are made of gold, and
unluckily the golden gods are generally outlandish heathen
deities, the best are mostly only marble or bronze, or perhaps a hollow shell of ivory and gold but wooden inside,
honeycombed by whole colonies of mice and rats. Jupiter
has decided they shall sit in order according to their value,
and Neptune is very wrath that a dog-faced Egyptian god
should sit above *him*. However they get settled at last,
amid great tumult, the more vulgar gods crying out—
"Divide, divide the sacrifices! This is thirsty work, where's
the nectar and ambrosia? One god, one victim." Jupiter
gets on his legs to make a speech, but is very nervous—
Mercury suggests he should begin with Demosthenes, so
he starts with a Philippic, slightly altered for the occasion:
"I believe you would give a great deal, men of—er—
Heaven, to know why it is that you are here assembled,

and therefore I beg of you to give me your best attention.
It is impossible to exaggerate the importance of the present
crisis, and yet *we* appear to pay no attention to it. I wish
now (for truth is Demosthenes is running dry) just to tell
you what is the matter." And so he explains. None of the
other gods have any advice to offer, but Mephistopheles
gets up and has the face to tell the gods it's all their own
fault—their oracles are so deplorably ambiguous—they
don't do anything but sit and gobble up sacrifices. This sets
some of the others on their defence, but they only make
themselves ridiculous. Meantime the controversy between
the two philosophers begins again upon earth, and the gods
lean downward and listen. The Archbishop brings his artil-
lery to bear on the profane Huxley, but is ignominiously
defeated at every point, until the dignitary of the Church
fairly loses his temper, calls the other all the bad names he
can lay his tongue to, accuses him of having murdered his
brother, of corrupting the youth like Socrates, and of
making speeches in the Union in defence of the Boers. So
ends the discussion, and the only consolation for the gods
is that all the rabble in Greece believes in them after all,
and *all* the savages without exception. "Ah," says
Jupiter sadly, "that is all very well, but you know what
Darius says in Herodotus, about Zopyrus who won
Babylon for him—I'd rather have one man like that on
my side than a million Babylons."

The more intellectual classes were the prey of philosophy.
Centuries before this Alexander the Great had murdered
his intimate friend Clitus in one of those fits of drunken
fury to which that great and amiable prince was given.
He shut himself up (being sober) in an agony of remorse

and shame—what did his attendants do?—they solemnly
sent in two philosophers to comfort him. I imagine to
myself an unfortunate student who in an unguarded moment has written down the statement that the vagus nerve
connects with the Fallopian tubes and has been consequently ploughed—I imagine him sitting with his head in
his hands and his whisky untasted beside him—I like to
dwell on the picture of the maid servant announcing two
gentlemen to speak with him and (in spite of his protesting
a desire for solitude) ushering in—Professor Read and Mr
Grieve. Yes, in those days philosophy was a serious matter,
and conceived that she had a work to do in the world. And
while Lucian was sharpening his jests in Athens the man
on whom rested the whole weight of the civilised world was
no other than the great and wise and good and sad Emperor Marcus Aurelius Antoninus, he round whose head
rests the last halo of the ancient world, fulfiller of the
dream of Plato, the philosopher made king. Like King
Arthur he fought in the mist the last battle of the old
against the new, and when he died the brand Excalibur was
cast away. So lofty, so severe are his *Meditations* that
they pierce us like the cold stars of winter; everything
human is purged out of him. This was the last word of the
wisdom of Greece:

Either gods or atoms. Either confusion and entangle-
ment and scattering again, or unity, order, providence.
If the first, why do *I* wish to live amid the clashings of
chance and chaos? or care for aught else but to become
earth myself at last? and why am I disturbed, since this
dispersion (death) will come whatever I do? But if the
latter case be true, I reverence and stand firm and trust
in him who rules.

Thus wags the world up and down from age to age. And either the universal mind determines each event; and if so, accept thou that which it determines. Or it has ordered once for all and all follows in sequence. Or invisible elements are the origin of all things. In a word, if there be a god, then all is well; if all things go at random, act not at random thou.

It is pure Agnosticism—for that also is no new thing in the world—but in that faith lived and died the highest recorded type of pure duty. It is good to go and look on his marble bust in the British Museum; it is not beautiful, but in gazing on it one feels there are better things in the world than beauty, and hears him saying in the last words of the *Meditations*: "Depart thou then contented, for he that releaseth thee is content."

Against philosophy in such a form what man should dare to breathe a word? Well, *some* people do—and their word is prig. But the world was full of philosophers of very different kinds. Quarrelsome were they, vain as peacocks, preaching one thing and doing another, wearing long beards and ragged cloaks and talking organised nonsense. Upon these Lucian fell with joy. He so bantered and badgered them that they got seriously angry (or else he pretends so) and he condescended to defend himself by saying that he only attacked impostors and not the real thing—just as Molière said, though with both Molière and Lucian it is difficult to distinguish. And indeed the man whose trade is to laugh has a way of laughing at what he respects as much as what he doesn't.

In one of his most celebrated dialogues Mercury is represented as holding an auction and putting up the philosophers for sale. He begins with Pythagoras. "Gentlemen," says the auctioneer, "we here offer you a philosopher of the very best and most select description—who buys? who wants to be a cut above the rest of the world? Who wants to understand the harmonies of the universe, and the transmigration of souls? Who would like to be a vegetarian and live a second life in the form of a peacock?" Pythagoras fetches a high price, being knocked down to a syndicate of philosophers from Asia Minor for £40. Diogenes the Cynic goes for three halfpence, and Mercury gladly jumps at even that offer. Socrates fetches £8, Aristotle no less than £80. Last comes the sceptic Pyrrho, what we nowadays call a neo-Berkeleyan, a sect which now flourishes at a place sufficiently described if I say that it is generally rather behind the times and in particular behind Cambridge. A customer asks him a few questions.

Customer. Tell me, now, what do you know?
Pyrrho. Nothing.
C. What do you mean?
P. That nothing seems to me certain.
C. Are we ourselves nothing?
P. Well, that is what I am not sure of.
C. Don't you know whether you are anything yourself?
P. That is what I am still more in doubt about.
C. What a creature of doubts it is! And what are those scales for, pray?
P. I weigh arguments in them, and balance them one against another; and then, when I find them precisely equal and of the same weight, why, I find it impossible to tell which of them is true.
C. Well, is there anything you can do in any other line of business?
P. Anything, except catch a runaway slave.
C. And why can't you do that?
P. Because, you see, I've no faculty of *apprehension*.

C. So I should think—you seem to me quite slow and stupid. And now, what do you consider the main end of knowledge?

P. Ignorance—to hear nothing and see nothing.

C. You confess yourself blind and deaf then?

P. Yea, and void of sense and perception, and in no wise differing from a worm.

C. I must buy you. (*To Mercury*) What shall we say for him?

Mercury. An Attic mina.

C. Here 'tis. Now, fellow, have I bought you or not—tell me?

P. Well, it's a doubtful question.

C. Not at all—at least I've paid for you.

P. I reserve my opinion on that point; it requires consideration.

C. Follow me, at all events—that's a servant's duty.

P. Are you sure you're stating a fact?

C. There's the auctioneer, and there's the money, and there are the bystanders to witness.

P. Are you sure there are any bystanders?

C. I'll have you off to the grinding-house, sir, and make you feel I'm your master by very tangible proofs.

P. Stay—I should like to argue that point a little.

The sequel to this dialogue is called *The Resuscitated Philosophers.* It begins with Lucian flying for his life, pursued by a multitude of wrathful philosophers who have got permission to come up from the world of the dead to punish him. They are led by Socrates, crying: "Pelt the wretch, heave half a brick at him—oyster shells—anything. Hit him in the eye, Plato, and you Chrysippus, and you! He is the common enemy of all. What, tired already, Epicurus? You luxurious idle dog! Be men, philosophers, summon all your pluck; Aristotle, do run a little faster. —Good, we've caught the beast." Then they propose

differcnt punishments, but Lucian demands a fair trial.
Diogenes (angry above the rest at having been sold for
such a trifle at the auction) acts as accuser. Of course,
Lucian is triumphantly acquitted.

The *Death of Peregrinus* is one of the works most interesting to us, because it is in that that we hear most of the
Christians. This Peregrinus had been a bad lot in his youth,
had then become a Christian and held high office in the
Church (I have known cases of the kind myself) but got
into trouble again, was expelled from the Church, expelled
from Rome by the authorities, tried to make the people of
Elis revolt against the Empire, an enterprise about as
hopeful as the Jameson raid, and at last finding his influence waning among them, gave out that he would
solemnly burn himself like Hercules at the next Olympic
festival. And he actually did—Lucian was present and
thus describes it.

The more foolish of the crowd shouted "Live, for the
sake of the Greeks!" But the more hard-hearted cried
"Fulfil your promise!" At this the old man was not a little
put out, for he had expected that they would surely all lay
hold on him, and not let him get into the fire, but force him
to live against his will. But this exhortation to keep his
promise fell on him quite unexpectedly, and made him
paler than ever, though his colour looked like death before.
He trembled, and became silent.... When the moon rose
(for she too must needs look upon this grand sight) he
came forward, clad in his usual dress, and followed by his
train of Cynics, and specially the notorious Theagenes of
Patrae, well fitted to play second in such a performance.
Peregrinus too carried a torch; and approaching the pile—
a very large one, made up of pitch-pine and brushwood—
they lighted it at either end. Then the hero (mark what
I say) laid down his scrip and his cloak, and stood in his

under-garment—and very dirty it was. He next asked for
frankincense to cast on the fire; and when some one brought
it, he threw it on, and turning his face towards the south
(this turning towards the south is an important point in
the performance) he exclaimed "Shades of my father and
my mother, be propitious, and receive me!" When he had
said this, he leaped into the burning pile and was seen no
more, the flames rising high and enveloping him at once.

It is evident that the Christians could not well blame
Lucian for his account of this impostor, who had made a
good thing out of it by swindling the Christians themselves.
And Lucian's account of Christianity itself is really a very
fair one and remarkably accurate. It is true it calls it an
"extraordinary philosophy," and says with compassion
"these poor wretches persuade themselves that they shall
be immortal and live for ever, so that they despise death
and some of them offer themselves to it voluntarily." But
on the whole he speaks of them with respect, and his
attitude is much that of an ordinary educated Englishman,
twenty years ago, towards the Salvation Army. Very
different was the general public opinion of those days.

However, in later times Christian writers were as angry
with him as ever the philosophers had been. They invented
a story that he died by being torn to pieces by dogs. Suidas
amiably observes: "Wherefore he paid a sufficient penalty
for his madness in the present life, and in the future he
shall inherit eternal fire together with Satan." Suidas, the
horrid dull dog! I remember what a wise man once
said—"If you want climate go to Heaven, if you want
society—."

The third great subject for the licensed jester is politics—
indeed it properly should come first. Unfortunately the

jester very often finds this field occupied with a large board and written upon it "Trespassers will be prosecuted. By Order." Neither Plautus nor Rabelais nor Cervantes nor Molière nor Voltaire could open their mouths upon this subject—they would have had the police down upon them and have been prosecuted for *lèse-majesté* at once. If any German happens to be present, I should like to explain that I am making no allusion to the great Kaiser. So great is the advantage of living under free institutions. Political satire was the life blood of the old Attic Comedy, it was one of the most formidable weapons in the arsenal of Swift and Byron. As for the unlucky Lucian, there were simply no politics to talk about. In Rome he might have been stopped by the police, in Athens or Samosata or Gaul he had no chance of arousing their suspicions. The great Roman Empire lay with a dead weight upon everything. He grew up under the rule of Hadrian, that admirable Emperor who spent his time touring about the Empire like the Viceroy of India and seeing that the machinery worked right everywhere. From 138 to 183, the period of his manhood, the two Antonines held the sceptre. The age of the Antonines is looked upon as a sort of golden age of happiness and tranquillity—happy the people may be that have no history, but the political satirist is not happy. The machinery worked right enough—men reaped the fields and women did the washing and talked about their work and deplored the weather, and the taxes were gathered in regularly and everything was managed for the best—it might have suited Pangloss, but everything was dead and dull. Now and then there might be a diversion somewhere: in the year 135 the Romans killed 580,000 Jews in Judea, in the reign of Aurelius there was a terrible plague and the barbarians began invading on the north-east frontier; but of political life there was none and I do not believe there is a single political allusion in all Lucian's works. One only has to think of the *Acharnians, Gulliver,* the *Vision of Judgement,* to feel what a loss this is to the satirist. In his last years the throne of Aurelius, by the irony of fate, was occupied by that brutal gladiator Commodus, as though Caliban were the son and successor of Prospero: it is all the same to Lucian—it was all the same to the vast machinery of the Empire.

But Sophocles well said that man can devise a remedy for all things but death. When literature has utterly run to seed, man writes novels. What we call novels now had not yet been evolved, but stories of a sort were beginning to be written. Lucian wrote a remarkable story called *The Dream* or *The Cock,* of which for several reasons I shall say nothing: a more celebrated work, which may be called if not a novel at least a romance, is the *True History.*

The *True History* is perhaps the most famous work of Lucian, certainly that which has had the greatest influence upon later literature. It itself derives from a no less venerable work than the *Odyssey,* as Lucian very fairly owns in his preface. Of all travellers' tales which have ever bewitched mankind the most enchanting are those which Odysseus told to the Phaeacians, concerning the Cyclops with his one eye, and Circe and the pigs, and the cannibal giants, and the bag of the winds, and his descent to Hades. Lucian says in his bantering way that Odysseus fired off all this stuff at the Phaeacians because he found them to be good simple easy-going folk who would swallow anything he chose to give them: Odysseus according to him was a de Rougemont and Alcinous was qualified by his innocence to be president of the British Association. Then there were other writers calling themselves historians who told enormous falsehoods, at all of whom Lucian is gibing. "We set sail once upon a time," he says vaguely, "from the Straits of Gibraltar." After some ten days during which their adventures are nothing very notable, they were seized by a whirlwind and carried up into the air some 350 miles—then they drove before the wind till they came to the Moon, where, being seized upon by the Vulture Guards, cavalry riding upon three-headed vultures as big as ships, they were brought before the king, no other than Endymion, who appears for a wonder not to have been asleep. Endymion was about to go out to battle against Phaethon, king of the Sun, and invited them to join as military attachés. The most remarkable of his troops were the flea-archers, who rode upon fleas each as big as twelve elephants. There is a pretty touch at the end of the catalogue of troops. "We heard that 70,000 Ostrich-acorns (whatever they may be) were expected from the stars beyond Cappadocia, and 5000 Horse-cranes, but I did not see them for they never came. So I thought it better not to describe their character, for what we were told of them was marvellous and quite incredible." The infantry fought upon a woven floor wrought by spiders, for the spiders there are about as big as the Isle of Wight. It really does not matter which side won, one cares no more about that than about the College Office. It is more interesting to investigate the customs of the inhabitants of the Moon and in particular their drink, which was "air squeezed into a cup yielding a

liquid like dew." We classical scholars are amused every
now and then by the scientific people proclaiming as a new
discovery something which was quite familiar to the
ancients—you see that liquid air is a regular chestnut—
and then Olszewsky and Dewar dispute about who discovered it! We could tell them a good many things if we
thought it worth while to condescend so far.

How they came down again into the Ocean, how a whale
of 200 miles long swallowed them, how they found inside
the whale an island with trees and cabbages, and cormor-
ants and kittiwakes roosting in the branches (rather odd
natural history, but perhaps birds who live in whales have
to change their habits), how they went on an exploring
expedition through the wood and found a temple of
Neptune and an old man who had lived there for many
years, how the imagination of Lucian gets heated with
driving and he proceeds to describe whole kindreds and
nations and tongues that dwelt about the mouth of the
whale, Turbotfeet and Lobstersons, and Thunnyheads and
Crabhands—how they planted vines and made wine, and
so lived one year and eight months in the whale, along with
many other things rather hard to believe, had best be read
in Lucian. At last they got tired of it, so they set fire to
the woods, beginning towards the tail, and the woods
blazed with a great conflagration. "For seven days and
nights the whale did not find out that anything was wrong,
but on the eighth and ninth we thought he seemed a bit
sick—at least he yawned more lazily than he used and
shut his mouth up sooner than before. Last of all the whale
died also and we got out. Then we came after a time to the
island of the Blessed, which is the most charming place I

ever saw—meadows full of all manner of flowers, violet,
amaracus and asphodel—but scenery is the last refuge
of the destitute—enough to say that all good Professors
go there when they die. There I saw Socrates cross-
examining Nestor and Palamedes, and round about him
a crowd of beautiful youths—but Rhadamanthus, who
rules there, was rather annoyed with him and threatened
to turn him out if he would still be talking nonsense and
would not drop his Socratic irony and revel with the rest.
Plato was not there, because he was gone to live in his own
Republic under his own laws with Dr Jowett and Dr
Jackson—by advices last received none of the three were
on speaking terms. There also I saw the Earl of Beacons-
field with a gold crown on his head, clothed in purple and
green and orange (as he loved to be in his youth in this
world), drinking Tokay wine out of great goblets with the
three beautiful Miss Gunnings and General Gordon, who
admitted that he had been quite wrong in his ideas about
the geographical situation of Paradise. And Lord Beacons-
field told me that it was a very odd thing, but however
much wine he drank he never became Dizzy, but I did not
understand what he meant. So great are the delights of
that Paradise. And there sat Cobet and Madvig making
emendations, and they said..., and a Quain Professor of
English editing *Beowulf*, very proud because he had recovered 2571 lines unknown before, but the others said he
ought to have gone somewhere else, if *that* was to be his
way of amusing himself.

"There I might have stayed to this day in great joy and
bliss, and there is no Literary Society there, but unluckily
Helen took the opportunity of running away from Menelaus

again with one of our crew, and the end of it was we were all turned out.

"One of the next places we came to was the Island of the Damned, over which Abdul the Sultan is king. This is a very unpleasant place, full of kings and prime ministers and bad poets and Deans and Mr Stead. Then I saw that Dante was right when he put the traitors in the lowest place of all, for in the worst pit were Judas and Ephialtes the Malian and Vellidos Dolfos and Mordred and Ganelon. Also those who had told lies and written them in books were hung up by their tongues, Ctesias the historian and Herodotus and Marco Polo and Sir John Mandeville and many others. Then I rejoiced exceedingly knowing I should never come to *that* torment, being by nature truthful and never having written down a false statement in my life. There also I saw a lecturer on physiology pinned out on a table and a frog lecturing upon *him*—the audience was mostly frogs and rabbits. The batrachian Professor was pointing out the disadvantages of a four-chambered heart and the superiority of the batrachian type. Altogether the place was very desolate and struck a chill into my heart—if you want to get an idea of it go to the Imperial Institute and explore the Education Exhibition.

"These are only a few specimens of the wonderful adventures which befell us. How we got back again I do not rightly know."

During the dreary Middle Ages Lucian found no followers—the mediaeval writers did not speak the truth much, being given up to vain imaginations. It is true[1] that Professor Wilamowitz-Moellendorff is of opinion that

[1] As true as the *Vera Historia*.

Dante's *Divine Comedy* is a mediaeval rendering of the *True History*—but I think there are serious difficulties in the way to accepting this view, as there generally are with the literary theories of that distinguished author. With the Renaissance, however, Lucian came back with a bound. The greater part of the amazing book which goes under the name of *Pantagruel* is directly inspired by Lucian. Rabelais, however, though a much smaller artist, was a much greater man than Lucian, and what in the Greek is only an amusing skit becomes in the Frenchman a fierce satire. The voyage of Panurge to seek the oracle of the Divine Bottle starts with no apparent meaning, but gradually it becomes more and more evident that the writer is inditing a parable of the vanity of human endeavours to solve the riddle of existence, to which the final answer is the Epicurean command "Drink"; and in particular it is a furious attack upon the Roman Catholic Church and the corruptions of society. Swift took up the same strain in *Gulliver's Travels*. Coleridge defines Swift as the spirit of Rabelais dwelling in a dry place; the satire in him is not bedewed with the juices of the Divine Bottle, but is fifty times more fierce and misanthropical, attacking not abuses nor religion, but the very nature of man. But Swift also went back to Lucian—especially in the voyage to Laputa, a good deal of which is a direct paraphrase of the Greek. Cyrano de Bergerac also, who has been lately resuscitated upon the stage, imitated Lucian in his fabulous voyage to the Moon—Swift is said to be more indebted to Cyrano than to Lucian himself. Lastly, the adventures of Tom in Kingsley's fascinating *Water Babies* are a softened copy of Rabelais, with the Epicureanism taken out and a gentle and charming light

of Christianity diffused over everything. But I do not
know that there is any evidence that Kingsley ever so much
as read Lucian.

However, the most truly Lucianic of all the moderns
is unquestionably Voltaire. With him we began and with
him we must end. He also, it must be admitted, was a
greater man than Lucian, but there can hardly be said to
be any difference in kind—he is Lucian raised to a higher
power—though a punster might say that they are both
noted for speaking very disrespectfully of higher powers.
I do not know that I ever observed any direct imitation
of Lucian in Voltaire—he has never adopted his methods
nor copied his jests. But both are typical mockers and
scoffers. Like his predecessor, Voltaire never wearies of
jeering at the established official religion of his time, and
at the philosophers; he gibes at them in serious tragedies
à la Euripides, in mock tragedies such as his *Saul*, in tales
and romances, in poems, in his Oceanic correspondence.
When Voltaire profanely makes one of his characters say
"The scape-goat will serve as an expiation; we will send
him into the desert, charged with the sins of the company;
he is accustomed to this ceremony, which does not do him
the slightest harm, and one understands that anything can
be expiated by a goat taking a walk," when we hear that
Zadig "knew of metaphysics what has been known in all
ages, that is to say precious little," we hear again the voice
of Lucian raised against the religion and the philosophy
of his age. Only in Voltaire it is refined and sharpened to
an inconceivable point; never had any man such an instinct for hitting the nail on the head. In their style also
is an extraordinary resemblance—both are swift and clear

without a superfluous word, both stick to one thing at a time and refuse to be diverted from their purpose by any alluring digressions, both are full of idiom. I speak of their prose, of course, for of Voltaire's tragedies the less said the better, Lucian would have laughed them to scorn—on the other hand, Voltaire's poems are another point which he scores over his rival, and on the whole Voltaire also is a much bigger man.

For indeed Lucian was not a great man, and that is the true reason why he is so much neglected in this busy world. He is an agreeable and amusing jester, but that is all, and there is no weight behind him such as there is with Rabelais and Swift and to a less degree even with Voltaire. And he lived in an age devoid of politics, where the established religion was an empty form, and the new ones were not yet taken seriously in literary circles, an age of emptiness and decay upon the whole, and he suffers accordingly—Aristophanes himself could not have made anything great in those days.

CERVANTES

(Literary Society, 1916)

Cervantes

Some people say that centenaries are nuisances, that there is no reason why you should make a fuss about a man precisely one hundred years after his birth or death any more than at any other time, and that such celebrations are mostly run in the interests of some noisy modern who is really rather celebrating himself. There is some truth in this, and certainly there is no justification for neglecting the great works of literature for the other ninety and nine years that you may gush about them in the hundredth. But alas! the flesh is weak, and the circulating library is strong, and centenaries have a real value for us in sending us back from our contemporaries to the eternal, from twaddly novels to the *Divine Comedy*, from Arnold Bennett to Cervantes.

This particular year of grace happens to be the tercentenary of the death of three of the very greatest men upon record; I need not say that I refer to Shakespeare, Cervantes and Iyeyasu. Now there are very good reasons why I should not talk to-day about Iyeyasu, which reasons I had rather not specify but will leave to your imagination. As for Shakespeare you are all sick to death of him, or if you aren't it must be the fault of your English staff. But Spanish literature is sadly neglected in England, a proof of which is that I should have the impudence to get up and talk about it, and Cervantes is the one supremely great name in it.

Miguel de Cervantes Saavedra—how lovely these Spanish

names are—came of a noble and ancient family, which is traced back to the mountainous wilds of Galicia in N.W. Spain, but which had flourished for generations in Castille. His life extends exactly over the period from the death of Henry VIII to the death of Shakespeare, and so his dates are easy to remember, 1547 (29th September)–1616. For the honour of giving him birth seven cities have contended, as seven cities did over Homer, one with a lovelier name than another, but the prize has been given, like the apple of Paris, to the loveliest of them all, Alcalá de Henares. That must be a place worth being born in. About his childhood and education little enough is clear and none of it matters: he certainly knew Latin to some extent, rather a small extent I fancy, and Italian; I do not know that he ever shows any knowledge of French, but he must have picked some up, one would think, in his adventures; he certainly never could have taken a degree in this University, but what graduate of this University ever did anything worth looking at? People of a superior and academic turn of mind sneered at Cervantes in his own day because of his want of learning, exactly as Ben Jonson did at Shakespeare and other folk at Dickens. But what *did* matter about all these people was that they had come in contact with all sorts and descriptions of men and had the eye of genius for understanding and reproducing them, not to say for greatly improving them. After his years of learning Cervantes spent his years of wandering in a school which certainly was not lacking in variety and adventure. He went on different journeys to the South of France and Italy in the retinue of an ambassador, enlisted as a soldier in the ranks and fought at the great battle of Lepanto. The excitement

and enthusiasm caused by that campaign is not now so
very easy to understand: enough for our purpose that the
Venetians were fighting the Turks, who had attacked
Cyprus; the Venetians called on the other nations of
Christianity to take part in a Crusade against the infidel.
Don John of Austria, son of the Emperor Charles V, led
the Christian fleet and won a great victory over the Turks
at Lepanto on the west coast of Greece in 1571, the year
before the massacre of St Bartholomew, an event which
throws a lurid light on the union of the Christians against
the infidel. In that battle Cervantes fought as a common
soldier; though ill of a fever he refused to stay in bed; he
distinguished himself by the most daring valour, and received three wounds, two in the body, and the third dis-
abled his left hand for the rest of his life. As he put it
himself, he lost his left hand for the greater glory of the
right, and he never wearied of referring to the great battle.
What he got by it all was three crowns in addition to his
pay. The remuneration is characteristic. After some
further stay in the Mediterranean he was sent back to
Spain in 1575 with letters of recommendation, which
turned out ill for him; for he was taken prisoner by the
Algerine pirates and carried off to Algiers. There he remained captive five years. The story of the Christian
captives in those parts is a horrible one which I need not
here go into; so far as Cervantes was concerned we have
fortunately a great deal of evidence, which is profoundly
interesting as showing what manner of man he was, for
I will give you a single instance. A plot had been made of
which Cervantes was the author and leader, for sixty of
the captives to escape, and was on the point of being

carried out, when a scoundrel informed the Turkish governor. The governor thought it advisable to dissemble his knowledge for a time that he might catch the Christians in the act and punish them accordingly. But the news got about that the governor knew everything; the captives were in great alarm, and one of them in particular thought that if Cervantes were seized the Turks would compel him by torture to reveal the whole affair and inform against his accomplices. This fellow entreated Cervantes to embark on some ships which were ready to set sail, offering to pay his ransom. Here was a splendid chance to escape out of Hell; did Cervantes jump at it? Not he: he thought it dishonourable to fly from the danger himself and leave his companions in so great a risk; therefore he not only refused the offer, but calmed the fears of the other, telling him that no torture nor death itself would make him betray any one of his companions; sooner would he lay the blame to himself alone to save them all.

Then for the first time we meet Don Quixote, do you know him when you see him? Is that not how Don Quixote would have behaved? Anybody can fight bravely, and the deeds of Cervantes at Lepanto could be matched doubtless by hundreds of others who fought upon that day. But the man who never thought of saving himself, and was ready to risk impalement and anything else on a point of honour; who not only does this but actually makes the other man believe that no torture will wrest the truth from him; that is indeed Don Quixote talking over Sancho Panza. This is only one specimen of his habitual attitude. Why he was not tortured and killed fifty times is a mystery; his companions constantly feared that he would be: he expected it himself more than once. But when it came to the point, he always somehow got off; there was something about him that overawed and imposed upon his brutal gaolers and tyrants. In truth the whole of the story of the captivity reads more like a fairy tale than real life; and if the evidence for it were not so good, it would be scouted frankly as incredible. As it is, it is not possible to understand it in many points; like the greater part of the life of Cervantes it is "wrop in mystery."

Be all that as it may, he was finally ransomed and restored to Spain in September 1580. During the next three years he continued his adventurous career, but I will not go into details, for they were of no interest in themselves and do not help us to understand him; it is high time to turn to his literary career. In 1585, aged thirty-eight, he published the first part of his *Galatea*, a pastoral romance divided into six books. On the pastoral I shall have more to say later on. I do not mean to read the *Galatea*; I have many other ways to die, and advise you to leave pastorals to rot in their graves. You remember what Horace Walpole said of Sidney's *Arcadia*: "a tedious, lamentable, pedantic, pastoral romance which the patience of a young virgin in love cannot now wade through."

About this time Cervantes married a young lady of nineteen, Doña Catalina de Palacios Salazar y Vozmediano.

He next tried his hand at the drama, which was then just putting forth its earliest blossoms in Spain as it was in England. His Quixotic enthusiasm for whatever he took in hand seems to have persuaded him that he could make a fortune by the drama; that is not strange, but he succeeded in getting managers to bring out his plays, which is stranger. One of them deserves notice, the *Numancia*. This tragedy has a kind of sombre grandeur about it, perhaps one might better call it a stilted sublimity: it deals with the heroic resistance of Numancia to the Romans, when the natives were finally starved out after fighting to the last gasp. It is a very bad play, a very bad play indeed, but there is a thing to be remembered about it which stirs the blood. When the Spaniards were holding Saragossa against the armies of Napoleon, when they like their ancestors were starving and facing overwhelming odds with a heroism which has become proverbial, then this play of *Numancia* was performed in the theatre amid frenzied enthusiasm to the accompaniment of the cannons of Mortier and Lannes. It was probably the first performance of the tragedy for over 200 years, and probably it was the last.

Anyhow as a dramatist Cervantes was promptly drowned by the amazing deluge of Lope de Vega. Zoologists talk of the fecundity of the herring and the oyster, but those interesting quadrupeds fade into insignificance beside the fertility of Lope. It is estimated that he wrote at least twenty million verses; epic poems, comic poems, romances, anything that came in his way; but his fame rests on his dramas, of which he composed at the lowest fifteen hundred.

About the year 1600 he was certainly in prison for a time, nobody quite knows why or where; he had got a small post under the Government and made a mess of his accounts. Legend says that he wrote, or at any rate conceived the idea of Don Quixote in prison; that like so many legends is highly questionable. At any rate in 1605 the first part of the incomparable masterpiece appeared in print, and the name of Cervantes immediately filled the civilised world. Everybody knows the outline of the story and how absurdly simple it is. An elderly gentleman living quietly with his niece and his housekeeper, having nothing much to do but read, has his brain turned by the romances of chivalry, imagines himself to be destined by Fate to restore chivalry and knight-errantry to the world, persuades a rustic named Sancho Panza to follow him as his squire, goes forth accordingly and meets with all sorts of ridiculous adventures, finally recovers his wits and dies, cursing the books of chivalry.

And what *were* these books of chivalry? No one can be expected to read them nowadays unless he is writing a dissertation. I haven't—except one. There *is* one which is pretty well known, Malory's *Morte d'Arthur*. But that I understand to be altogether an unfair example; it is a million miles too good; it is unspeakably tiresome to read through, and most of it is inconceivably silly if you think about it seriously, and it is horribly immoral, but for all that the Arthurian legend is an interesting thing, and the *Morte d'Arthur* contains many very fine passages. But the sort of romance which turned Don Quixote's head was very different. The stories of Amadis of Gaul, Huon of Bordeaux and so on, had not the interest of Arthurian romance because they were merely silly inventions of professed literary people, not the genuine popular tradition. The characters are reputed to be idiotic, their behaviour and adventures on a par with their characters, their morality as bad as Malory's. Yet people read this rubbish by bucketfuls because they had nothing else in the way of fiction to read and they were so silly themselves for the most part that they couldn't read anything but fiction. Nay, in the seventeenth century that divine creature, our lady of Livry, Madame de Sévigné herself, reads and delights in the novels of chivalry written by Mademoiselle de Scudéry: she is a bit ashamed of it as she confesses, but read them she does in spite of Don Quixote.

The knight of course has a lady-love, probably somebody else's wife, he fights giants and other knights and performs incredible feats of valour, he is beguiled and bamboozled by enchanters, and he is supposed to ride abroad redressing human wrong. All these features in him are of course parodied in *Don Quixote*, not once nor twice, but over and over again. There is an enormously long novel of George Meredith called *Evan Harrington*, built entirely upon the fact that the hero is the son of a tailor, and there is something very funny about being a tailor—you get sick to death of it before you are half-way through—at least I did. But somehow you never get weary of the adventures of Don Quixote, though it is a much longer book than *Evan Harrington*. What does bore one in it are just those parts which are *not* on the gibe of knight-errantry. The rest is eternally amusing, but it is a great deal more than that.

There is a story that King Philip III saw a man with a book in his hand overcome with inconsumable laughter. "Either that man is mad," quoth His Majesty, "or he is reading *Don Quixote*." And that indeed is the first aspect in which the book presents itself to us. To enjoy it truly you must do two troublesome things; you must learn Spanish and you must grow old. But even if you know no

Spanish and even if you are young, you cannot resist its gaiety and absurdity. At the same time those who only want to laugh may quite easily be disappointed in it. I have heard grave persons of taste and education call it "dull." The fact is that much more amusing books have been written since, if by "amusing" you mean provoking laughter. There are numbers of modern French farces which it is hardly possible to get through for sheer laughter —though they have no literary merit to speak of and though in consequence you can hardly read them a second time. *Don Quixote* no longer produces the effect noted by King Philip III. While a book is at the height of its immediate popularity, it is almost certain that it will be producing its effect upon the public by something superficial, something which will not wear well. The public of those days were consumed with laughter, I am afraid, to a very large extent exactly because of the features in the book which now rather repel us. What amused people then was to see somebody whacked with a big stick. That part of the business now repels us—but what still delights us is the grave and serious humour which spreads a serene light over the whole. It may not make us laugh so much as a Parisian farce, but it abides with us, if we are persons of taste, like you and me, and we can go on reading it all our lives. But I tell you again that you won't appreciate it till old age begins to come upon you—suppose you wait to try it, till you are forty—and by that time ten to one that you will not be reading anything but the last new twaddle from Mudie's.

However, here is a bit which I will translate as well as I can—but unfortunately for my present purpose *Don*

Quixote cannot be represented in extracts; it must be taken as a whole. Let us take one specimen, the battle with the sheep. Don Quixote and Sancho having ridden up to the top of a hillock to get a better view, Don Quixote proceeds to hold forth in the following strain: [Part I, chap. 18].

Such is the first aspect in which *Don Quixote* presents itself—as an extremely amusing book. But presently it begins to dawn upon one that it is a great deal more. It is not true, as has been said, that all great authors necessarily become symbolic, but it is true of many and especially of Cervantes. This knight errant going out on his broken-down old horse to conquer giants and overthrow armies is not merely a skit upon the old books of chivalry, such as the adventures of Amadis or the *Morte d'Arthur*; he is also a satire upon every single one of us, for we are all in our humble way Don Quixotes; he is an ironical type of all the proud imaginations of man. He is going to redress human wrong, and what is the result? He sets free a gang of criminals who are being taken to the galleys. He is going to kill a giant, and he is knocked flat by the sails of a windmill. He has a lady-love, the peerless Dulcinea del Toboso, whom he has never seen and who is really nothing but a blowsy farmer's daughter. Well, is not that so with all of us? We set out nothing doubting to become distinguished scholars and are knocked flat in the Matriculation. Don Quixote says it is due to the malignancy of an enchanter; of course it is not his own fault; *we* say that it is the malice of examiners. We set up some imaginary phantom to worship; it may be a young lady or perhaps more likely a young gentleman in khaki; it may be a determination to square the circle or to put a stop to the wicked practice of vaccination, or to persuade the world to believe in spiritualism; and many people go on worshipping such fetishes all their life long. All their efforts prove fruitless, they only get themselves laughed at, but nothing can shake their belief in themselves and their Dulcinea. "My writings," said Pascal, one of the greatest of men, "may be condemned by the Sorbonne, but they are approved in Heaven." On which Voltaire sarcastically commented that in the court of Heaven they had something else to think of than Pascal's writings. And Voltaire himself? is he not as much of a Don Quixote? He wrote bad tragedies all his life and thought them very fine; he preached all sorts of fine things and never dreamt that he was paving the road to the French Revolution, which would have driven him mad with horror. A certain Swedish philosopher wrote a book to prove that the Swedish constitution was impeccable and indestructible. As he was finishing his last chapter some one came and told him that the King had destroyed the constitution with a stroke of the pen. "Sir," said the philosopher, "he may destroy the constitution but he cannot destroy my book." But there is simply no end to the applications that may be made. Dulcinea is peerless: "Deutschland über alles." What the world wants is knights errant: "We Germans are the salt of the earth."

As we have all a Don Quixote inside us, so we all have a Sancho Panza. Sancho is a dull man who has never seen a heavenly vision, who knows which side his bread is buttered, who is an amazing compound of shrewdness and stupidity; he knows very well that Don Quixote is mad, and yet he follows him because he hopes to get something out of him; he sees him battered with blows and he takes

good care to keep out of their way himself, and yet he
follows at his heels without knowing why. So in every one
of us the lower nature is led grumbling after the higher,
and the ill-assorted couple jumbles through the chaos of
life as it can. But the parable is plainer if we look at the
two characters as disjoined from one another. Is not the
socialist party in Germany exactly like Sancho? It went
grumbling after the military party with a thick bandage
over its eyes because in a muddled way it thought it was
going to get something; now that it sees its leader
thwacked and is itself tossed in a blanket, it begins to
reflect what a fool it has made of itself.

Such is the second aspect in which this book reveals
itself, a dazzling commentary on human life, so universal
in its application that it completely transcends every other
novel ever written. And it is all treated with such grave
and delicious irony that one never wearies of it. There is
nothing like irony for keeping a book green.

But there is one irony upon another in it. In the second
part especially it somehow begins to dawn upon us that
the madness and misadventures of Don Quixote are wisdom
and happiness as compared with this world. That is the third
stage of our experience in studying it. Dulcinea may have
appeared to Sancho as a blowsy rustic, but which was the
happier, Sancho knowing the truth or his master nursing the
illusion? As Rostand says in his enchantingly beautiful play:

> Le seul rêve intéresse,
> Vivre sans rêve, qu'est-ce?
> Moi, j'aime la princesse
> Lointaine.

And how distant Dulcinea was!

...let us thither, Sancho, for though I but see her, be it through fences, or windows, or openings of doors, or garden grates, this shall I gain—that whatever ray of the sun of her beauty reaches my eyes, it will enlighten my mind and fortify my heart, so that I shall be unique, and without equal in wisdom and prowess.

(Duffield, trans. 1881, vol. II, p. 526.)

All those other people in the book, and there are more than six hundred of them as it is reckoned by the curious, begin to seem like shadows, like people who have somehow missed the only things worth having in life. They may eat more bacon and receive fewer hard knocks, but we begin to look upon them with disdain. And there are times when even the madness of Don Quixote carries all before it and justifies itself. Once at least was he made manifest in the flesh. There sat in a place called Vaucouleurs a battered old captain of the wars, sick at heart, I think, and if he knew his Virgil saying to himself "Una salus victis nullam sperare salutem." And there came and stood before him a peasant girl of seventeen who could neither read nor write, and said to him: "I come to you in the name of God who is my Lord, that you may tell the Dauphin that God will send him succour in the mid Lent. In spite of his enemies he shall be king and it is I who will lead him to be crowned and sanctified at Rheims."

Which is the madder? Don Quixote going forth on Rozinante to deliver the oppressed, or the peasant girl who summoned to battle the shattered and despairing chivalry of France and by faith put to flight the armies of the aliens? Mad as March hares both of them. Nay, we become ashamed of ourselves; why did we begin by thinking it funny to read of Don Quixote's disasters? We begin to think that it wasn't funny at all, but tragic—the eternal tragedy of lofty aims thwarted by the horrible hard facts of life. In fact we fall in love with Don Quixote. There is a story that six people being asked to write down the name of the finest gentleman they knew of, one and all wrote down his name. This feeling culminates when we read the tale of his final overthrow. A certain bachelor of arts, Sampson Carrasco, goes forth to cure him of his madness at the beginning of the second part; he arms himself like a knight and challenges Don Quixote. But unluckily the bachelor gets the worst of it and is overthrown himself, and commanded by the victor to go and yield homage to Dulcinea. After that we hear no more of him for some hundred pages. Then he appears again on the outskirts of Barcelona as Knight of the White Moon.

...Don Quixote commending himself to Heaven with all his heart, and to Dulcinea, as was his custom at the beginning of all the battles which were offered him, turned to take a little more field, for he saw that his adversary had done the same, and, without sound of trumpet or other martial music to give signal for the onset, they both wheeled their horses at the same instant. And as that of the Silver Moon was more swift, he met Don Quixote before he had run a third of his career, and with such great force, that without touching him with the lance—for it appears that he carried it aloft on purpose—he gave Rozinante, and with him Don Quixote, a parlous fall to the ground. Foot-hot he ran to him, and bringing his lance to his visor, he cried:

"Thou art the conquered knight, and even a dead man, unless thou confess to the conditions of our challenge."

Don Quixote, bruised and stunned, without raising his beaver, and as if he spoke from within a tomb, in a sick and feeble voice said: "Dulcinea del Toboso is the most

beautiful woman of the world, and I the most miserable
knight of the earth; nor is it right that my weakness should
belie this truth. Strike home, knight, thy lance, and take
my life, seeing thou hast taken away mine honour."

(Duffield, trans. 1881, vol. III, p. 639.)

Do you laugh at it or do you cry? Humour seems to me,
so far as I can attach any meaning to the word, to be just
this in its highest manifestation, that one doesn't know
which to do over it. And how thin is this line which divides
comedy from tragedy! Treat the irony of fate and of the
world in one way and you have Oedipus, in another and
you have Don Quixote.

It is because of this approximation of laughter and tears,
because of the development of Don Quixote into something
higher than he was at the start, that many of his lovers
prefer the second part to the first. There are other reasons
also. Into the first part Cervantes threw all sorts of things
which he had handy, a whole novel of considerable length,
the story of the Moorish captive, and so on. Also he
yielded to his old fancy for the pastoral, as he had done
before in the *Galatea*. Now you may say a great deal for
the pastoral in its proper place. The ideal Arcadia invented by Sannazaro, which ran like wild-fire over all
Europe, was a very pleasant dream. Shepherds with
pretty names hanging odes upon hawthorns and elegies
upon brambles, shepherdesses of amazing beauty and
simplicity, sheep which apparently can look after themselves, eternal spring and a capacity to live without food,
all these make a very pretty picture. And the story of
Cardenio and Dorothea is told in such enchanting language
that no one can have the heart to be severe on it in itself.

But there is a glaring defect about it; it is utterly out of place. Don Quixote depends for his effect upon being a dreamer brought in contact with the hard facts of life; pastoral is a denial of these facts. To drag the knight and his squire into the midst of it is as if you should plant Sir John Falstaff and Pistol amid the shepherds of *As You Like It*. Just fancy Falstaff listening to the confidences of Orlando, or Pistol weeping over the sorrows of Rosalind. Then too there is another trouble about the pastoral and about Cervantes in general: the ladies are really all too beautiful. They all have red hair and green eyes, and every one of them outgoes her predecessors. When the Moorish lady removes her mask:

And so she removed it, and disclosed a face so beautiful that Dorothea held her to be more fair than Lucinda, and Lucinda said she was more beautiful than Dorothea; while all those who stood by knew that if any could equal the beauty of these, it was the lady Moor, and there were some who thought she surpassed them in one thing.

(Duffield, trans. 1881, vol. II, p. 191.)

One phoenix in a nest is very good business, but three phoenixes in one cage are, in vulgar parlance, all my eye.

A third objection to the first part is the amount of buffeting and, to this squeamish age, the sometimes disgusting disasters of the hero. Charles Lamb protested that they pained his heart.

Whether other critics protested at the time, or whether Cervantes criticised himself, I do not know. Certain it is that in the second part he cleared all these things away; there are no irrelevant novels inserted in it, pastorals are only laughed at and the big stick is reduced to a minimum.

Yet we must admit that though the second part is to be held superior for all the reasons here alleged, yet the first part has the most amusing scenes and conversations in it and the events which are most familiar to all the world. What does it matter anyhow? Let us enjoy them both.

But I go back to the point that there are three stages to be gone through, first mere amusement, secondly the feeling of the universal irony as against Don Quixote, thirdly the feeling that after all Don Quixote is worth all the rest of the people and that his madness is nobler than their sense. And I ask a question which has been often put and answered in many ways. What was the object of Cervantes in writing this amazing book?

The answer, I think, is that he went through two and a half of those stages himself. He began the representation of a comic elderly gentleman going off his head and acting the knight errant just as a prodigious lark. Then as he went on the irony of the situation and the way in which it can be allegorically applied to all human life simply forced itself upon him. Finally he, like everybody else, fell in love with his hero. But I much doubt how far he really intended at any time whatever to make his readers understand that the lunacy of Don Quixote is really better than the common sense of the world. I think that it is we, or at any rate some of us, who largely read that into the story. We have no right to do so, you may say; yes, but we have. When a man has created such a portent and has conquered the whole world without knowing it, he has lost his own rights over his own creation; he has lighted a train of gunpowder and the resulting explosion is no business of his, or to express it better he has discovered a new

chemical element which produces one result in contact
with his own mind and other results which may be quite
different in contact with other minds.

It is only fair to say that Cervantes himself gives quite
a different account of the matter; he says, if you can believe
him, that his object was to destroy the popular romances
of chivalry. The last words of the book are "my desire has
been nothing else than to bring into the abhorrence of
mankind the false and crazy histories and books of chivalry
which already go stumbling to their fall because of those
of my veracious Don Quixote, and which without any
doubt must fall altogether." Some people have taken
those assertions very seriously; Mr Duffield's notes are
one continued outcry against the immorality and wicked-
ness of those unhappy books, and he really thinks their
destruction was the great achievement of his hero. But if
that really was the object of Cervantes, one can only say
that he was as blind as a bat; Don Quixote *did* destroy
them, but if that was all should we now be talking about
him? When an author tells you what his object was in
writing a poem or a novel, you can bet what you like that
he is deceiving you—probably he deceives himself too.
Milton said that he wrote *Paradise Lost* to justify the ways
of God to men: if so, he was only fit for a lunatic asylum.
Cervantes may have *begun* with that intention, but it is
obvious that he went on with others—mainly for the sheer
joy of creating an enchanted world and because his radiant
and delightful character must needs overflow in some way
or other.

For that is another great quality of the book, its radiant
good humour, its cheerfulness and brightness. There is not

a drop of gall or bitterness to be found in it, and this it is which makes one feel how delightful and sunny a nature its author's must have been. Compare his external life with his great contemporary's. Shakespeare was a prosperous stage-manager, he amassed a fortune and bought a country place at Stratford, he brought out his plays before princes, and we know of no particular grievance of his against the world. Cervantes lost a hand, was prisoner in a horrible captivity five years, was a consistent failure in literature till the age of fifty-eight, was a poor man all his life. Yet it was Shakespeare who at one time turned as sour as vinegar and drew a picture of the world as savage almost as Swift's; it was Cervantes who remained as cheerful as Falstaff, as gay as Rosalind, as good-humoured and wise and tolerant as Don Quixote himself. Yes, as wise, for Don Quixote's wisdom, except on one point, is prodigious, and bursts forth in a perennial stream on every subject of conversation that arises, insomuch that all those who hear him marvel. "Your worship," says Sancho on one occasion, "is better fitted for a preacher than for a knight errant." "Knights errant have to know everything," responded Don Quixote, "there was one in past ages who was as ready to deliver a sermon or an oration as if he had been a graduate in the University of Paris."

But when Don Quixote begins talking there is no end to it, and I must get on.

This book is Cervantes and Cervantes is this book. But he never knew it, the simple old creature. Between the first and second parts he produced his next best work the *Exemplary Novels*. I will only say of them that if they had not been by Cervantes nobody would ever have heard of them. And at his death he was feverishly putting the last touches to a long romance about Persiles and Sigismunda, of which all I know is that I have read an account of the plot and that it must be enough to drive the most enduring of readers into a strait waistcoat. But there is a description of himself in the Prologue to the *Exemplary Novels* which is worth quoting:

He whom you see here with aquiline countenance, chestnut hair, a smooth and open forehead, cheerful eyes, the nose curved but well proportioned, the beard of silver (less than twenty years ago it was of gold), the moustache large, the mouth small, the teeth none the better for wear, since he has only got six and these in bad condition and worse placed since they don't correspond with one another; the body between two extremes, neither great nor small, the colour fresh, rather fair than dark; somewhat bowed in the shoulders, and not very light of foot—this, I say, is the visage of the author of "The Galatea" and "Don Quixote," etc., commonly known as Miguel de Cervantes Saavedra—he was a soldier many years—

and then of course follows a flight of rhetoric about the battle of Lepanto and the victorious banners of the son of that thunderbolt of war, Charles V, of happy memory.

Only one portrait of him exists, and it corresponds much better with the description I have just read than the author's upper and lower teeth did.

But his mind, his character, his real essence is not so easily described as his outward person. The more one gets to know about him the more one sees how closely he is akin to his own masterpiece. He certainly was not mad, not by any manner of means; *he* never saw St Michael appearing to him in a glory and telling him to go on and prosper (and that in spite of the fact that he was born on

St Michael's day), he was never, so far as we know, affected
by any such illusion as was Pascal, nor diseased in his
nervous system as so many great authors have been, nor
is there any shadow of a cloud of melancholy upon him
such as we feel brooding over Molière. Clear shining of the
sun upon a smiling landscape seems to be the atmosphere
in which his spirit moves, a perpetual serene happiness
which no external discomforts or disasters can mar. The
kingdom of heaven was within him. And so it was with
Don Quixote; what did it matter to him what befell his
unlucky body? Take away from Don Quixote his delusion
and there, I think, is the author himself. As the knight of
La Mancha was utterly fearless of all dangers, insomuch
that he opened the door of the lions and defied them to
come out and fight him, so Cervantes defied his Turkish
masters and was ready to face much worse than death
without turning a hair. As the former drags Sancho after
him, inflaming even that fleshly nature with a spark of his
own enthusiasm, so the latter persuaded everybody with
whom he came in contact to follow his lead, whether
they were captives in Algiers or stage-managers in Spain.
But why then did he not prosper better in this world?
Because though he was not mad he was nevertheless all in
the dark about himself, as so many of these geniuses are.
O, the time he wasted over trying to write poetry, and the
naïveté with which he palms off his verses upon us!
Cervantes had no ear for verse, no instinct for finding anything to say in verse if he could have written it, yet he
went on pegging away at it just as Goethe did at his
perfectly disgusting attempts at making pictures. He
wrote plays by the dozen, and except for the doubtful case

of *Numancia* they are failures too. And the pastoral
romance hung about his neck like a millstone all his life.
And why did he never succeed as a soldier? The answer to
that question can only be a guess, but my guess is that he
was a great deal too like Don Quixote again. Certainly it
was not for lack of valour, but I suspect that he was devoid
of the sense of what was practicable and what was not.
Alike as soldier and as writer I picture him to myself as
moving recklessly in the pursuit of flying stars through
a wilderness of bog and brier, never heeding the hard facts
of life, never losing heart, never without a smile on his lips
at his own misadventures. He looks on the pageant of life
around him, and illuminates it all with his own brightness.
But to this you must add his delicious humour, a quality
in which his hero was perhaps a little deficient. A man
with humour in him would certainly never have behaved
like a Quixote. But Cervantes had not only a Quixote
within him; he had also a Sancho Panza, and we may be
sure that he provided his own commentary upon his own
extravagances. Indeed you have just heard him do it:
the hero who followed the banner of the invincible Don
Juan has only six teeth in his head, and they do not correspond.

There out of Cervantes' own lips is the description of
the knight errant and the practical remark of the honest
and unromantic squire. Indeed there is a passage of which
one is irresistibly reminded by this description. Directly
after the adventure of the sheep, Don Quixote holds forth
on the heroic deeds and wisdom of knights errant and
presently adds "but just put your finger in my mouth and
see how many teeth are missing on my upper jaw upon the

right, for that is where I feel the pain," the shepherds having hit him there with a stone from their slings.

I do not know whether I have succeeded in making in any way clear my notion of the sort of man Cervantes was, but indeed if you want to get any impression of him worth having I repeat again that you must learn Spanish and must grow old, and I know very well that you are immutably determined to do neither the one nor the other. "Paciencia y barajar," as Durandarte said when he woke up.

JULIAN

'Literary Society, 1903)

Julian

THERE is a vast chasm in the knowledge of most of us, a great gulph fixed between the two worlds ancient and modern. The names of Socrates and Caesar, Alexander and Herod the Great, Solomon and Marcus Aurelius are familiar to all even if they be not professed students of antiquity. Greece, Rome and Judaea in a word still live for us. But then comes a great waste chaos lighted by scarce a star; we know that Muhammad and Charlemagne and one or two others are weltering somewhere in it and that is about all. There is indeed a bridge across this chaos. Edward Gibbon, resembling Sin and Death in *Paradise Lost*, and indeed he was as ugly as sin, built that bridge with wondrous art; it stands high, spanning that thousand years more or less; and scarce a brick in the majestic structure shows trace of decay. Everybody must read Gibbon once in his life, but I suppose not many of you have done it yet.

Meantime the last figure which still stands on the shore of that ancient world has still a strange fascination and romance about him. By the triumphant party which he opposed he has been pilloried under the name of apostate, which after all only means a man who has changed his mind. Yet somehow or other the Apostate has remained a far more vivid figure than any of his opponents, however triumphant their cause. More vivid and more romantic. Who knows or cares anything about Ambrose? Ambrose, the author of the greatest of Christian lyrics, reformer of

Church music, priest and statesman, perhaps a greater man than Julian—he is as dead as last year's cricket averages—that is to the ordinary reader. He advanced the cause he had at heart, Julian lost his. Perhaps that is just it. The descending sun of Rome, and all the glorious memories evoked by the name of Rome, cast a gleam of light upon the head of her last defender even as he was swallowed up in the rising tide, and that last gleam is more pathetic and more romantic than the blaze of sunshine. The legend invented against him by his enemies has helped to consecrate him, for the picture of the dying warrior crying "Thou hast conquered, O Galilaean" is as familiar as that of Alfred burning the cakes, and as moving as the last hour of Socrates. And it may be added it is equally false—it shares the fate of so many of those pretty historical anecdotes, it may have all sorts of merits but its evidences will not bear inspection. But it shows the fear and hatred with which the Galilaeans, as he calls them, regarded him, and it typifies better than anything else the attitude he bears in history; it is a crowning example of the truth of Aristotle's profound saying that poetry is truer than history.

On the other hand he has been applauded and beherofied in late years by a very different set, by people who have in their turn apostatised from Christianity and who think any stick will do to beat a dog with. Their puffing of Julian is like the pilgrimage to the shrine of Giordano Bruno which is undertaken every now and then in Rome simply to annoy the Pope and give the police something to do. Julian would have given these amiable enthusiasts as short shrift as he gave the Christians.

For in fact he was an eminently religious person; had

he not been so he never would have apostatised at all. Gallio does not trouble himself in that way, especially when it is tolerably evident that he will be on the losing side.

By the time that Julian assumed the purple and threw off the mask, that surely must have been evident. The edicts of Milan had granted peace and toleration to the Church in the years 311 and 313, the last great persecution in the days of Diocletian having proved a sad failure; Constantine had declared for Christianity himself, and it had become the established religion of the Empire; no calm judge can well have doubted by the time of Julian's birth, about 330, that it had won the day. Julian was the nephew of Constantine and was himself brought up as a Christian—one of his instructors being possibly a bishop. But perhaps this was not much in his favour, for de Quincey has remarked that the sons of bishops are always disagreeable.

Possibly the circumstances of his early life were not calculated to inspire him with a great love for his Christian relatives or great faith in their professions. Julian was about seven years old when Constantine died and was succeeded by his three sons. Their accession was celebrated by a general massacre of all their relatives, which secured their position, and from which Julian only escaped because of his extreme youth. But the whole character and behaviour of his kindred was calculated to fill him with disgust. His cousin Constantius, who reigned more or less alone during the next twenty-four years, was a jealous and contemptible tyrant for whom it is vain to attempt apology. And as for Constantine himself, though we are apt to regard him with reverence as the patron of Christianity, yet a nearer view rubs all the gilt off the gingerbread. Among other trifles he murdered his own son. Even his conversion has been doubted by many writers who think it is no more sincere than that of Henry IV of France. But there is one circumstance which leads me strongly to believe in his sincerity; being precisely that on which many doubts have been founded. He was never baptised till he was on his deathbed. He had been trying a water cure for his body and when that had proved unavailing he took one for his soul instead; it may sound profane to put it in that language, but it is the literal fact; baptism was in those days held to be somehow a passport to Paradise. And in postponing the ceremony to his deathbed Constantine resembled many other persons of the time. Baptism absolved you of all past sins, but not of any in which you might indulge after it, and if you felt a strong presumption that you would indulge in them pretty freely (as Constantine must have done) it was as well to wait. Such was the orthodox view. But suppose now that Constantine was *not* sincere and consider the natural course for him to take. Surely he would have got baptised at once to show that he really was a Christian. To defer it was bad policy because it would infallibly give rise to those very doubts about his sincerity which *have* arisen, and if as a matter of policy he wished to be thought one, clearly he would have got baptised at once. Therefore I hold that his conversion was perfectly genuine—why not? It is unfortunately only too certain that a genuine belief in any religion may go along with crimes innumerable.

But this is a digression. Anyhow Julian had good enough reason to doubt the moral value of Christianity—the

difficulty rather is to know why he should have been so
enthusiastic in favour of Paganism. That was neither
moral, nor up to date, nor the winning side—so at least
it appears to us from our point of view. But though we
think of Paganism as a whole as immoral, yet it proved
capable of satisfying the moral sense of eminently moral
men and men of the very first intellect. Hostile criticism
of it there had been in plenty before any thought of
abolishing it had arisen. The criticism had caused thinking
men with moral and religious tendencies to read new
meanings into the old texts. They interpreted them to
suit their own convictions when they could no longer
swallow their literal statements. So all the Homeric
figures became to them allegories—Jupiter was the aether,
or the creative force of nature, or the Sun. If he quarrelled
in a most unseemly manner with his wife, and kicked
his son out of heaven, that forsooth was only a way of
explaining or disguising some natural phenomenon or
inculcating some profound religious maxims—what particular one you liked to choose was your own affair. Above
all, the old Greek and Roman pantheon had been enlarged
to make room for an Oriental deity who had become of the
highest importance in the eyes of mystics of that date. His
name was Mithras, and he started life in Persia as a per-
sonification of sunlight. Gradually he became more and
more important, and was taken into partnership with the
strange group of metaphysical abstractions, emanations
and the like, which were talked about by the neo-Platonists.
He is closely connected with the Sun, but in the opinion
of the more elevated philosophers, such as Julian, was by
no means to be identified with him.

To go into the bastard system of metaphysics and religion would only bore you, even if I could understand it sufficiently myself to make it intelligible. One of the principal authorities is Julian's own oration on the subject, which I can honestly recommend anyone whatever to flee from as the plague.

The *Orations* are the earliest in date, the most elaborate, and the most tiresome of all the works of our author. They do not redound to his credit. The first especially is a rather shameful performance. It is an elaborate and monstrously highflown panegyric of that very Constantius who was the Emperor, being Julian's cousin, and of whom I have had to speak in very uncomplimentary language before. But Julian was in an awkward place. He was of course celebrated for his learning, for his love of poetry and rhetoric, for his literary capacity. At the same time he was a near relation and at the Emperor's mercy. It is rather a wonder that he was spared at all, and he certainly would not have been if he had ventured to reveal his real sentiments. Consequently he was forced into an abject hypocrisy in every word and act. Of course he *might* have acted openly, he might have said to his cousin that he did not feel capable of giving him a testimonial which after all would be no use, he might have said in like manner that he found it no longer possible to believe in Christianity. We know of plenty of men in history who would have done so—and there were plenty of men then living who would have declined to abjure their religion, plenty who if they had been converts to Christianity would have said so even if the result had been martyrdom. But who will be a martyr for a metaphysical abstraction?—for the flimsy relics of a soap-bubble, even if it be as gaudily coloured as neo-Platonism was by its rhetorical professors? Anyhow, one can't help agreeing with Gibbon that this oration is equally disgraceful to both parties concerned. Constantius is compared in it and preferred for genius and morals to Alexander the Great, Agesilaus and other heroes of the past, he is a finer fellow than Achilles, a greater orator than Demosthenes, his magnificence, temperance (good Heavens!), eloquence, military skill and clemency to the vanquished are all remarkable.

No sooner was Julian himself Emperor and his lamented cousin dead, than the tune changed. In an elaborate epistle to the Council and People of Athens, Julian defended his conduct and spoke out what he thought about Constantius. "This most humane of princes," he says with bitter scorn, "murdered without trial six of his own cousins and mine, and my father who was his own uncle; as for me and my brother, he wished to kill us, but ended by banishing us instead."

One observes that he is not content with facts but imputes to his enemy evil thoughts besides. How could he know the secret wishes of Constantius? If Constantius wished to kill him why didn't he? This habit of pushing your points to the utmost, of exaggerating wherever it is to your interests to do so, of making out your own case to be better than it really is and your adversary's worse than it really is—all this is unfortunately a characteristic of Greek generally—at any rate from the fifth century B.C. onwards. The habit of turning everything into a field for rhetorical discussion, a subject for a debating society, is one that is very tempting to an acute mind, and the Greeks were acute beyond any other nation. They loved to debate questions themselves, they loved to hear others debating them too, alike in the public assembly, in the law court, in tragedy or comedy, at a drinking party—in short all day and every day.

If this habit is discernible in the great authors of the past, when all the free states of Greece were flourishing and life was more fully life indeed than it has ever been since, how much more deplorable did it become when the Roman Empire had crushed everything under its level uniform weight and political life was utterly extinct! The degenerate Greeks went on arguing and debating—if they could no longer shake the arsenal and fulmine over Greece, they could at least go on inventing sham speeches to put into the mouths of historical characters—much as if we nowadays were to amuse ourselves with publishing imaginary addresses by William the Conqueror to his troops before Hastings. In this artificial dead wearisome school of rhetoric Julian was brought up; he was himself a type of the argumentative chattering Graeculus of the decadence if ever there was one. When he sits down to compose an oration in praise of his deadly enemy or to defend his action in rebelling against the same enemy, you feel all the time that it really doesn't much matter which he is doing, that he is really interested in putting literary touches to his work, not in the work itself—that he wants to show how clever a fencer he is according to the rules. You don't feel that with a great orator. The result accordingly of reading these works is extreme depression and a sort of nervous irritation.

Still worse are his rhapsodies about Mithras and Atys,

emanations and essences and existences. For not only do
they ring insincere but they are mainly unintelligible.

You may feel inclined by this time to ask: Why then
trouble oneself about Julian at all? How can anybody think
him a great man in any way? What has he to do with
literature? And yet in his way he *was* a great man. As
such he impressed the most impartial and keenest-sighted
of his contemporaries, the historian Ammianus Marcellinus.
For he was fortunate in this also, that his life is recorded
by a great historian, one who if compared with the other
historians of the Empire after Tacitus, is a perfect giant,
and who will indeed bear comparison with any Roman
historian whatever. At least he is incomparably the most
impartial and honest among them all. So much is this the
case that it has always remained uncertain whether he was
or was not a Christian, though for my own part I have no
doubt whatever that he was *not*. Though Julian is his great
hero, he never shrinks from blaming him when he thinks
him wrong. But his style is generally deplorable, he tries
to be fine, and isn't; he indulges in foolish and unintelligible
speculations about rainbows; people call him turgid and
coarse and other pretty epithets; he came too late and so
is ignored by classical scholars, though I *have* seen a piece
of him set for translation in the M.A. He was a good soldier
and a man of sense.

There can be no sort of doubt about the impression
Julian made upon *him*. He cannot have cared a straw
about his neo-Platonism nor about his rhetoric, and he did
not approve of his attitude towards the Christians. But
it is plain all through that he thinks Julian the one great
man of his time—he speaks of him as Milton spoke of Crom-

well. And the one passage in which his swelling efforts to reach the sublime are for once successful, is that in which he recounts the elevation of Julian to the Caesarship.

For Constantius after massacring nearly all his relations found himself at last in a fix which was common to Roman Emperors of those times. The Empire was so unwieldy and unmanageable that one man could not look after it. This led them time after time to try experiments in the way of dividing it, but these divisions made things worse because the rival rulers sooner or later always flew at one another's throats. Constantius, feeling the necessity for devolving some part of the government on another, accordingly looked about him for a partner, for there were threatening clouds all round the horizon, and he had no son of his own to succeed him. Indeed, owing to his own thoughtful measures, he had no relations at all by this time except Julian. So he took the astounding and desperate step of giving Julian the title of Caesar. This was not equivalent to Emperor, but a sort of Prince of Wales.

Julian at this time was studying philosophy and literature at Athens, the city he loved best in the world. He had a great reputation among the students there, the sort of reputation of a senior wrangler; nobody thought of him as anything but a hard-working devotee of literature. Probably Constantius thought such a man was safe enough and would give him no trouble, but if so what was the good of making him Caesar? It is a hopeless puzzle.

Julian obeyed the summons with great reluctance. He was leaving his books and everything he valued, and for what? He came to Milan and there with great pomp and magnificence was endued with the purple, which in his eyes

was but too ominous. It was Nov. 6th, 355. As the
soldiers clashed their shields upon their knees and broke
into applause, the new Caesar repeated to himself the line
of Homer, "Purple death and violent fate seized him."
He departed for Gaul, and in a few months the world was
filled with his renown.

There does not seem to be any parallel in history for the
change. This awkward long-legged student, with his eager
restless way of walking, his nervous excitable outbursts
of talking, his loud undignified laughter, his silly rhetorical
school exercises, who had been heard to murmur "O Plato"
as he practised the goose-step after his promotion, who had
mourned at having to shave off his philosophical beard and
adopt the soldier's coat for the student's gown—this
Brutus suddenly threw off the mask and appeared as the
greatest warrior of his age. Though his inexperience, and
a rashness which never deserted him and finally ruined
him, caused him some sound losses at first, yet in 357 he
won a great victory over the German invaders of Gaul at
Strasburg. His administration of Gaul, both civil and
military, was in the highest degree practical and successful.
He lived like an ascetic or a Stoic, refusing to have a fire
in the coldest winter, eating little, sleeping less, sitting up
all night to compose some literary performance and working
all day at the business of the Empire.

There is no time to go into the final quarrel with Constantius which led to Julian becoming Emperor. Enough
to say that he was blameless, that the soldiers got excited
and alarmed, and insisted on their beloved general assuming
the sovereignty. One night he was awakened by the din
of armour and the cry of "Julian Augustus," a cry which

was treason. He vainly tried to pacify the soldiers—they broke in and raised him on a shield, and a standard-bearer placed his military collar on his head as a crown. Julian, for whatever reason, yielded—some said in fear of his life— he himself said to prevent anyone else being made Emperor, but that I cannot believe.

Constantius might have accepted the elevation, irregular as it was, and the two emperors might have reigned together. But he was already consumed with jealousy and hatred of his rival, and refused to recognise him. Civil war was assured. But neither party was in a hurry to begin— both in the East and West their hands were full, campaigning against enemies of the Empire. When Julian did at last strike, he struck like lightning. The military situation will be most easily imagined by you if you suppose a small army throwing itself with inconceivable rapidity from Paris upon Vienna, and supposing it to have taken Vienna it has then got to attack a superior force and make its way through immensely difficult country to Constantinople. This bare sentence shows the enormous difficulty of Julian's undertaking, one which he could have hardly ventured on perhaps, if he had not expected and had not hoped for treason on the other side. He may well have had reason to believe that he would be welcomed in the East.

Anyhow, he carried out the first part of the programme in so masterly a manner that one is irresistibly driven to think of the similar campaign of Napoleon in 1805. Julian from Paris, Napoleon from Boulogne, advanced in one case on Sirmium in the other on Vienna (it comes to the same thing) with a wonderfully similar series of converging columns and with the same amazing rapidity which

completely threw their enemies into bewilderment. But one
cannot help observing that Napoleon risked nothing and
Julian risked everything. His reckless audacity, however,
served him well—everywhere he was successful, and was
welcomed by admiring crowds in Sirmium itself, then one
of the great ganglions of the Empire. Then he halted and
just at the nick of time Constantius had grace enough, to
die—nothing in his life became him like the leaving of it—
he could not have better timed his exit from the stage. By
this "crowning mercy" Julian found himself in 361 sole
master of the Roman world.

His next two winters were passed at Constantinople and
Antioch. Amid the enormous labours of reform of various
kinds, and the administration of the over-swollen Empire,
he found time to write his three most celebrated and
principal works—and others besides for that matter.

These were first a treatise against the Christians which
has naturally perished and is only known in fragments from
those who again wrote against it, secondly the *Caesars*
and thirdly the *Misopogon*. He wrote with amazing swift-
ness—as he did anything else—and one is astounded to
hear that some of his orations were composed in a single
night.

The *Caesars* is a prose satire written at Christmas-time
A.D. 362. The plot is thus. Romulus invites the gods and
the Roman Emperors to a banquet—the gods take their
places first and watch the entry of the Caesars one by one.
The drunken and bloated Silenus, companion of Bacchus
and a sort of Falstaff of mythology, acts the part of jester,
and it is his satirical and comic remarks that are the real
essence of the piece. Julius Caesar came first and is taunted

with his ambition. Then Augustus, changing colour like
a chameleon, first making up to Venus and the Graces and
then handed over by Apollo to Zeno the Stoic philosopher,
who turns him out a decent and respectable member of
society. Every one of them is gibed at for some defect
except Julian's great model Marcus Aurelius—and even
he is reproached for his indulgence to his good-for-nothing
wife and son. When all the company are assembled, a
competition is started between Julius, Augustus, Trajan
and Alexander the Great to decide which is the greatest
hero—Marcus Aurelius is also thrown in to represent
philosophy—and Constantine is allowed to go in, really in
order that Julian may make an attack upon his character
and his religion. After they have all made speeches for
themselves, the gods award the palm, as you might expect,
to Marcus the Philosopher, but each of these heroes is
allowed to choose a special patron among the gods that he
may not depart unhonoured. Alexander chooses Heracles
and Trajan runs after Alexander, Augustus takes Apollo,
Marcus Jupiter and Saturn, Julius Caesar Mars and
Venus. But Constantine, says the writer, "not finding
among the gods the pattern of his own life, spied out
Luxury and ran to her, and she embracing him and decking
him up in fine raiment took him to Profligacy—and then
he found Christ wandering about and proclaiming to all:
"Whoever is a corrupter of others and guilty of blood-
shedding, accursed and abominable, let him come with
boldness, for with this water I will wash him and make him
clean, and if he again fall into the like iniquity, I will grant
unto him to become clean by just striking his breast and
beating his head." And Constantine met with him gladly

and departed, he and his sons, from the assembly of the gods. But nevertheless did the avenging furies make havoc of him for his godlessness, exacting vengeance of him for shedding of kindred blood, until Zeus granted him a respite for the sake of his ancestors. As for Julian, he is dedicated by Mercury to Mithras.

I have read this passage because it is the most illuminating of all Julian's written words. The first thing that must strike you on hearing it is the singular and unexpected fact that what Julian blames in Christianity is not lack of evidence for the doctrines nor the ruin it was sure to bring on the ancient life he loved—not what you would expect at all—but its immorality. Astonishing indeed must that seem to us, in whose ears have rung so long that appalling denunciation of the Greek and Roman world in the first chapter of St Paul's Epistle to the Romans. Astonishing to all classical students who have investigated the sink of iniquity into which the Roman Empire had sunk by the time that the leaven of Christianity entered into it, who have read their Petronius (which *I* haven't), their Juvenal and their Tacitus. All the more remarkable for us to be waked up to consider this passage; written by a man whose own morality was blameless and who believed himself even more superior than he was. How blind even the wisest among us are to the great stream in which we move! especially how blind is the Pharisee to human life! And the Pharisee is as rampant now as ever he was.

That is the second point—that Julian was a Pharisee of the strictest sect. Outside his own Little Bethel of Mithras and moonshine there was no salvation, and he thanked Mithras that he was not as other men. And with that forsooth he was going to convert the world and dam up the torrent of Christianity. Here is a specimen of his religion for you, a prayer addressed to the Mother of the Gods. "O mother of gods and men, that sittest enthroned with mighty Zeus, O fountain of the divine intelligence, companion of the pure essences of the intelligible gods, that hast received the common cause of all things from all and dost give them to the divine intelligences, mother of life, Wisdom, Providence, Creatress of our souls, thou that lovest the great Dionysus and didst save Attis when he was cast forth and bring him back when he entered into the abyss of earth, thou who leadest the divine intelligences in the path of all good things and fillest the visible world therewith and hast granted of thy munificence all good things to us in all."

I should think that is enough of it. There is not much immorality about that, and it must be a great comfort to the unhappy and the weary, and all those that seek to cast their burdens upon some divine helper. It is as bad as the Athanasian Creed. "Come unto me all ye that labour and are heavy laden and I will give you rest." But that, we see, was an abomination to Julian—the sinner was *not* to be cleansed and there was to be no redemption for him. And he is surely, we may hope, unfair in suggesting that the Christians of his time did not insist upon repentance and a better life. Of course the case of Constantine himself, with his baptism deferred to his deathbed that he might sin at leisure and repent in haste—that was enough to cause a scandal. But it is a pity that kings and emperors should be expected to live virtuously or decently—Julian is really unconscionable.

But what astonishes me most is that this passage should have been handed down to us at all—what were the Christians who transcribed it thinking about?

The *Misopogon* or *Beard-Hater* is an extraordinary production which Julian composed at Antioch while there engaged in preparation for his great enterprise against Sapor, the famous King of Persia. The people of Antioch and Julian could not get on together at all. Most of them were Christians, divided into three sects who quarrelled with one another as bitterly as if they had had an Education Bill before them. The Pagans were a luxurious and idle lot, caring for nothing but games and shows. Julian despised all parties and all parties hated Julian. The Christians hated him as an Apostate to their religion, the Pagans because he was too superior and philosophical—Julian was disgusted with them also because they didn't even keep up the Pagan religion respectably. He went to a temple to celebrate a great festival, expecting a multitude of votaries and rich sacrifices—he met one priest bringing a goose provided at his own expense.

A dignified prince would certainly not have condescended to take any notice of the rabble who laughed at him and misunderstood him. But Julian's dignity was a frightful minus quantity, and it is evident that he had vanity enough to make him smart under the annoyance of the flies who stung him into angry retort. This it is which makes one feel a painful littleness about him, that makes a strange mixture with his great qualities.

The title *Beard-Hater* is due to the beard being regarded as the sign of a philosopher. Julian cherished as fine a beard as he could grow as the external and visible sign of his calling. This was apparently most unorthodox for a general or a ruler, and afforded a handle for the laughter of the satirical populace.

But the Emperor could hold his own in the domain of satire. The *Misopogon* is written from the point of view of the inhabitants of Antioch who hate beards—i.e. hate all philosophy and culture; with elaborate irony Julian attacks and ridicules himself, jeering at everything of which he was really proud. This irony is so elaborate that it has deceived many people in later times and most extraordinary to tell, even the great master of irony, Gibbon himself. Here is a specimen:

I cannot flatter myself that my countenance is peculiarly beautiful or comely to look upon, but so boorish and un-polished am I that I have made it worse by the addition of this thick beard, punishing it, it seems, purely and simply for not being beautiful. That is why I put up with—er—insects which run about it like animals in a forest.

Gibbon has positively been deceived by this into talking of Julian's being proud of the size and populousness of his beard!

In reality the whole piece is a bitter attack upon the luxury, the utter absence of any intellectual life, and the general degradation of the Antiochenes, and a lofty defence of himself; and it ends up with the ominous words: "Hence-forth I will try to be wiser in my conduct towards you, and may the gods give you the fit reward for your benevolence to me and the public honour you have done me."

Besides these two satires, the letters are worth reading; nothing ever throws so much light upon a man as his correspondence, and luckily a great deal of Julian's is preserved. They show him in all sorts of lights, as a lofty, noble and amiable man in his intercourse with the chosen few, as an intolerant despiser of the multitude.

To Ecdicius, prefect of Egypt.

Though you write to me on no other subject, you ought at least to have written concerning that enemy of the gods, Athanasius, especially as you have long been acquainted with our edicts against him. I now swear by the great Serapis that if the enemy of the gods does not leave Alexandria, or rather Egypt, before the calends of December, the officers of your government shall be fined a hundred pounds of gold. You know my temper: I am slow to condemn, but I am slower still to forgive. (*Postscript in autograph*) His contempt for all the gods fills me with grief and indignation. Nothing that you can do will give me so much pleasure as to hear that the abominable Athanasius, who has presumed in my reign to persuade several Greek ladies of rank to be baptised, is expelled from all Egypt. (Epistle VI.)

It was at this time, while the Emperor was in the full flush of his prosperity, engaged in preparations for the overthrow of Persia, rebuilding the temple at Jerusalem, and finishing off Athanasius, that the famous oracle came to him from Delphi, whither he had sent to enquire of Apollo. The temple was destroyed and the vale of Castaly was desolate, but somehow an answer was given.

Go ye and tell the Emperor that the carved work of the sanctuary is cast down upon the ground, and the god thereof hath no longer where to lay his head. And the laurel of his divination is withered, and the waters that spoke with voices are dried up.

"A strange coincidence!" writes Myers in one of those purple patches of which he was so fond, "that from that Delphian valley, whence as the legend ran had sounded

the first of all hexameters—the call as in the childhood of
the world to 'birds to bring their feathers and bees their
wax' to build by Castaly the nestlike habitation of the
young new-entering god—should issue in unknown fashion
the last fragment of Greek poetry which has moved the
hearts of men, the last Greek hexameters which retain the
ancient cadence, the majestic melancholy flow.''

With this ominous answer and no other from any oracle
of the dead gods Julian set forth on his great enterprise.
But his rashness this time was not condoned by Fortune.
He got to Ctesiphon indeed on the Euphrates, but found
it necessary to retreat, over a desert country, in want of
supplies, harassed incessantly by an active and pertinacious
enemy. Even so he still devoted his nights to study and
meditation. On his last night we are told the Genius of the
Empire appeared to him (not for the first time), but now
covered with a funeral veil and retreating from him—he
leapt up and stepping out into the cool night saw a blazing
meteor shoot across the sky and vanish. In the morning
as he led the van of his army he heard that the Persian
horse had attacked the rear—he seized a shield and hastened
to their relief; the attack became general, but was repelled,
and as Julian on horseback led the pursuit, calling on his
troops and exposing himself with reckless valour, under
the burning sun and amid a whirlwind of sandy dust and
stamping chargers, he was struck by a flying javelin in the
side, and fell from his horse. The victory of the Romans was
complete, but the soul of their army lay dying in his tent.

His death is compared to that of Socrates—Ammianus
puts into his mouth a philosophical discourse the authen-
ticity of which is doubtful to say the least, but it is certain
that he passed his last hours in conversing with two

philosophers on the nature of the soul. He died without pain about midnight, June 26th, 363.

And then falls the curtain of history upon living men, at least in Europe, not to rise again till that day in 1274 when in Florence appeared to Dante that Beatrice of whom he was to write things never before written of mortal woman, clothed in a most noble colour, girt and adorned as became her tender years. In all the 900 years before is nothing but ghosts and shadows moving in the mist, and "in all the endless roads they tread there's little but the night." They have fine names, some of them wore crowns, and some were great saints and great men of all kinds, St Louis and Alfred, Benedict, Charlemagne, Theodoric, Stilicho—but there is not one whom I feel that I know or care about. But Julian is a man whom we *can* know, one whom in spite of his errors we can admire and even love. Had he fallen on happier times he might have been among the principal names of either history or literature, and even as it is he is quite worth reading and studying.

THE RELATIONS OF POETRY AND SCIENCE

(Literary Society, 1912)

The Relations of Poetry and Science

It is a common opinion, I believe, that poetry and science are antipathetic things, and this opinion may be bolstered up by quotations from representatives of both Faculties, if I may so call them. I have long thought myself that this opinion is, however, one which has been very hastily formed, that there is no real evidence to be adduced in its support, that the evidence is in fact the other way round. That is to say, that the poetic and scientific types of mind are by no means mutually exclusive, but touch on one another in many points, and though it is true that excessive addiction to either pursuit will probably render the mind incapable of the other, yet the two will run very well in harness.

It is just as well to begin by defining one's terms—one of the principal reasons for the deplorable nature of most literary discussion is the neglect to begin by doing this. Consequently, as the brothers de Goncourt observed, it almost invariably degenerates into the position "My taste is better than yours"—either asserted boisterously or hinted under a pretence of modesty. Then people begin to raise their voices and get red in the face and make themselves ridiculous.

But in literature one cannot define one's terms with mathematical accuracy any more than one can in ethics. Different people have very different notions about what they mean by poetry, and nobody need quarrel with his neighbour's using it in any sense that seems good to him, if only he will state as clearly as possible to begin with what that sense is. So for the purpose of this present paper I declare that by poetry I mean any good literature written in verse and not prose. That I take to be more or less the sense in which the word is understood by the general public in England, and though in German and in Cherokee the word may cover different ground, I am neither a Cherokee nor a German myself, and have a very absurd and unreasonable fancy for talking plain English. And by science I mean what is commonly understood as natural science, exclusive of mathematics and the application of science to practice.

Certainly nobody will suggest that poets are given to mathematics. I can only think of one instance of their combination in the same individual, Omar Khayyám, who was, I believe, a great mathematician for his age and country, and who reformed the calendar of Persia, even as he says himself:

> Ah, but my Computations, People say,
> Reduced the Year to better reckoning? Nay,
>   'Twas only striking from the Calendar
> Unborn To-morrow, and dead Yesterday.

It is true that the peculiar merit of Manilius, according to his latest editor, who certainly knows plenty about poetry, consists in his skill in doing arithmetical sums in verse, but Manilius does not come under the head of "good literature in verse," and is so ruled out by my definition.

But when we turn to the other sciences, we find quite a different story to tell. It is true that certain poets have lent their aid to foster the popular belief; two of the greatest poets of the last century in England have perhaps done so more vehemently than any others. I mean, of course, Wordsworth and Keats. Wordsworth is eternally declaring in good verse and in bad verse alike that you ought to open your mouth and shut your eyes and ask no questions.

> Enough of science and of art;
> Close up these barren leaves;
> Come forth, and bring with you a heart
> That watches and receives.

It was this attitude of mind that so much allured Matthew Arnold. A. C. Bradley has fallen foul with justice of Arnold's famous lines at Wordsworth's grave:

> The cloud of mortal destiny,
> Others will front it fearlessly—
> But who, like him, will put it by?

"Shut his eyes to human trouble?" cries Bradley indignantly—"not he," and he produces a multitude of instances to the contrary where Wordsworth has painted in blackest colours the misery of life. Very true, and yet what Arnold says is true too. Wordsworth knew well enough that the world was full of affliction, and did not attempt to forget it, but what he *did* attempt to escape from was the scientific spirit, which enquires into things. That is the real moral of that remarkable poem the *Advice to Fathers*. It is true that he heads the poem by a pretence that it has a different moral, that it is intended to show how easily the habit of telling lies may be implanted in the youthful mind. But that, as Charles Lamb would have said, "was only his fun." You all remember how the

father worries the unhappy child to tell him why he likes
one place better than another,

> And five times to the child I said,
> "Why, Edward? tell me why."

At last the unhappy infant, goaded to desperation by his
tormentor, answers that it was because there is a weather-
cock at one place and none at the other, and the poet lifts
his eyes to Heaven and thanks his Creator for teaching him
so many lessons at the hands of babes and sucklings. But
what *was* the lesson? Not, as he says, that the habit of
lying may easily be taught, but that you ought to enjoy
Nature and not go grubbing up the reasons for it. Accept
the simple impressions of things upon your mind, and do
not investigate them scientifically. One might quote fifty
poems to illustrate the same thing; I content myself with
one pyramidal example:

> One impulse from a vernal wood
>   May teach you more of man,
> Of moral evil and of good,
>   Than all the sages can.

That is to say that you learn more about virtue and vice,
and the true end of human life and so on, by lying on the
grass and listening to a cuckoo than you can by studying
Aristotle's *Ethics*. This amazing nonsense has seriously
perturbed some of the poet's admirers; Morley tries to
make out that he did not mean what he said, but Raleigh
more wisely takes the bull by the horns, says he did mean
what he said and was quite capable of talking nonsense.

That anyhow is Wordsworth's attitude, and I take it
that it is very much the same as the Apostle's attitude in
religious matters when he tells us to quench not the spirit.

Let your instincts have full play and don't apply your intellect to their conclusions. Dozens of people declare every Sunday that if you use your intellect you will go to the Devil.

"Spirit" and "intellect." There we come upon the great mental division which corresponds within our brains to the outward manifestations of poetry and science. It has become fashionable in some circles to talk about the difference between the "subliminal consciousness" and the "supraliminal consciousness," but these are long and clumsy words, and I prefer to call them for the purpose of this paper the "spirit" and the "intellect," assuming that I have Apostolic warrant at any rate for the former. This "subliminal consciousness" or "spirit" is that part of our mental activity which emerges in dreams and visions, partly under the control of the intellect often even then, and which creates the works of the poet, the artist, the musician, being then much more under the control of the intellect. "Let no man imagine," said Goethe, "that by the ordinary operations of the mind, or by any amount of thinking, he can make music like Mozart or pictures like Raphael." And indeed Raphael himself is said to have seen the Sistine Madonna appear visibly before him, he knew not how nor whence, and his active and conscious participation in the matter consisted merely in transferring his vision to canvas. So also in poetry the spirit supplies a constant stream of ideas and words and phrases, which the intellect controls, from which it selects and arranges, and which itself only partly understands. When these two work harmoniously together and the balance between them is perfect, then we get really fine poetry, but when

one or the other predominates unduly, then there will be
something wrong.

Blake is an example of the extreme predominance of the
spirit. In Blake, perhaps more than in any other, we seem
to get poetry in its purest essence now and then by fits and
starts, but at an early age, perhaps from birth, something
was wrong with his intellect. The longer he lived the more
did he trust to the inspirations of his spirit, and the more
he condemned the intellect, and Nemesis came upon him.
From the enchanted *Songs of Innocence* he slid downward
into the monstrous abortions of *The Marriage of Heaven
and Hell*, and *Albion* and *Jerusalem*, and the spirit itself
was wrecked for want of its pilot; instead of verse that
ripples like a river, he pours out oceans of turbid stuff that
is scarcely even prose. But as a rule what happens to poets
is just the contrary. They begin with an excess of spirit in
consequence of which they write harmonious magic without
much content, then, if they are great poets, they arrive at
the proper balance between the two faculties and write
really great poetry, then in the third stage the intellect
begins to get the upper hand too much, they may think
more and may have more to say, but the natural gush is
quenched and they write verse which is flat and feeble.
This is particularly visible in Wordsworth himself; by an
irony of fate he who had fought against the intellect was
himself overcome by it; he who had kept on crying
"Quench not the spirit" had his own spirit quenched by
a thick blanket of moralisation and preachification, and
the beauty of it was that he never knew what had befallen
him. Browning is another conspicuous example of the
same thing. These and many others go on writing verse all

their lives, but in many cases the poet is wiser; feels the inspiration flag and betakes himself to something else; so for instance did Coleridge, Arnold.... But the great poets of the first order are those in whom the two faculties are in perfect harmony all their lives; there we get Sophocles, Dante, Shakespeare, Milton, Goethe.

This change takes place in all of us, or at any rate in nearly all of us. In youth we love dreams and delusions, we know nothing about logic or the value of evidence, we do not like to apply our minds to any hard thinking, and so far as we think about it at all we rather despise the operations of the pure intellect. The whole tendency of education is to correct this, to make us think, to make us work at intellectual things in an intellectual manner, to get us to look at things as they are, not as we should like them to be. It seeks to make us scientific instead of poetical, one might say; that is, it tries to correct the reliance upon instincts and make us follow evidence instead of impulse. Possibly it nips a good many youthful poets in the bud in consequence, but I do not think we need fear its doing any real harm in that way. For in the first place people with the poetic instinct but with no brains to speak of mostly let their education go to the dogs, and in the second place nobody is the worse for the loss of such; there are feeble minor poets enough about as it is in all conscience. And when you come to the great poets, the only ones worth troubling about, you find that they are eager to get all the education they can. Nobody can possibly be more educated than were Milton and Goethe.

In the poets of the first order, then, we find spirit and intellect walking hand in hand. They are not content with the one without the other. *They* do not think that there need be any conflict between the two, and so far from hating and fearing science, they embrace it eagerly. For that is the particular direction of all others which their intellect is apt to take. They want to know things, they are consumed by an insatiable curiosity. Before Dante and Goethe one stands aghast, in helpless amazement. They were walking encyclopaedias; whatever was to be known they had amassed and absorbed. Goethe is, of course, the grand example of the union of science and poetry. About the latter it is needless to speak, but I will briefly recapitulate his achievements in science, because to literary people they are but little known. Of their value indeed as advancing science it is difficult to speak, because there are very diverse opinions among scientific men on that point. But when all deductions have been made, it seems impossible to deny that Goethe more than any other one man founded the whole vast subject of the morphology of plants, a subject the importance of which was not truly understood before Darwin revolutionised biology, but which is now one of the staples of all botanical teaching and research. He is hailed, moreover, as one of the forerunners of evolution, and though his ideas on that seem to have been of a hazy metaphysical kind in general, yet one cannot get over the fact that he definitely asked the luminous question which Darwin was to answer: "The question among naturalists," said he, "has been: for what does the bull use his horns? the question of the future will be: how did he get them?" It was Goethe who started the theory that the skull is a modified vertebra, a theory in which there has turned out to be a certain amount of truth.

Again, people used to assert that man was not made on the same plan as other animals, and pointed as a proof of this to the alleged fact that a certain bone was missing from man in the upper jaw; Goethe proved triumphantly that the bone was there. It is true that Vicq-d'Azyr had discovered it fifteen years before, but that does not alter the fact that the author of *Faust* made this discovery in human anatomy independently. All his life long he was absorbed in such things; for years he studied colours and wrote a great book upon them, but there he was frankly a failure, and as so often happens he was prouder of his failure than of anything else. "There have been greater poets before me and will be greater hereafter," he said, "but my glory is that I overthrew the Newtonian doctrine of colour." And again: "To make a name in the world you need two good things, a good head and a great inheritance; Napoleon had a good head and inherited the French Revolution; I inherited the Newtonian errors concerning light and colour." In his old age it became a mania, and his attitude upon the subject is distressing to his admirers. Geology, too, was a favourite subject, and when at the University he actually attended lectures on midwifery. It is this attitude of Goethe's which so vexed the soul of Mazzini. Commenting on his *Campaign in France* Mazzini cries indignantly, "Everything interests him, the skeleton of a sheep, the bones of a fish, everything except the movements of masses of men." And it is easy to see why Goethe could not tolerate the sort of windy atmosphere of gaseous gammon in which politicians dwell. I thought of that passage in Mazzini when I read a book by Wells called *Ann Veronica*. The heroine thereof after contact in London with politicians and suffragettes and such *bêtises* goes back to the room of Comparative Anatomy in this very College—and what a blessing she feels it to get back into that orderly domain, where something really is known, where one generation bequeaths its wisdom to another and one is rid of violent assertions about the unknown and the attitude of mad bulls in china-shops.

Therefore it was that that famous scene took place when a certain person went to Goethe at the time of the July revolution in 1830. A great dispute about cuttle fish had broken out at the same time in the scientific world in Paris and Goethe was full of excitement about it. When his visitor began talking about the importance of what was going on, Goethe said "Yes, indeed, it can no longer be kept hid—it will all to light" and so on, and the visitor couldn't make out what he was at, and began talking again about *his* exciting news. When Goethe saw what he was at, he said with great contempt "My good friend, I perceive that we are at cross purposes—I am talking not about these people at all, but about the report of St Hilaire; *that* is something important."

But Goethe may be exceptional, you will say. Take then Dante. The *Divine Comedy* is full of science, such as it was in the middle ages; in particular there is a most masterly résumé in the *Purgatory* of Aristotle's work in embryology, and in the *Paradiso* a most elaborate discussion of the markings on the moon. Dante wrote a scientific work himself; I do not mean the treatise *De Vulgari Eloquio* which is the first contribution to philology since the dark ages, the first extant since the *Cratylus* of Plato, but a lessknown work, the question on Earth and Water. In the year 1320 Dante read at Verona an elaborate paper to prove that the earth sticks out of the water, not the water out of the earth. Such was the condition of science at that time that this was a disputed point, and Dante successfully solves the problem on the right side. Among other things he has to prove that water finds its own level. Imagine it! he must in all probability have been putting the finishing touches at that time to the ineffable last cantos of *Paradiso*, and yet he descends to discuss such a question as that with, to all appearance, just as much interest as when he is describing the mystic rose of Paradise in what is perhaps the highest reach of human song, in what is certainly unique in its ardent rapture and dazzling splendour in all the world.

And when we descend from the heights of Dante and Goethe, we find the same combination of interests in plenty of humble followers. Redi in the eighteenth century in Italy was a famous poet, but he not only wrote the delightful *Bacco in Toscana*, he also was the first man to knock on the head the theory of the spontaneous generation of animals which had been an article of faith ever since Aristotle, ever since the beginning of enquiry in fact, and which still flourishes in a certain corner of this College. Chamisso in Germany not only wrote the beautiful *Frauenliebe* which has been immortalised by Schumann's exquisite setting, but went on a scientific expedition to the South Seas and was one of the principal authorities on coral reefs before Darwin. Gray was a professor of history and drowned some of his poetry with it, but Gray was also an enthusiastic student of zoology and botany and according to his friends might equally well have been a professor of *them*. Tennyson is notoriously soaked in science; in fact a whole book has been written on his relation to it.

If we go back to the ancients we find the most remarkable instance of all in Lucretius, who wrote one of the great poems of the world on the atomic theory! It is true that the more scientific parts of that poem are the least poetical. Virgil in lines known to everyone regrets that the "cold blood about his heart" as he expresses it, prevents his following in the same line, but there is a certain want of sincerity in Virgil and I do not believe he was entirely serious in his complaint. Yet in several other passages he seems to think natural science is the ideal subject for a poet; such is the subject treated by Silenus in the *Eclogues*, and by long-haired Iopas in the *Aeneid*. Last, and dearest of all to me, Sophocles to one who can read between the lines is tarred with the same brush. Little things here and there show that he was master of the science of his times, such as it was.

This brief review is surely enough to show that the alleged antagonism between poetry and science simply does not exist. The names I have mentioned include four out of the seven great masters of European poetry, if we may take Tennyson's list as valid. Four out of seven is a pretty good percentage, and I think we may defy anybody to discover any other characteristic which marks so many as four of them—bating, of course, those special things in which every poet has got to be interested.

How different is the case if we look at metaphysics for example. Coleridge is, I believe, the solitary instance of any poet doing any kind of work in this line. Their general attitude towards it is rather that represented by Goethe, who told Jacobi that his metaphysical *tic* was a compensation for all the goods the gods had given him, "house, riches, children, sister and friends and a long etc., etc., etc. On the other hand, God has punished you with metaphysics like a thorn in your flesh; and me he has blessed with science, that I may be happy in the contemplation of his works."

What is the cause of this remarkable difference? The answer is obvious enough perhaps. The poet, the scientific man and the metaphysician are all alike consumed by the best gift nature can give to man, an insatiable curiosity; they all want to know things—at least most of them do. But the sort of things they want to know are distinct. The metaphysician wants to know some abstract truth, far removed from the panorama which nature spreads before him; the poet and the scientific man both want to know the panorama itself. They do not care about the abstract idea of ash-buds, nor the question whether the colour of the ash-bud exists only in the mind of the spectator thereof, or whether it has an objective as well as a subjective existence, or in general what is its relation to the percipient subject. No, but they like it as it seems to them, they note it as a living thing, and then use it as a simile:

More black than ashbuds in the front of March.

Everybody knows the old farmer in *Cranford* who had been walking among the hedge-rows for fifty years and never knew that, "and now comes a young gentleman from Cambridge and tells me that the ash-buds are black, and I look at them, and so they are." Professor Ker has

observed that Pope is just like Tennyson in his noting of
little things like that; only Pope as the poet of a frivolous
society shows his observation on playing-cards instead of
nature. That is the way of them all, more or less; they
want to know the scientific facts, and they do not care
about the rest in comparison. For the particular and the
concrete is the life-blood of poetry, but the general and
the abstract is death to it. Besides they want to know what
can be known, and they think they see that metaphysic has
only a doubtful claim to come under that head. Consequently their attitude to these mysterious subjects is
apt to be one of agnosticism and indifferentism.

> When Bishop Berkeley said there was no matter,
> And proved it, 'twas no matter what he said.

And this type of mind is naturally led on to note the
differences between the inflorescence of ash and of oak, to
try and find out what are the natural causes at work in
them, to devote itself in fact to science.

If then any poet attacks science, he is probably very
young and his intellect has not yet begun to assert itself.
So only can we excuse the extraordinary outbreak of
Keats in *Lamia*:

> Do not all charms fly
> At the mere touch of cold Philosophy?
> There was an awful rainbow once in heaven:
> We know her woof, her texture; she is given
> In the dull catalogue of common things.

By "Philosophy," as the whole context shows, Keats meant
science. Keats was surely the most glorious creature in
himself whom we know of in our poetic roll since Shake-

speare—if only he had had time to realise himself; but along with his radiant and supernatural splendours he had sad defects to which we may shut our eyes in reading him, but which we cannot ignore in applying to him the touch of cold philosophy. In particular we may say of him what Goethe said of Byron: "So soon as he reflects, he is a child." Why, at the very time when Keats was writing *Lamia*, a far greater poet than Keats was spending laborious days in investigating this very question of the colours of the rainbow—though to no good end. But Keats never lived to learn to think severely about anything; if he had, he might in poetry have rivalled Goethe himself. Of course the great comic poets jeer and fleer at science, as they do at other things; it is their business and it would be foolish to complain of them for it. What can be better fun than the *Clouds* of Aristophanes or the *Femmes Savantes* of Molière? Nay, Goethe himself can do the same when he likes; remember the scene between Mephistopheles and the student. But these people all do it in the right way, not like petulant children.

Akin to this notion that you cannot enjoy a rainbow properly if you know about the refraction of light is another heresy which is very common among the uninstructed. It is one which is always likely to be common because it appeals to two of the principal ingredients of the common mind, idleness and vanity. The heresy I mean is that you can enjoy things better if you know nothing about their technique; it is in fact simply the Wordsworthian doctrine about nature applied to art itself. It is, of course, in no way necessary to salvation to investigate the technique of verse; if any one likes to enjoy poetry and ask no questions, there is no reason why he should not behave in a concatenation accordingly. But he should not give himself airs about it, nor suppose that the application of the intellect to the works of the spirit will in any way interfere with his enjoyment. On the contrary, it greatly heightens the enjoyment; I do not say this depending on my own experience, but on the fact that the men who produce great poetry and who enjoy it most, one may suppose, are just exactly the men who do take interest in and investigate such things. And everybody who does understand the technique of any art whatever will bear witness that it adds to his pleasure. I will give two examples of the sort of thing I mean.

In Greek, Latin and Persian poetry a singularly beautiful effect is often gained by shifting the metrical accent and value of the same word when repeated; this can be done with ease in those languages because their poetry is quantitative. In English this effect can only be gained in a comparatively feeble manner and practically only with combinations of two monosyllables. A good instance is the first line of *Lycidas*

> Yet *once* more O ye laurels and once *more,*

where the accent first falls on the *once* and the second time on the *more*. There are a great many instances of this in Shakespeare's sonnets. But perhaps the prettiest specimen of it I ever saw is in a poetess who was not by any means a great one, Mary Coleridge:

> Over the blue sea goes the wind complaining,
> And the blue sea turns emerald as he goes.

How beautifully there the change of the colour is echoed by the changing accent of the two words "blue sea."

My second instance shall be a method of expressing reflection in poetry, of which I know two very beautiful examples. Shelley in one of his most lovely lyrics describes the poet dreaming all day by the water side:

> He will watch from dawn to gloom
> The lake-reflected sun illume
> The yellow bees in the ivy-bloom.

No analysis can exhaust the charm of such lines; partly it is due to the repetition of the letter *l*, especially in the triple "rich rhyme" as the French call it, gloom, illume, bloom. That is why the bees in this passage are "yellow," not humming or buzzing or banded or fifty other words which would fill up the verse. But now for the way in which the reflection of the bees in the water is painted: "The lake-reflected sun illume." The enchantment of this greatly depends upon the fact that the second syllable of "reflected" itself reflects in a weaker form the sound of the word "lake," just as the water reflects in a weaker form the bees. If you doubt this, try the experiment of substituting any other word for either "lake" or "reflected" and see how the picture disappears.

My other example shall be taken from Shropshire. For Prof. Housman has now left us so long that we may be permitted to speak of him in this Society as what he is, the most exquisite poet of our own times. Two of the most beautiful lines in those beautiful if melancholy elegies are these:

> And like a skylit water stood
> The bluebells in the azured wood.

Here again is a reflection in water, and this time the magic effect is produced by repeating the syllable "like" inside the word "skylit," but inverted as a reflection is inverted in water.

Consideration of these details has led me further astray than I intended, and indeed there is no end to the mazes of this fascinating forest. Of course nobody ever yet wrote poetry by deliberately trying after such things: they are crystals created by the mysterious alchemy of the spirit, the intellect can only marvel at them. What the intellect has made, that the intellect can understand, but what the spirit makes is a mystery to it. Nobody will ever know exactly what makes the difference between a good verse and a bad. Spenser speaks of "the roses reigning in the pride of May," and everybody, I hope, can see what a line it is; it tastes like raspberry jam—why is "the roses blooming in the pride of June" such a bad one? Of course these delicacies are not *the* important thing in poetry; in fact there is a poetry which shoots up into an atmosphere where such ornament can hardly exist, a region crowned with snow, and much of the very greatest poetry is written in a style to which ornament is impossible. It would be so obviously to *King Lear*, to the passages in the *Prelude* about the soldier on the road and about the blind man in London, to the last lines of Emily Brontë, which I reckon to be probably the greatest short poem in the English language. All that I have been insisting on is that the analytic appreciation of the qualities and effects of the elements of verse is no hindrance to the enjoyment of the complete product, but quite the contrary. The more you *know* about anything the more you can enjoy it.

I have been dwelling on an application of science to poetry. Let us now consider the application of poetry to science. That poets are apt to be addicted to it I have shown, but how ought they to use it? Perhaps the less they use it, the better it will be for them and for us. In spite of Lucretius and Virgil science is not a fit subject for a poem, and those two giants alone have ever succeeded in doing anything with such a subject. The poet's business is to address the general public after all, and not to puzzle them more than he can help; he always does puzzle them of course, but that is because he *can't* help. But so far as he does touch upon science, it ought to be correct according to the lights of his time, and in the case of the great poets it always, or nearly always, is. If so, it becomes itself interesting to later generations. I have not often read anything more interesting than Psichari's papers on Sophocles and medical science, but they are so interesting because Sophocles was up to date in his medicine, and if he had not been so his science would have been simply a blot upon him and a nuisance to his readers. Again everything in that vast cathedral and store-house, Dante's *Divina Commedia*, is now interesting. Even the politics are so, even the Aristotelian philosophy or rather the blend of Aristotle and Christianity so cunningly compounded by Thomas Aquinas, even the exposition of the spots on the moon. All these things are now as dead as last year's cricket scores, and yet in Dante they are all alive. But it is because they do represent the truth as it was then not only to Dante, but to all the best men of his time. If they did not, they would simply bore us. It is amusing to compare the interest of these poets in science with the interest shown in it by their commentators. Virgil knew what was to be known in his time about bees, he loved them and was profoundly interested in them; but the modern commentator on the fourth *Georgic* does not seem to know the difference between a bee and a bull's foot, as the old saying goes.

It is true that there are certain poetic traditions which pass current because of their antiquity, mere commonplaces which nobody minds. Shakespeare may set a female nightingale singing with her breast against a thorn, if he likes. But when Wordsworth solemnly tells us that

> The blackbird amid leafy trees,
> The lark above the hill,
> Let loose their carols when they please,
> Are quiet when they will.
> With Nature never do *they* wage
> A foolish strife; they see
> A happy youth, and their old age
> Is beautiful and free—

then we cannot help being disgusted. It is not so much that Wordsworth knew nothing about "Nature red in tooth and claw" (though he might just as well have known that as Tennyson did), for the idea of the struggle for existence was not then familiar. But to talk about the beautiful and free old age of thrushes and blackbirds shows that Wordsworth was not up to the level of ordinary information and intelligence in his own times; Homer would have blushed to talk such nonsense. That I suppose is what comes of giving yourself up to poetical and natural impulse and neglecting science and the intellect. I am really sorry to knock up so often against Daddy Wordsworth, as Fitz-Gerald called him; he was a most respectable old gentleman and he wrote some magnificent poetry, but it is hard to keep from laughing at him.

But a more common mistake is to drag in science *mal à propos*. When Tennyson says:

The swallow and the swift are near akin,

one is shocked. It is pedantic and unpoetical. It so happens, too, that it is one of the few mistakes, I believe the only mistake, Tennyson ever made in science. So not even the ornithologist is pleased any more than the public is, for he knows that the swallow is no more akin to the swift than a hippopotamus is to a giraffe. But the moral on the whole perhaps is that if you are as great as Dante or Goethe you can do what you please; everything in such men is interesting, and you dare not meddle with it, and the longer time goes on the more interesting do they become. "You cannot touch it," said Heine of some passage, "you cannot touch it; it is the finger of Goethe." But if you are comparatively little, only a Wordsworth or a Tennyson, you had better mind your P's and Q's. And it will take you all your time to be only a Tennyson.

But there is no denying that the gradual growth of the intellectual powers and interests is a terrible danger to the spirit and to poetry especially. Few indeed are they who can hold the balance between them to the end, few highly favoured by impartial Jupiter. The classical example of such a downfall of, not poetic genius, but poetic taste, is Darwin himself; over and over again has it been commented on. When he was young he was an enthusiastic admirer of poetry, and one is not surprised to find in such a man, so remarkable for judgment and sense, that the poetry he admired was the best he knew. He was not taken in, as scientific men so often are, by the third and fourth and tenth rate—indeed nearly all young people are so taken in, even if they flatter themselves that they are poetical and thank God that they are not as these scientific students—no, but his particular idols were Milton and Shakespeare. When he was absent from England on the famous voyage of the *Beagle*, if he went on an expedition and could only take one book with him, that book was Milton. In his old age he laments pathetically, with that charming humility which made him the most lovable of men, that he had entirely lost this taste. He had been peculiarly fond of Shakespeare's historical plays, but on looking at them after an interval of many years, found them so dull that, says he, "they nauseated me." Remembering the condition of his health, I think the phrase is to be interpreted quite literally. And it is really no wonder. For many years, under constant pressure of wretched health, he had been struggling to work at scientific questions, and everybody knows what an astounding work he had done. It is not strange at all that he should have lost a taste which most people never have to any extent worth mentioning, and which most of those who do have it lose in later life without any excuse at all. And indeed one is often tempted to think that such a mind as his exceeded in the grandeur, sublimity and simplicity of its ideas the imaginations of any poet. But he grumbled himself that he had become a mere machine for grinding out general laws. Anyhow it is quite certain that if you want to retain the taste you must cherish it, or it will die away. And cherish it how you will, you will find it change.

Gibbon observes of Claudian that he does not often satisfy or silence our reason. No poetry can ever satisfy the reason, but it can silence it by, in a sort of way, hypnotising us. Certainly good poetry throws one into a sort of trance, and if the trance be deep enough the poet may defy reason in the most audacious manner. Perhaps the most astonishing instance of this is the adventures of Odysseus as recounted by himself in the *Odyssey* ix–xii; for obvious reasons I will not dwell upon these books, but will take a parallel case from Shakespeare. When Othello is asked by what magic he secured the love of Desdemona, he answers by telling us that he talked to her about his own adventures. That is natural; the reason or intellect has nothing to say against it. But watch how he continues:

> The Anthropophagi, and men whose heads
> Do grow beneath their shoulders. These things to hear
> Would Desdemona seriously incline.

Well, if Othello had really told Desdemona about such things, she would have laughed at him, let us hope, instead of seriously inclining. Yet it is all right, and nobody ever cavilled at it. And the reason why is that the intellect is entirely caged and bound by that magnificent scene, and in the second place the instinct of both Homer and Shakespeare has acted in the same way: they both make the hero tell these stories, but do not themselves represent him as doing these things; the impossible is removed into a distance and can be accepted. In fact Shakespeare could not even have made Othello tell Desdemona such stories upon the stage, or he would be hissed off it. It would be like Mr Hoopdriver telling Jessie Milton how he ate stuffed ostriches at the Cape. When on the other hand the battle of Shrewsbury is actually represented on the stage, with kings and princes whacking at one another like common soldiers, the intellect is disgusted; the play degenerates into a wretched farce. I don't know how I could live without Sir John Falstaff, but when I come to that battle I skip over it as fast as I can and cannot pretend to like it. It does very well for boys. But there is no saying where to draw the line. When I was a boy myself I could read the whole of *Paradise Lost* with equanimity, even the battles of the angels with their gunpowder. Now I confine myself to about half the poem.

As one gets older and the intellect more and more asserts its sway, these misfortunes are bound to happen; common-sense rises in revolt against the spell of dreams. If it is allowed to have its head, it may end by shattering the talisman, and that is what one must guard against. But *if* one sticks to both one gains more, much more, than one loses. One learns the difference between the best and the second best, a difference which young people hardly ever know. *You* all know it, of course, but it is not all young people who are endowed with your instinct. Outside this Society I think you will find they *don't* know the difference, as a rule. Certainly I did not—it wasn't only *Paradise Lost*—I did not see really the difference between Shakespeare and Marlowe, nor between Shelley and Swinburne, nor fifty other like cases. And I have observed that always without exception I have ended by coming round to the general opinion of the world; you can easily be cleverer than one man, said La Rochefoucauld, but you cannot easily be cleverer than the world. And the best becomes a treasure such as one never dreamt of.

In the second prologue to *Faust*, the prologue on the stage, in which is packed together perhaps more wisdom and shrewdness, more common-sense and knowledge of the world, and more poetical beauty than can be found in an equal space anywhere else—in that prologue the poet, regretting the loss of youth, says of himself as he remembers himself in that delightful period:

I had nothing, and yet I had enough,
The impulse towards truth, and the delight in illusion.

There in a nutshell is all I have tried to get clear, at, I fear, undue length. Goethe retained both all his life; try to do likewise.

CAMBRIDGE PRELECTION
(5th Nov. 1921)

Cambridge Prelection on Plato, Phaedo, chaps. 45–48, pp. 95 E–100 B

I HAVE chosen to speak upon these chapters on this occasion mainly because I think that I have a good deal to say of them which is new and important; partly also that it is a melancholy satisfaction to me to discuss in this University a passage in which I first became interested under the guidance of that great man[1] who has left a void which can never be filled, and upon whom so many of us will look back with affection and veneration to our dying day. I never propounded my own theory upon it to him, for by the time I had elaborated it he was too ill to listen, and it is entirely different from his own views.

95 E. The point at which we have arrived in the dialogue is this. Socrates has put forward the first proof of the immortality of the soul, namely the proof which is given by the combination of the two theories of antapodosis and anamnesis. He has then added supplementary evidence of a general kind to show that soul is altogether more divine and more permanent than body. The majority of his audience were apparently convinced, but the two Thebans, Simmias and Kebes, still raised objections. Simmias produced the old theory that the soul is merely a name for the harmonious tempering of the bodily elements, as a lyre may be said to have a soul when its strings are tuned in any given musical mode. This has been quickly disposed of by Socrates to the satisfaction of Plato, perhaps hardly to the

---

[1] Henry Jackson, Regius Professor of Greek 1906–1921.

satisfaction of his readers. But the objection raised by Kebes seems even to Socrates to be really fatal to the proofs which have been offered since the conclusion of the argument from antapodosis and anamnesis.

I observe parenthetically that Kebes has certainly not overthrown that argument; he has not even attacked nor so much as mentioned it. The reason for this omission— surely a very strange one if you look on the conversation as a real one—is purely dramatic; it is as if you were first to prove Euclid i 47 as Euclid does, and then add some vague arguments which are *not* mathematical proofs, and then some one were to attack the latter without a word of the former, and *then* all the audience should be downcast, not one of them remembering Euclid's proof. I do not go further into this point here, but call attention to it as one of the many proofs that Plato writes as an artist, not as a historian, throughout this dialogue, and that it is quite impossible to accept it as a true representation of anything said upon the last day of the life of Socrates. So potent is Plato's magic that he carries every one away and they do not notice it. Kebes however certainly shows that the supplementary evidence put in by Socrates is defective; it only proves that soul is tougher and longer-lived than body, it does not prove that death may not after many conflicts advance his pale flag over the soul herself. In order to prove that soul is really immortal and imperishable, Socrates will have to show that death cannot under any circumstances whatever enter into the soul, that nothing can bring about her destruction, that no *cause* can be found sufficient for this, seeing that the *cause* of life is necessarily and eternally exempt from all contact with the cause of death. "What you desire to know, Kebes, is no trifling matter," says Socrates (95 E); "it involves nothing less than raising the whole question of the causation of generation and destruction."

With a view to leading up to his own account of this causation Socrates then gives an account of his own experiences. So says the Platonic Socrates. But it has been long an article of faith, alike with ancient and modern expounders of Plato, that what the Platonic Socrates says need not be taken to apply to the historic Socrates; that in the earlier dialogues indeed he may be only a glorified presentation of the real man, but that in *Meno* and all the later dialogues he is mainly a mouthpiece for proclaiming Plato's own theories.

Lately an attempt has been made to maintain that this is a mistake, that what Socrates says is to be taken quite literally as representing the views of the real Socrates, dressed up no doubt in flowing robes and ornamental attire and put into a literary form, but still substantially historical. To defend this position it is necessary to throw overboard the evidence of Xenophon as worthless, as merely the vague reminiscences and deliberate fictions of a rather stupid military man with no turn for metaphysics; it is necessary to belittle the express statements of Aristotle, who had every opportunity for being well informed on this point, and who was neither stupid nor military nor unmetaphysical; it is necessary to fly in the face of Plato's own equally express statements in the *Apology*, surely a more historical work on the face of it than the *Phaedo*; it is necessary to ignore the fact that in all Plato's earlier works there is not a word to be found about the theory of ideas either earlier or later, and that we can see him gradually excogitating it in (for example) the *Euthyphro*. This attempt therefore, in spite of the high authority of its daring authors, may I think safely be dismissed, and in the course of what I say I think I shall provide further proof of its impossibility.

If however the passage is not a history of the thought of the real Socrates, the obvious alternative is to suppose that the experiences of Socrates as here narrated are really those of Plato himself. The difficulties in the way of believing this ἁπλῶς will be developed in the course of my comments on the account here given. For the moment I will only say that I believe the greater part of them to be nothing of the kind, but part really to be so.

Plato wants to prove the immortality of the soul, and he thinks he can do so by developing a correct theory of causation and applying that to this particular question. Now what is the natural thing to do if you are going to put forward a new theory of causation? What for instance did Aristotle do in like case? The answer is evident; he wrote the first book of the *Metaphysics*, reviewing therein the theories of his predecessors from Thales to Plato. I quote his own words from the beginning of that book:

We have studied these causes sufficiently in the *Physics*, yet let us call to our aid those who have attacked the investigation of being and philosophised about reality before us. For obviously they too speak of certain principles and causes; to go over their views then will be of profit to the present inquiry, for we shall either find another kind of cause or be more convinced of the correctness of those which we now maintain.

He points out that the early Ionians or hylozoists only looked at *one* cause, the material; that Anaxagoras introduced two new causes of the very greatest importance, the efficient and the final, but that Anaxagoras failed to work out the latter or to apply it to his theories of cosmogony and of the ordinance of the Universe; that Plato then added the last, the formal cause.

Now is it not as plain as daylight that all this is exactly and precisely what the Platonic Socrates does here in *Phaedo*? I say it is as plain as daylight—but for years I used to knock my nose up against all this, like a pike in an aquarium. Like Aristotle, Plato wants to preface his own theory by a review of his predecessors and of their theories. But Plato at this period of his life was a great dramatic artist, the greatest and most fascinating of all dramatic artists who ever wrote in prose. Therefore he does not give us a dry matter-of-fact statement of what Thales said or what Anaximander said, but, seeking as ever to make his exposition lively and not reckoning on the dulness and lack of imagination which unfortunately are only too prevalent among mankind, he turns the whole story into a sort of allegory; the slow course of thought as developed by one school of philosophers after another is condensed into a fictitious account of the wanderings of one soul in quest of truth, and that soul is of course called here Socrates, for the purpose of his dialogue. Certainly I do not mean that Plato supposed the individual generally to go through this development; he never did go through anything of the kind himself in spite of his being at first a disciple of Cratylus; I mean that it is more lively, more interesting, more poetical if you like so to call it, to put the work of generations into the pretended reminiscences of an old man calling it all up as his own past.

No doubt he could have made Socrates recount it all as dryly as Aristotle does. But could anybody have thanked him for it if he had? None who has ever read it can forget how the Athenian youth heard some one reading from a book of Anaxagoras (as he said), how his heart was filled with the prospect of a glorious truth to illumine and redeem all the world, and how the cup was dashed from his lips. As soon should we forget how he pressed down the springing curls upon the neck of Phaedo. By this fictitious setting Plato has burnt what he had to say into our brains; such is the power of imagination. But it needs imagination to answer it; he who comes to knock at Plato's door without that will not perhaps go empty away, but he will not divine the true meaning of the oracle. When I say that imagination is needed, I only mean that you must put yourself into Plato's position, see what he was aiming at, see why he chose to put things as he did. There is another representation of Socrates in literature which makes the same requirement, and which shows the amazing liberties the Athenians took in such matters—the *Clouds* of Aristophanes, which I here allude to because you there have a pretty close parallel to this passage of the *Phaedo*. Whereas Plato represents a number of different theories which belong to a number of different persons as *succeeding* one another in the development of the mind of Socrates, Aristophanes represents him as holding a number of theories of other persons all at the same time. Why did the poet attribute all that amazing farrago of nonsense to Socrates? Not because Socrates really troubled his head about such things; he neither investigated, as Aristotle might have done, the *incessus pulicum*, nor taught rhetoric like Gorgias.

Everybody knew this. But Aristophanes wanted to attack the whole tendency of the new thought; to do this in accordance with the methods of the Old Comedy, it was not merely convenient but absolutely necessary to embody those tendencies in one man. Granted that, all the rest follows; Socrates was the only man he could by any possibility have picked for the part. What Aristophanes did on the stage, Plato in his own way has done for the closet or the lecture-room; both of them make many voices speak from behind the mask of Socrates.

So much for preliminaries. I propose now to give you a brief summary of my interpretation of all this passage. It will be necessary to make so many digressions and speak on so many topics that, to use a homely phrase, you might not be able to see the wood for the trees if I did not first sketch out the main outline; you will then be able to follow me filling it up. Thus do I translate the essential portions of the story into the historical truth which it has so long disguised like the sun in an eclipse. Indeed I conceive that I am doing what the great Aristotle did, for I believe that in the first book of the *Metaphysics* he had all this passage in his mind and was playing his usual game of reducing to black and white what Plato left glowing with iridescent fire.

96 A. The question raised is the question of the causation of γένεσις and φθορά. I (Plato) will give a sketch of the views of my predecessors on this. When Philosophy (not Socrates) was young it was wonderfully enamoured of this which they call natural science, thinking it a fine thing to know the causes of phenomena.

96 B. Accordingly different thinkers put forward dif-

ferent views. Some for example said, as Anaximander, that animals were formed out of decaying matter; Empedocles said that we think with the blood, Anaximenes with air, Heraclitus with fire, Alcmaeon and the medical school with the brain.

96 c. But in the end this early school of natural science was convicted of incapacity by the criticism of the Eleatic philosophers. Owing to its persistently looking at only material phenomena and material causes, it was so stupefied that it could not even explain why a man grows. Anaxagoras had said, and it had certainly seemed reasonable enough, that it was because particles of flesh, bone and so on in the food we eat were added to the flesh and bone in our bodies. But when the Eleatics propounded their arithmetical puzzles, it became evident that the natural science philosophers had no answer to give them; they could offer no explanation for instance of how one and one become two. So feeble was their notion of causation.

97 c. A far nobler and more brilliant theory of causation was however put forward by Anaxagoras; it was only thrown out in an isolated manner and had no connexion with the rest of his speculations or with the Ionian school in general, but noble and brilliant it was. Reason, said he, ordered all things with a view to the best.

98 b. But unfortunately he did not apply this theory to his explanation of the universe in detail; he only talked of material causes like any other Ionian.

99 d. Plato himself would have liked to follow up the hint of Anaxagoras, but did not see how to do so. He fell back therefore upon the next best theory which he could devise. Physical science having failed in the investigation

of the truth of things, he took warning by the fate of his predecessors, and feared that he like them might be blinded in consequence of tackling physical phenomena with his senses. He sought refuge therefore in λόγοι, assuming the truth of the Theory of Ideas as the strongest he could attain to, and putting down as true whatever agreed with it. And in particular he asserts that the true theory of causation is that which makes the phenomena depend upon the Ideas.

Now let us go back to the text.

96 A. "When I was young," says Socrates, "you cannot believe how enthusiastically I pursued this wisdom which they call the investigation of nature; I thought it a glorious thing to know the causes of everything—why each thing comes into being, why it is destroyed, and why it is. Many a time and oft did I swing to and fro from one theory to another. Are animals formed by putrefaction of the hot and the cold? Do we think with the blood, or is it by means of air, or fire? Or are all these views wrong; does the brain produce in us the sensations of hearing, sight and smell, and thence arise memory and opinion, and knowledge springs again from these when they have settled down? Such were the questions I asked, and I asked too what again destroys all these things; and I searched out the phenomena of the heaven above and the earth beneath. And what was the end of it all? Why, I found myself the stupidest creature in existence in these investigations."

There, I say, you have Plato's history of the Ionian philosophy, including the medical school of that period. And you have his terribly severe indictment of it—it turned out to be the stupidest creature in existence. He does not put it in chronological order like Aristotle, but he quite agrees with Aristotle in substance. The early philosophers set out to discover causes of things, *rerum cognoscere caussas.* When Virgil wrote that famous line was he not translating this very phrase of Plato's, ὑπερήφανον γάρ μοι ἐδόκει εἶναι, εἰδέναι τὰς αἰτίας ἑκάστου? And the only sort of cause they could suggest was a material one. As for the reason why the question what we think with is made so prominent, it is surely obvious that Plato lays particular stress on this *one* question because he considers the inadequacy of the material cause to be especially glaring here, as indeed it is; "I cannot conceive," said Huxley, "how matter can think."

"It is as if," says Socrates presently, "you should say that I sit here because of my bones and sinews, not because of my sense of duty." So to say that the cause of *thinking* is blood, as Empedocles thought, or air as Anaximenes, or brain as Alcmaeon of Crotona, is an even more inadequate statement than to say that earth and water are the cause of our bones. Therefore it is that Plato picks out this special point for emphasis.

With regard to the alternatives proposed, it is interesting by the way to see that Plato allows the medical authorities a place. It appears to have been Alcmaeon of Crotona, that shadowy elusive alluring figure, who if we could only get a better sight of him might perhaps be rightly called the Harvey of the ancients—*he*, I say, first clung obstinately to the view that the brain is what thinks, but the philosophers have never been willing to admit it. Plato however had the sense (at any rate in his later days) to take his physiology from Hippocrates, and was not inclined to ignore the medical faculty as completely as many of his brethren. The conflict between the two parties is very visible in Aristotle and elsewhere; how eloquent is the fact that he never mentions Hippocrates but once, and that in the *Politics*! The medical writers retorted by ignoring Aristotle's science, so there is not much to choose between them. But all that is another story, which this is no place to go into.

Here Plato dismisses both classes of speculators with equal contempt. Neither Ionian science nor Italian medicine find any favour in his sight. Socrates found himself the stupidest creature in existence. In modern language and properly interpreted this statement is only another way of proclaiming what has been called the "bankruptcy of the Ionian science."

And what convinces him of stupidity? Listen to his own words (96 c):

My sight was so blinded by this enquiry that I unlearnt again even what I thought I knew before. For example, why does a man grow? I had supposed it obvious to anybody that it was because of eating and drinking, that particles of flesh and bone out of our food were added to our own flesh and bone, and so on with the rest of our bodies, that this process of addition resulted in making a small mass into a large one, and that this was how a small human being becomes a big one.

But, he continues (I will not go minutely into what follows), he gave up this plain and simple view because he got involved in logical puzzles, such as that addition of one to one cannot make two, in which for all I know Mr B. Russell and Mr Whitehead may agree with him.

I must enter into several digressions here. There is a point of great importance. The theory about the flesh out of the food being added to the flesh in our bodies is that of Anaxagoras, and so far as we know of nobody else. Socrates

therefore is already acquainted with the philosophy of
Anaxagoras. Yet we shall be told presently that he knew
nothing of his book and apparently had never heard of his
name. This is very strange if we suppose all this history
to be that of the mind of the real Socrates or of Plato himself. It is worse than very strange, it is a flagrant self-
contradiction. Hence Mr Archer Hind denies that we have
here a reference to Anaxagoras at all, and thinks that this
is simply the common-sense view of the average unthinking
man. But that can hardly be the case. The average man does
not think that flesh and bone are in bread; so far from that
it does not appear that Anaxagoras ever converted anybody
to this opinion. But this self-contradiction is quite natural
if we suppose, as I do, that Plato is giving in a parable the
history of philosophic thought. This part of the speculations
of Anaxagoras is quite germane to the rest of these purely
material causes, and Plato was perfectly justified in committing this little anachronism, he who did not care a snap
of the fingers for anachronisms, whatever Wilamowitz
may say.

There is another interesting point to make here by way
of parenthesis. Lucretius asserts that the meaning of the
homoeomeria of Anaxagoras is this:

> ossa videlicet e pauxillis atque minutis
> ossibus hic et de pauxillis atque minutis
> visceribus viscus gigni (putat).

If now we compare the words of Lucretius with the words
of Plato we see the Latin to be virtually a literal translation
from the Greek. That means, I take it, that both Plato and
Lucretius, which is to say Epicurus, are quoting the very
words of Anaxagoras with their curious plurals σάρκες and

viscera, ossa and ὀστᾶ; curious because they mean *bits of*
flesh and *bits of* bone as well as flesh and bone as wholes.
In any case I can have no sort of doubt that the reference
here *is* to Anaxagoras.

And there is another point of some consequence. M.
Tannery, a name never to be mentioned without respect,
and certain eminent authorities following in his wake, have
declared that Aristotle misunderstood or at any rate mis-
represented the doctrine of Anaxagoras by describing as
material particles what in reality were only qualities.
Anaxagoras talked of "the hot" and "the cold"; Aristotle
substituted material atoms and thereby took in and deceived the whole world. I am astonished again at the easy
way in which we moderns throw over the authority of
Aristotle whenever it suits our convenience, and I cannot
believe that the ancients who followed Aristotle were so
ignorant as not to know that they could buy the works of
Anaxagoras for a drachma at the outside and confute
Aristotle from the original text. Well, but here Plato says
exactly the same thing; *he* also talks of material particles,
not of qualities; will it be asserted that it was Plato who
"went about to banter the world with an enchanted"
Anaxagoras transformed from the real thing?

The real truth about it seems to me obvious enough.
Try to put yourself into the state of mind of a man thinking
about these questions at a time when there was no word yet
invented for *matter*, no word for *quality*. Speech creates
thought, as Shelley says; when a vocabulary is not yet
developed, thought suffers and is cast into dire confusion.
These early speculators had no word for *matter*; consequently they call it "the hot and the cold" and such

phrases; how then could they help confusing matter and quality? This confusion crops up in many places; it is at the bottom of the four elements of Empedocles, which have no sense in them except as signifying the four conditions in which we know matter, and yet you know that is not what Empedocles meant by them; it is at the bottom of the Aristotelian doctrine of the four elements, a doctrine which is not much to its author's credit, with its jumble of earth and water, air and fire, hot and cold, liquid and solid. No wonder then that Anaxagoras also, who had not the advantage of the Aristotelian vocabulary, groped about in the dark and did not distinguish properly between σπέρματα of gold, and its qualities. But to the minds of Plato and Aristotle the distinction was clear, as it was to Democritus; if they choose to speak only of the material particles of Anaxagoras and to say nothing about their qualities, that is their own affair, but they were in their rights; a modern investigator ought to distinguish sharply between the two, dividing them with a hatchet, to adopt the old philosopher's own metaphor; but he ought *not* to cleave to the one and ignore the other, nor to accuse Aristotle of reckless misinterpretation.

Early philosophy then had thought that a body grows greater by addition of particles to particles. Then it found itself stranded in a mist of metaphysical puzzles. (The coming of metaphysics upon the scene is like the coming of the Albatross to the Ancient Mariner.) Precisely then came the Eleatic criticism of the earlier thought, in particular Zeno, the founder of dialectic as Aristotle calls him, Zeno who revelled in arithmetical quibbles. Of him has it been written that men were doubtless puzzle-headed before him, but nobody ever had such a capacity for bringing out that quality, and that is just what he does here. My interpretation of all this passage then is simply this. Ionian philosophy thought it knew certain obvious things, such as the cause of growth as expounded by Anaxagoras. Then came the criticism of the Eleatic school and showed that people could render no intelligible account of even the addition of two units to make two.

Philosophy in their hands began to turn from contemplation of the material universe to contemplation of logical questions. The eternal dispute whether Zeno should be placed in order of date before Anaxagoras is of course an uncertain question, but it is not a matter of any consequence for our present purpose. Anyhow Plato handles these matters freely. If he represents philosophy convicted of stupidity by the Eleatic criticism before he introduces the new cause of Anaxagoras, this is not necessarily because Anaxagoras preceded Zeno, if he did precede him; it is because he wants to finish off his criticism of the first stage in the history of causation before he goes on to the second. It is quite immaterial to his purpose to ask whether Zeno really perplext men with his problems before Anaxagoras wrote.

Next therefore we now come to the famous passage in which Socrates heard one reading from a book the epoch-making words: "Mind came into Chaos and ordered all things for the best" (97 B *ad fin.*). καὶ οὐκ ἂν ἀπεδόμην πολλοῦ τὰς ἐλπίδας..., "not for a great sum," says he (98 B), "would I have parted with the hope I then conceived. In great excitement did I lay hand upon his books as soon as I could get them, and began my reading that I might know

at once the best and what is worse than it. High indeed
were my hopes, my friend, and great was my fall, when
as I advanced in my reading I found my author making
no use of his mind whatever" (there is here a play on the
words "his mind" which has generally been missed), "nor
bringing into play any causes fit to be called *causes*, but
airs and ethers and waters and other such absurdities."
Plato then proceeds to his severe criticism of the failure of
Anaxagoras to apply his idea, his new cause. But he does
not deny the importance of this cause; in his opinion it
is *the* cause which is the highest of all, and if a man could
but gain a knowledge of it he might count all else as dross.
ἐγὼ μὲν οὖν τῆς τοιαύτης αἰτίας ὅπῃ ποτὲ ἔχει μαθητὴς
ὁτουοῦν ἥδιστ᾽ ἂν γενοίμην· ἐπειδὴ δὲ ταύτης ἐστερήθην
καὶ οὔτ᾽ αὐτὸς εὑρεῖν οὔτε παρ᾽ ἄλλου μαθεῖν οἷός τε
ἐγενόμην, τὸν δεύτερον πλοῦν ἐπὶ τὴν τῆς αἰτίας ζήτησιν ᾗ
πεπραγμάτευμαι βούλει σοι, ἔφη, ἐπίδειξιν ποιήσωμαι;

"Most gladly," says Socrates, "would I sit at the
feet of any one whatever who would teach me the truth
about it. But since this was denied me, being unable
either to discover the truth for myself or to learn it from
any one else, I have contrived a crutch instead to aid my
steps in the search. Shall I explain its nature to you?"
(99 c).

Before going further, I wish to call attention to the fact
that we have here applied to a particular case a general
principle laid down some way back. At 85 c Simmias has
observed that certainty in this life upon such questions is
difficult, perhaps impossible; "yet" says Simmias, "it
would show a sad want of grit in a man not to thrash out
the current statements about them, declining to give up

the attack before he is exhausted by investigating the question on every side. For it is our bounden duty to bring to pass one of these three things, either to *learn* the truth or to *find* it, or (if we can do neither of these) at least to take hold of the best and most inexpugnable of theories (λόγος) known to man, to ride upon this as upon a raft and sail through life trusting in it at all hazards." Why this general principle should be given to Simmias to proclaim is rather puzzling at first sight. Anyhow here at 99 D we find all the conditions fulfilled; Socrates can neither *learn* nor *find* the truth; he is exhausted by investigation; therefore he falls back upon a λόγος. As Simmias had described this λόγος as a raft, a makeshift when no better vessel is to be had, so Socrates describes his own procedure as a δεύτερος πλοῦς, rowing when he cannot sail. This comparison adds further proof, if further proof were needed, that the δεύτερος πλοῦς means "a second best course."

But in truth the principle was not altogether new to readers of Plato, for part it had been laid down in the earlier dialogue of *Meno*; Simmias therefore is perhaps only repeating what he had learnt before as a member of the Socratic circle, just as he repeats elsewhere what he had picked up from the Pythagoreans. There is no originality about him anywhere. It is first laid down in *Meno* by Socrates himself; being presumed familiar it is now put into the mouth of a secondary character—so delicate are the links which bind the Platonic dialogues to one another.

We come now to the well-known passage which has been the despair of commentators, 92 D. If my view of the proper interpretation of the whole story of the adventures is correct, it should enable us to throw some light upon these crucial sentences, and I am bold enough to think it does. I will go through them piecemeal and minutely.

First of all, we must ask what is the exact meaning of τὰ ὄντα. There has been considerable difference of opinion on this point. It means τὸ δέον καὶ τὸ ἀγαθόν, says Mr Archer-Hind; Socrates wanted to see that the view of Anaxagoras was the right one, and that all was regulated for the best. Others say it means simply "things." I hold that the latter view is the correct one, for these reasons. If τὰ ὄντα meant the true essence of things, τὸ δέον and τὸ ἀγαθόν, Plato would have made this clearer; he would have said at least τὰ ὄντως ὄντα. And he uses τὰ ὄντα about a dozen times in this dialogue, and in all those passages it means simply "things" in the widest and vaguest possible way—it may include the ideas in one place and implicitly exclude them at another, but it is just like the English "things" and never means the reality behind them as distinct from them.

But if τὰ ὄντα here means nature in general, *not* the glorious revelation promised by Anaxagoras, it follows further that we are not continuing the thread of the previous paragraph at all. For the connexion of thought we must regard chapters 46 and 47 as parenthetical; the beginning of ch. 48 articulates in reality with the end of ch. 45. The whole passage about Anaxagoras is an episode and excrescence on the main history. And so the theory of Anaxagoras was.

And by the way I cannot resist the pleasure of quoting from Sir Herbert Warren's reminiscences of Mr Bywater the sentence: "I well remember especially how he brought

out with great *empressement* the appearance of Anaxagoras
and his discovery of νοῦς which made him appear like
'a sober man after the wild talk of his predecessors'"
(*Life,* p. 69). The book of Anaxagoras belonged in its
details to the same category as the books of Anaximenes,
Empedocles, Democritus; it was of the earth, earthy. The
single hint which it threw out about some higher cause was
no doubt a brilliant flash, but it never came to anything
and did not disturb the current of Ionian philosophy from
its bed. Plato has done it full justice, as he always did in
speaking of his predecessors.

Observe indeed how wonderfully Plato has treated it
from the purely artistic point of view. The other early
philosophers are identified with the poetical and mythical
story of the adventures of Socrates, but the episodic nature
of this outburst on the part of Anaxagoras is brought out
strongly by the device of making Socrates hear somebody
else reading it out of a book. It comes in from outside like
a bolt from the blue, it is weighed in the balance and found
wanting as applied by its author, and now we drop it again
altogether and go back to the main stream of the history.
Socrates then continues thus (99 D):

It seemed to me at this stage, since I had failed utterly
in the investigation of things, that I must be careful lest
I should share the fate of those who contemplate and
examine the sun in eclipse; for you know they sometimes
ruin their eyes unless they look at the sun's image in water
or some similar mirror. So I too bethought me of something of this kind; I feared lest I should utterly blind my
mind by looking at things with my eyes and seeking to
grasp them with each of my bodily senses.

There is a serious confusion in the expression of this

paragraph. "I thought," says Socrates, "*after* this, that I ought to be careful. I feared lest I *should* be blinded by examining nature in the Ionian manner. I feared this *after* I had failed in looking at things." Let me offer a respectful parody of this. "I spent ten years in playing cricket without pads, and found it painful. After this, when I had given up playing cricket in consequence, I feared lest I should hurt my shins, and so I took to another method and adopted the use of gloves."

The editors skate hastily over this thin ice, and hold their peace. Let us see whether any explanation can be given of it; the contradiction is there and cannot be explained away. I have tried hard to get round it and I cannot see how it can be done. In such a case there are three roads open: first, we can shut our eyes and pretend that nothing is wrong; secondly, we can proceed to do violence to the plain meaning of the words and twist them into something we prefer; thirdly, we can acknowledge that something *is* wrong and then try to explain *why* the author put it wrongly and how the trouble came about. For myself I greatly prefer this third course, and I think that we really can see very easily *how* it was that Plato came to express himself in this manner, illogical as it seems at first sight. Interpret Socrates again into terms of the first book of Aristotle's *Metaphysics*.

When the Ionian philosophy had broken down in its effort to explain the universe, being reduced to absurdity by Eleatic criticism, Plato next thought the right plan was to seek refuge in the theory of ideas. For Plato thought that the material method could only blind the soul by turning its gaze earthwards; accordingly he fled for shelter to the ideas.

You see now, do you not, how the contradiction arose? Socrates stands neither for the son of Sophroniscus nor yet for Plato himself, but for the history of philosophy down to and including Plato. Now it is quite natural to say that the Ionians failed in their investigations and that Plato learnt wisdom from their failure and consequently took care to avoid falling into either the error of the gross dealers in material objects, or the error of Anaxagoras who thought he was going to storm heaven right away with his theory of Mind ordering all to a good end. But when both the Ionians and the Eleatics and Plato himself are all identified for dramatic purposes with one solitary individual, then the allegory, as allegories will, breaks down. It is possible that Plato might have avoided this awkwardness if he had liked. But I imagine that he did not care to trouble himself about it. For one thing he rather had a fancy for puzzling people, and if that was his object he has certainly succeeded.

Socrates stands for the Ionians. Therefore it is necessary that he should fail after protracted endeavours to get at truth with his material causation. Socrates stands for the Eleatics. Therefore he has to convict his Ionian self of stupidity by mathematical puzzles. Socrates stands for Plato himself. Therefore he has to take warning by his Ionian self, and avoid studying the very things at all from the beginning which, as typifying the Ionian philosophy, he had been studying for years and years with all his might.

That is what comes of writing allegories. But the game is worth the candle; who would not rather read Plato's allegory than Aristotle's sober statement of fact? Plato knew well enough that the contradiction was there, I do not see how he can have helped knowing it; but he did not think it mattered; how he would have been amazed to see the way in which he has been interpreted by the literal moderns! That is what comes of expecting other people to possess imagination.

But after we have cleared up all this confusion we are bound to enquire what is the meaning of the parable of the astronomers and the sun. "I feared lest I should share the fate of those who contemplate the sun in eclipse, for you know they sometimes ruin their eyes unless they look at the sun's image in water or some similar mirror." I think it has been shown pretty clearly that the meaning of Plato in this passage is simply that after the Ionian philosophy had failed, because it only recognised material causes, he (Plato) therefore took up an introspective line of enquiry. It has been shown, if I have been successful so far in my endeavours, that there is here no question of the sublimer cause of Anaxagoras. Therefore it follows that the simile of the sun is not to be pressed, that we must not seek for some explanation of it which will represent Plato as fearing that he would be blasted by the excess of light of the Anaxagorean $νοῦς$. It has been truly observed that astronomers only look at the sun in eclipse or at least did in those days, and that accordingly Plato need not mean anything subtle by adding the word $ἐκλείποντα$. This view is borne out very strongly by a passage in the fifteenth chapter of the Life of Pythagoras by Iamblichus, which is plainly written with the Platonic passage in mind.

"Pythagoras was of opinion," says Iamblichus, "that other men must be content to gaze upon the Creator in

P   14 images and patterns, δι' εἰκόνων καὶ ὑποδειγμάτων, for their benefit and instruction, because they are not able to attain to the pure and original archetypes, just as those who are unable to gaze stedfastly upon the sun by reason of the surprising splendour of his beams have eclipses shown to them in a deep pool of water or by means of melted pitch or a dark mirror."

I gather from this that the forgers of Pythagorean Apocrypha plundered this passage of *Phaedo* among so many others and ascribed its doctrine to their own hero, and *they* did not understand the reference to the sun in eclipse to have any profound significance.

At the same time I cannot agree with those who maintain that the expression δεύτερος πλοῦς and the simile of the sun are both ironical. I see no sign or symptom of irony in the whole passage. Plato really would have liked to see the ἀγαθόν of Anaxagoras if he could, but he does not yet see his way to doing so; in the *Republic* he does see his way, as he thinks, thanks to the invention of the Idea of Good. Meantime the δεύτερος πλοῦς really is a second best course, and remember how he asserts in the *Republic* that the most noble and lofty of his ideas only derive their value from that Idea of Good. So also Plato wanted to know the truth about things; he believed this truth to be something inexpressibly magnificent; both the garment of the outward universe and the mirror of our own minds are reflexions of this; in both alike a man may well seek for revelation. But experience shows him, as he thinks, that looking at material things will *not* lead to such revelation; on the contrary it only blinds the mental eye of the enquirer. That is just what metaphysicians go on saying about natural science to this day. Our only course is to give up physical science therefore and take to mental; not that mental is in the least inferior, as he is careful to add. ἴσως μὲν οὖν ᾧ εἰκάζω, τρόπον τινὰ οὐκ ἔοικεν· οὐ γὰρ πάνυ ξυγχωρῶ τὸν ἐν τοῖς λόγοις σκοπούμενον τὰ ὄντα ἐν εἰκόσι μᾶλλον σκοπεῖν ἢ τὸν ἐν τοῖς ἔργοις: "perhaps the simile is not perfect; for I am very far from admitting that he who considers things in propositions is viewing them in images more than he who views them in actualities" (99 E).

We may here well ask a question; what is the connexion of these clauses? "My simile is not exact. For λόγοι are no more εἰκόνες than τὰ ἔργα." If this refers only to the words beginning at ἔδοξε χρῆναι, then there is no connexion, no coherency at all. Therefore this refers to something more: what Plato says, or should have said, is something like this: "λόγοι are εἰκόνες of the truth, and I fled for refuge to them because I feared being blinded by the phenomena, which however are also only εἰκόνες of the truth, although I did just now compare them to the sun itself. That was an oversight which I now correct." If you will consider carefully that clause οὐ γὰρ πάνυ ξυγχωρῶ you will see that it is absolutely necessary, if you want it to be coherent, to assume that the sun represents τὰ ἔργα for the nonce. And Archer-Hind was therefore wrong in contemptuously throwing over that notion. But Plato has, perhaps on purpose, been a bit careless in expression, as people are in developing their ideas in real speech. Socrates *ought* to have said that the truth which lies behind and gives rise to both material and mental phenomena is like the sun. He is still struggling in the confusion into which the allegory has thrown him, and I do not see how it can be denied that he has got into another confusion between being blinded by poring on things and being blinded by gazing at something too bright. At any rate I cannot see my way to getting this passage clear and can only console myself by reflecting that no one else can either.

But it will be said that Plato does not take such an indulgent view of the phenomenal universe as I have here represented him to have taken. No, not in certain of his later writings; but in *Phaedo* he has not yet proceeded so far as he does later. In no early work of his does he express an opinion that the world of matter is so contemptible as he declares it to be in the *Republic*; neither in *Phaedo* nor in any other earlier work does he say that the material universe is intermediate between Being and Not-being. The one truth which underlies both nature and mind is one and the same; both are manifestations of it; if you can get at it through either, do so by all means, but as a matter of fact you can't get at it by physical science: *that*, as I conceive it, is his attitude at this period. Then he becomes more and more contemptuous of material phenomena, but the *Timaeus* is enough to show that to a certain extent he reverted in his age to the position of his youth. He always looked with dislike upon matter; but he could not and did not deny that it was an outward and visible manifestation of the reality he sought; the earth spirit weaves for God the garment thou seest him by; the material object exists because it participates in or copies the idea. But if you want to know that idea you must look rather within than without.

I suppose I ought to give here my reasons for assuming the *Republic* to be a later work. I am fully persuaded that it is such for these reasons: (1) The psychology of *Phaedo* is less developed than the psychology of the *Republic*. (2) The tenth book of the *Republic* is of the nature of an appendix to *Phaedo*, as well as to the *Republic* itself; now it is evident that at the same time it is an integral part of the larger work and that Plato never intended to stop at the end of the ninth book; therefore, if he added a supplementary proof of immortality in that tenth book, it shows that *Phaedo* was already published, and indeed he actually as good as quotes *Phaedo* in 609 D and as good as refers to it by name in 611 B. (3) In *Phaedo* he has not been able yet to link together the cause of Anaxagoras with his own theory of Ideas; in the *Republic* he has succeeded in doing so by the Idea of Good. (4) In *Phaedo* Socrates is still a real man, and the dramatic setting of the dialogue is masterly; in the *Republic* Socrates is a mere vehicle for Plato's own notions, and the author has largely lost his interest in the dramatic side of the dialogue; he has become more of a preacher and less of an artist. (5) This very comparison of the truth of things to the sun is here confused and sketchy, I might say unintelligible; in the *Republic* VI it is elaborated and vastly improved. (6) In *Phaedo* the ideas are still of an ethical and mental kind only, ideas of equality and the like; in the *Republic* we hear of ideas of all kinds of things, cats and dogs, even manufactured articles.

Had the *Republic* been the earlier dialogue of the two, it would have been difficult to avoid supposing that the sun of the one illumined with its light the sun of the other. But if the truth is the other way about, we need not suppose any connexion between the two. For in the earlier work we have here merely a casual illustration, which has not *yet* become a matter of any importance.

100 A. ἀλλ᾽ οὖν δὴ ταύτῃ γε ὥρμησα...

"However that may be, such was the line I took. Not only in regard to this question of causation but in regard to every other I assume as my starting-point the theory which I judge to be the strongest. I then put down as true or false whatever appears to me to be or not to be in harmony with this. But I should like to explain to you more clearly what I mean; for I think you do not see it at present."

"No indeed," said Kebes, "I do not."

"Why, this is all; no new thing, but what I have continually told you before and have never ceased repeating in the discussion to-day. So I will now proceed to try and disclose to you the sort of theory of causation which I have struck out for myself; I will return to that old story of the ideas and begin with them, assuming the existence of absolute beauty and goodness and greatness and so on; if you allow their existence, I flatter myself that I can explain thereby my theory of causation and discover a proof of the immortality of the soul."

I also will go back to what I have been saying before; look again at 85 c *fin.* "One must lay hold of the best and most inexpugnable human theory one can get, and rely upon that." "If indeed," Simmias says there, "we had a revelation from heaven, that would be another matter." Plato, then, represents Socrates here as still carrying out the scheme laid down by Simmias. He has failed himself, has had no divine revelation from either Anaxagoras or anybody else, and so he falls back on the best human theory he can get, which for Plato is of course the theory of ideas.

It may again be objected that Plato would never have spoken of this, the theory of ideas, as a δεύτερος πλοῦς from Plato, as we have just seen in the simile of the eclipse, not that Plato stole from Pythagoras, except in one point, which I will admit to be as important as you like— namely that he mixt up Pythagorean arithmetical nonsense with his ideas in the later and esoteric development of which we know nothing except what Aristotle tells us.

And the conclusions we may draw from this interpretation of the whole passage are:

First, that it is not of any avail to appeal to this sketch of the history of philosophy in order to draw any inferences from it about the teaching or the thought or the development of the real Socrates. Indeed the real Socrates, the son of Sophroniscus, does not appear in the allegory at all: we jump in it straight from Anaxagoras to Plato himself. And this was necessary; Plato could not bring in Socrates for the simple reason that Socrates took no interest in such questions. What he thought about them appears very plainly from the statement of Xenophon, which there is really no reason to doubt; *Mem.* ι i 14. The substance of that statement is that Socrates thought scientific speculators no better than madmen, for some of them thought one thing and some another exactly contrary to it, for example one set asserted that everything γίνεσθαι καὶ ἀπόλλυσθαι and others that nothing could ever do either the one or the other. These were the opinions of the historical Socrates about γένεσις καὶ φθορά, that nobody knew anything about them. And if he had read the *Phaedo*, he would, I fear, have thought Plato just as mad as the rest of the philosophers.

Secondly, that Plato did not regard himself as affiliated to the Pythagoreans, but as being led to his theory of causation by the Eleatic criticism of the physicists, and by the Eleatic logical puzzles. And this agrees excellently with the way in which the Eleatics are brought into connexion with the Ideal Theory in *Parmenides*. It was only in later days that he began to draw in an evil hour upon the magic fountain of moonshine which had sprung up in the Pythagorean school.

Such is my view of the true meaning of this enchanting but enigmatic passage, such are the conclusions which I hope may be legitimately drawn therefrom. It is just possible that some of my audience may have grown a trifle rusty in their Greek philosophy and may have found it difficult to follow me in all the ramifications of my exposition: if so, I apologise to them and trust they will forgive me for endeavouring to make a serious contribution on such an occasion to a great subject, even at the expense of their convenience.

CAMBRIDGE: PRINTED BY W. LEWIS, M.A., AT THE UNIVERSITY PRESS

Glory

Blue Girl

jodi lynn

PUFFIN BOOKS

Blue Girl

PUFFIN BOOKS
Published by Penguin Group
Penguin Young Readers Group,
345 Hudson Street, New York, New York 10014, U.S.A.
Penguin Books Ltd, 80 Strand, London WC2R 0RL, England
Penguin Books Australia Ltd, 250 Camberwell Road, Camberwell, Victoria 3124, Australia
Penguin Books Canada Ltd, 10 Alcorn Avenue, Toronto, Ontario, Canada M4V 3B2
Penguin Books (N.Z.) Ltd, 182-190 Wairau Road, Auckland 10, New Zealand

Published by Puffin Books,
a division of Penguin Young Readers Group, 2003

1 3 5 7 9 10 8 6 4 2

Copyright © 2003 17th Street Productions, an Alloy, Inc. company
All rights reserved

Front cover photography copyright © Barry Marcus, 2003

 Produced by 17th Street Productions,
an Alloy, Inc. company
151 West 26th Street
New York, NY 10001

17th Street Productions and associated logos
are trademarks and/or registered trademarks of Alloy, Inc.

LIBRARY OF CONGRESS CATALOGING-IN-PUBLICATION DATA

Lynn, Jodi.
Blue girl / Jodi Lynn.
p. cm.—(Glory ; 3)
Sequel to: Shadow tree
Summary: While becoming sicker, Glory tries to do the things she and Katie had planned to do in
Boston and tries to find her place in her foster home, at school, and with a new friend.
ISBN: 0-14-250045-3 (alk. paper)
[1. Foster home care—Fiction. 2. Sick—Fiction. 3. Guilt—Fiction. 4. Schools—Fiction. 5. Boston
(Mass.)—Fiction.] I. Title
PZ7.L9945Bl 2003   [Fic]—dc21   2002037083

Printed in the United States of America

FOR THE BRUNCH CLUB:
KIM, KAITLIN, KRIS, ANDY, ERICA . . . AND SHIRA

PROLOGUE

What if you were thirteen years old, and someone told you your life was going to end tomorrow? Or next month, or the month after that? It sure would be a shock, wouldn't it? You probably wouldn't believe it.

Well, dying tomorrow would not shock me. Since being cast out of my home and being made to drink from the vial of judgment—a mix of poison, folks in Dogwood say, handed down from our ancestors—I've come to accept that I'm going to die, and soon. That's all there is to it. And I won't be surprised in the least when it happens.

What surprises *me* is all the beginnings. All the days I don't die. All the days that start instead of end. I mean, here I am, waiting for my life to flicker out, and I keep running into these fresh starts—new towns, new homes, and now they say I'm going to have to go to a new school. And to tell you the truth, it almost seems it would be better to just have it over with and be gone. Because the thought of all these starts makes me want to curl up in a ball and disappear.

I am standing on the front porch of a sky blue house on the outskirts of the city of Boston, about to meet my new foster

parents, and all I can think is, *Maybe I'd rather keel over and die.*
What are these folks going to be like? How can I come to them
knowing what I know—that there is this poison inside of me,
killing me bit by bit—and act normal? How can this possibly
turn out all right when all I can do is die in the end?

I really and truly do not want to be dead. After all, I haven't
done what I came all this way to do. Back home, Katie and I
promised each other we'd make it to Boston together someday.
And now that she's gone because of me and I can never go
home, that's all I have. That, and this list I've made of everything we wanted to experience here. I have to do it for the both
of us now—because Katie can't anymore. And I've got to do it
soon, before I die for real.

Even though I arrived in the city weeks ago, I haven't
checked one thing off my list. I haven't ridden the swan boats,
or eaten in a restaurant, or read a real city newspaper. . . .
Instead I've starved, I've been homeless, I've gotten caught by
the police (and turned in to Child Welfare). And not once have
I glimpsed the Boston Katie and I dreamt of. Either I've failed
the city or the city has failed me. I feel like the gristle in a piece
of meat—like Boston has chewed me up and spit me clear
across the room.

So why not give up?

Because I can't. And because I'm hoping that things will be
different now. I'm hoping that maybe my foster parents, whoever

they turn out to be, can help me find Boston—the real Boston—
for Katie. I *owe* her. I would face a million beginnings if that'd
bring me one step closer to making up for what I've done.

Standing on the porch, I don't pray. But while I wait, I do
send a silent thought up into the air—maybe up to Katie herself, sitting in heaven and watching. *Please don't let it all be in
vain. Please let me get this done.*

CHAPTER
ONE

"They're awfully slow. How old did you say they are?"

I tapped the heel of my right foot on the porch below me and looked up at Sherry, my social worker. She pretended like she hadn't heard. Her hands were crossed politely in front of her, and I tried to do the same. But gosh, was it hard to stand still. Here I was, waiting on tenterhooks to meet the folks that would be taking care of me from here on out. These were the people who would be in charge of the little bit of future I had left. And they were slow as molasses. I tapped my foot again.

Anyone in the town of Dogwood would tell you—if they'd tell you anything about me at all—that patience is not one of my virtues. In fact, it's one of the qualities they'd say I most lack, next to manners and modesty and whatever trait it is that makes you mind your elders. Some of my earliest memories are of me pitching fits over things that made me impatient as a kid—not being allowed to run wild with the boys, sitting in church on a dizzyingly pretty spring day, having to wait my turn for a helping of my favorite supper. So you can probably imagine what my patience is like when it's tested by much bigger, much more important things. Right then, I was filled with the most painful impatience of my life.

As Sherry and I waited for the door to open, I noticed a window to the left and sidestepped a little, tilting my head, trying to peer inside. I couldn't make out a thing. I couldn't even *hear* a thing. Maybe they weren't home. Part of me hoped they weren't.

"Glory." It was Sherry, giving me a look that said, It's rude to stare in people's windows.

"Sorry." I pulled back to her side, blushing and biting my fingernails. I wanted to be on my best behavior. Whoever or whatever these Kellys turned out to be, I wanted them to like me. Sherry had sworn up and down that they were "upstanding candidates" and very kind people to boot, but still, I felt like it was important to make a good impression. I needed them to be on my side.

I just hoped they made a good impression back. They were likely the last people I was ever to live under the same roof with.

Sherry pushed the doorbell again, and this time a noise came from deep inside the house. A voice—I couldn't tell what it was saying—and then footsteps, making their way toward us. I held my breath. My stomach dropped.

Then came a sickening *creeeak.* The doorknob turned, the door cracked open, widened, and there she was. Mrs. Kelly's hair surrounded her head in a curly white circle, the color perfectly matching her straight white teeth, which were bared in a smile. She wore a pale blue pants suit, with a silver brooch on the collar of the jacket. She was old, but I'd been expecting that. Sherry had explained a lot while I was at the center.

Seeing her now, I couldn't imagine ever calling her what Sherry had said she was going to be. My foster mother. *Mother.* I mentally compared the woman before me to my own mama, whose hair was long and brown, who was strong and slender, who wore simple dresses sewn by hand. There was not a speck of resemblance.

"Glory, welcome," Mrs. Kelly said through her smile, kind of jerking toward me. Suddenly I was enveloped in a stiff hug, her papery cheek pressed against mine and her hands grasping my shoulders. She smelled like the lilacs in my mama's back garden, and her bones felt tiny. "It's so nice to finally meet you!"

I put my hands on her back stiffly. "Pleased to meet you, ma'am," I warbled back. "I mean, Mrs. Kelly."

Finally? I felt like it had been no time at all since Sherry had told me the news. They had matched up a set of foster parents for me, who had come through all the "interviews" and "record checkings" and such scot-free. It had taken just about two weeks from the time I got caught that night at the train yard to now.

To my relief, Mrs. Kelly pulled back quickly. She looked from me to Sherry and back to me. Her hands fluttered to her throat like moths to a flame, all jittery and restless. I reckoned her big, forced smile was meant to look welcoming, but it only made me feel more nervous—if that was possible.

"Well . . ." She stood a second longer. "Well, come in, you two."

As I stepped into the house, both ladies followed me, exchanging greetings. The hall was extra dark after the bright sunlight outside, and it took a few seconds for my eyes to adjust.

"It's nice, isn't it, Glory?"

"I beg your pardon?" I turned toward Sherry.

Sherry smiled. I'd been learning that folks up north thought my talk was as funny as theirs sounded to me. "The house. Isn't it nice?"

The house was . . . divine. We were standing in a wooden-floored hallway with deep red-colored walls. A small, fancy bundle of lights dangled from above, each bulb surrounded by glass and reflecting off the lights around it. To our right was a staircase that rose to a landing, then backtracked its way to the floor above. To the left was a wide-open room, also with wooden floors and flooded with light. I could only see one wall from where I stood, but that was lined with shelves filled with vases, tiny glass figures, silver and brass trinkets. It felt unreal that I should be standing here. That I would be living here.

I realized my mouth was hanging open and shut it quickly. This house was a lot fancier than the last one I'd lived in. After I was cast out of Dogwood, I'd stayed in the nearby town of Shadow Tree for a while, saving up money from my job at a local store to afford the rest of the trip to Boston. My boss at The Rock Shop, Becky Aiden, eventually insisted on taking me into her home with her family. The Aidens' house had seemed like a palace to me—full of modern gadgets and carpets and a television. But this was *even nicer.* And it was a million times fancier than home. Still, that was no reason to look flabbergasted. As usual, I didn't want to reveal the ignorant girl I was. "It's . . . it's very . . ."

"Antique?" Mrs. Kelly asked, her smile never faltering. "Jim and I have a lot of things that are about as old as we are. But I promise I dusted before you came." She leaned forward a bit. "Not myself, just the antiques." She laughed then, putting her hand on my shoulder as she did. I stiffened—I couldn't help it—and her hand danced back to her throat and tugged at a heart-shaped pendant.

"We've collected them from all over. England, Germany, even Bangladesh. Jim and I love to travel. We haven't done it so much recently, but, well—Jim, Glory's here," she interrupted herself as she backed down the hallway and gestured us to follow. "He's in the morning room," she said more quietly, then added, "Football. He just loves it. He can sit in front of that TV for hours if sports are on. Otherwise it's books, magazines. . . . He loves reading. . . ."

The room we entered was to the right beyond the stairs. It was smaller and humbler than the front room. It gave you the feeling the Kellys had lived here forever—the way the shelves were piled with books and knickknacks and the curtains all faded and settled into the great window across the room. In the center was a round table with four chairs. Off to one corner was an impossibly tiny television, much smaller than the Aidens', mounted high on the wall. And opposite the television, so that the two were kind of tucked away in their own little section of the room, was a rocking chair containing Mr. Kelly.

The volume was turned up loud, and Mr. Kelly seemed engrossed in the action on-screen. But when he felt his wife's hand on his shoulder, he looked up, smiled, and stood, reaching out his hand to me. "Welcome, Glory," he said as I shook the hand he offered and said I was pleased to meet him. He was rounder than his wife, especially in the middle. "Sherry." He nodded over my shoulder. He turned back toward the screen and lowered the volume all the way, seemed unable to tear his eyes away for a spell, but then turned back to us. He didn't seem half as jittery as his wife or me. In fact, he was very calm and quiet—almost like this was any other day and I was just a visitor. I swallowed.

"Did you bring your bags in?" he asked.

He was looking at me, but Sherry answered. "They're still in the car. There isn't much; we'll get them."

"I'll get them."

In a moment he was gone. Mrs. Kelly wrung her hands a time or two in the silence, then nodded at the television. "He wanted a real TV—a big one, I mean—in the front parlor. But I didn't think it would look very nice. So this is our compromise." She swung her head around to indicate the room.

"Unless we're having company, this is also where we eat. You can help yourself to anything you like, Glory. We have lots of fruit. I go to the farmer's market, and . . ."

I listened politely, but I felt like a part of my brain was far away, seeing this all from above—sizing things up, figuring out what these few minutes meant about the rest of my life. Mostly I felt relief—Mrs. Kelly seemed very friendly. I had expected to be so scared of her, and I *was* nervous, but she seemed more scared of *me*. I could see right off she wasn't like the foster parents I'd heard about from Greta, the homeless girl I'd met when I was living on the street when I first came to Boston. Greta had said that foster parents were all mean and bossy, always ordering you to do all this work for them. But then, Greta's stories were probably all bunk to begin with. Anybody who could take you under their wing like she did for me—showing me how to survive being homeless in the city—and then betray you like she'd betrayed me couldn't be trusted. That, at least, I was learning.

"You do have a lovely home, Caroline," Sherry said. "I've told Glory a lot about it. And a lot about you." She squeezed my shoulder. "I'm sure she'll be very happy here."

While Mr. Kelly trudged inside and upstairs with the bags, his wife led us back to what she called the parlor, the room I had glimpsed when I came in. At first I shied from sitting on any of the chairs—they were too fancy, covered in soft yellow fabric that shone brightly—but when Sherry took one, so did I. The light was coming from a wall of windows behind us—the windows I had tried to look through from the porch—illuminating the chairs and a matching settee, the shelves with all of their fine doodads, and across the room, a large and very fine piano. Resting on top of it was a photograph in a frame, but I could only see the back.

We'd had a piano back in Dogwood, but it wasn't nearly as grand as the one before me. Several of the keys had been missing off ours. And it had probably never been used for anything but hymns. But Mrs. Johansen had, on special occasions, made it sing for us from its nook in the back of the church. Seeing this one filled me with longing for her. I wondered if she played anymore, since losing Katie.

"Cookie, dear?"

Mrs. Kelly was standing before me, a platter of cookies balanced on her left hand. More out of politeness than anything else, I took one. Oatmeal raisin. I *knew* oatmeal raisin. They were Teresa's favorite. Anytime mama had time to bake us a treat, that was what she'd asked for. I'd always liked gingersnaps myself. "They're very good. Thank you, ma'am."

"What manners! Have some milk, too," she said, setting down the tray on a low table that stood between the settee and the chairs. From another table at the corner of the room, she lifted a clear pitcher full of milk and poured me and Sherry each a glass. Then she sat on the couch just as Mr. Kelly appeared in the doorway.

"Jim says, 'Caroline, kids don't eat cookies and milk these days. They drink soda. They eat . . . what are those things . . . *Nerds. Sweetarts.* Glory isn't five. She's not going to want cookies and milk.' But I told him, 'Kids don't change.' Right?"

She was looking at Sherry, who nodded and laughed. "No, they don't change much," she replied. Then she cast a glance at me and pulled her hands together on her lap. "Speaking of change, we might as well just go over everything we need to. . . ."

Mrs. Kelly nodded agreement. I knew Sherry meant the business about me living here.

"Right. Glory will be starting school Monday, yes?"

Mrs. Kelly rubbed her hands together and glanced toward her husband. "We both agreed with the center that it'd be best to get her started right away. And that still gives us time to do some school shopping."

"And she'll be taking the school bus," Sherry said.

I tensed up, squeezing my knees tight against each other. A school bus. The Aiden kids had taken one of those. It had always sounded terrifying to me.

Mrs. Kelly nodded again.

"Were you able to get her all the supplies you needed, or—"

"We're going to do that this weekend," Mrs. Kelly interjected, winking at me. I attempted a smile back.

They went on talking, about something called a "class schedule" and these confusing tests they'd given me at the center (the ones that had told me I needed to be in the seventh grade, whatever that meant).

A couple of times I darted a glance at Mr. Kelly, still standing in the archway. He didn't speak at all. Maybe he didn't really care about all of this either way and he was just being dragged into this whole foster care thing by his wife. It made me feel even more out of place, if that was possible. Me, Glory Mason, sitting in a parlor in a house near Boston, listening to somebody called a "foster mother" talk about sending me to school. And not a one-room school like the kind I'd gone to back home. A real, *modern* school. With modern kids. It was so unlike anything I'd ever imagined for myself.

How had I ended up here? What was I doing in a town called Brookline, with a foster mother and a foster father and with plans to start school on Monday?

I had a sudden urge to dart out the front door and keep running until I found my way back to the Aidens. With them, life had been strange, for sure, but at least they hadn't made me go to school. Their house hadn't been home, but Becky and her family had seemed so warm and familiar, not delicate and quiet like these people. And they'd still been in sight of the Appalachian Mountains that had surrounded my home. I missed them. I missed my job at Becky's shop. Of course, I didn't miss Becky's suspicious husband and all of his questions—the reason I'd had to leave there when I did.

The grown-ups talked and talked, not seeming to notice me sitting there, even though I was the main subject of their conversation. And I was content to keep hushed. But when Sherry finally got up to leave, panic and worry welled up in me again, and I clung to her arm as she walked out to the porch.

"Do you have to leave so soon?" I asked, real low. We had only been here an hour at the most. I'd pictured Sherry staying all day. I could hear my voice catching in my throat and knew she must have heard it, too.

She put a hand on each of my shoulders. "You'll be fine, Glory. This will be a great environment for you. And if it isn't, or if there's anything you need to talk about, you know you can call me. You have my card." Seeing all the worry in my face, she sighed, but it was a pleasant sigh. "Remember, I'll be here exactly a month from now to see you, and I'll be calling periodically in the meantime."

I patted my pocket where I'd carefully tucked that card—the one with her telephone number on it. But a card wasn't the same as having a familiar face around. Even one that had only been familiar for a couple of weeks.

"Honestly, Glory, you'll be fine. And like I said, I'll be checking in, I promise." Sherry bent over and gave me a brief little hug. Then one more smile, and she turned down the walkway toward her car. My heart ached.

How awful good-byes are. In Dogwood we didn't have them. Nobody left town ever except by dying or being forced out, like me. Most of us weren't even allowed to leave, except Daddy and Mr. Johansen and a few others when they went off for supplies. Half a year ago I'd never said an actual good-bye to anyone in my life. Now a string of them stretched out behind me like clothes on a wash line. To Jake, the boy who'd let me live in his barn on the edge of the woods for a while just after I was cast out. To Becky and the rest of the Aidens, in a note I'd left by my bed. And of course, there was Mama and Daddy and Teresa and Theo and baby Marie, trudging away down the hill without me, the night I was cast out. I'd wanted to say good-bye then, but I couldn't.

I'd never gotten to say good-bye to Katie, either.

Sherry and I hadn't known each other long, but like the Aidens and Jake before her, she was all I'd had for a little while. It made me sad to lose her. Now, like everyone else I'd known, she was just a memory blowing in the wind.

We ate dinner quickly—me gobbling up a bowl full of something called pasta primavera while Mrs. Kelly eyed me from across the table and pretended not to. She said she needed to fatten me up. I made a big show of eating as much as I could, though I didn't have the slightest appetite. All I really wanted was to get off to myself, alone.

After dinner, Mr. Kelly sat in his chair, reading a book and seeming oblivious to me. As much as his wife was intent on my every move, he acted completely uninterested. I wondered if he was annoyed to have me there. Even though I had no control over getting taken in by these folks, the thought made me feel embarrassed.

"Your room is just up here on the right." Mrs. Kelly was at the top of the stairs with me close on her heels. She turned toward a door that was already half open and pushed it all the way, then stood back to let me enter.

She was quiet as I took in my room. *My* room.

A *whoof* of air reached my nostrils as soon as I poked my head through the door. The smell was musty and old. It was a combination of creaky old wood and time and dust, a mixture I hadn't smelled since leaving home, it seemed. The picture it brought to my mind—which was only there for a split second but still crystal clear—was of the back staircase at Zeke Brown's house, where Katie and I used to go to pet his latest batch of kittens. Standing in Mrs. Kelly's house all the way over in Boston and hundreds of miles from home, I could still feel how soft those kittens had been. Katie used to press them against my cheek. . . .

"I'll give you your privacy, dear. Call down if you need anything, all right?" Mrs. Kelly looked uncertain for a second, as if she didn't want to leave me alone. I tried to give her a reassuring smile and a nod. Then she was gone, closing the door behind her.

Phew.

Alone. In my room. I'd never expected to have a room again. And I'd certainly never expected to have one that was so . . . *pink.*

A lamp stood by the large double bed, shedding warm light on the soft pink quilt, a bedside table, my knapsack, and the suitcase of hand-me-down clothes from the center that Mr. Kelly had brought in. Across from the bed was a curved wall, with two long pink curtains hanging in the middle and pulled together tightly. I walked over and spread them open, revealing a large window that, with a click of the middle latch, opened out onto the evening air. I leaned over the sill and breathed deeply, happy to be alone.

Lord, it was pretty out. The smell of spring was in the air. What I could see of the street was dimly lit by lamps turning on in the various houses, all of which were big and fetching. Some looked to be what Sherry had called the Kellys' house— *Victorian.* Somewhere a dog barked. Leaning out farther, I saw that part of the Kellys' parlor jutted out below me. Its roof formed a kind of platform that stretched off to the right and met—somewhere out of view—with the gently tilting line of the main roof. It would be nice to climb out onto it sometime and use it as a place to sit and think.

I sighed. I felt like a princess from one of Mrs. Johansen's stories . . . one who was wasting away, I guess, like Rapunzel, but a princess all the same. Sad and scary as my life was, and panicked as I felt even at this moment, it was lovely to be here in this beautiful house, in my own room, smelling the blossoms on the air.

Leaving the window open, I ducked back inside. There was a door opposite the one I'd come through, and I opened it to reveal a large closet. Unlike the rest of the room, which was very clean and empty except for the furniture, the closet was full of boxes, some of which were taped shut and a few of which were open to reveal girl's clothes, plush animals, a couple of books.

I shut the door quickly, feeling like I'd been snooping (even though, after all, the closet would be mine for as long as I lived here). I remembered something else Sherry had told me at the center. The Kellys had lost a daughter, years and years ago. I hadn't really given it much thought when she told me, seeing how it had happened long before I was born and I hadn't met the Kellys yet. But now, suddenly, it felt a little bit more real, and it made me feel bad for forgetting. It made me think about Mrs. Johansen growing old without Katie and my mama growing old without me. Three lost daughters.

I sat on the bed. It sank deep under my weight. I leaned over the suitcase Sherry had given me and began pulling out my clothes. Then I started putting them in a chest of drawers, covered in pink rosebuds, near the window.

Next I removed what few knickknacks I had. A cake of soap, shampoo they'd given me at the center. Finally I got to the piece of paper folded up on the bottom. My list.

The things I have to do in Boston:
Ride the swan boats
Eat in a restaurant with a real waiter
Read a newspaper all the way through
Go to the top floor of a skyscraper
Ride in a taxi
Go to Mrs. Johansen's church
Be happy

All the things I'd set out to do when I got here, to make sure that I saw Boston the way Katie would have wanted to. It was my reason for being here. It was the only way to do something good for Katie, to make up just a little for getting her to drink spirits that night, for bringing her down to the lake. It was my one reason to go on living.

Yet I still hadn't done one thing on it.

I curled my toes into the ground. I was just so mad at myself.

I thought about Rapunzel again and the other heroines in Mrs. Johansen's old stories. They had always gotten saved by someone. Now I wondered if I could be saved, too, by the Kellys. Not from dying—that was already written, and it couldn't be changed. But from missing my chance to set things right. If I could just win them over, I could get them to take me to Boston (it was only a short ways off). Or let me go in by myself. I could do all the things on my list, bit by bit, and not just spend all my time scraping to live, like I had before. I had to get back into the city, without having to sleep there and fend for myself. The Kellys had to help me.

I folded my list and put it in the drawer of the bed stand, then reached into the front pocket of my knapsack for my other valuables: a note from Jake, wishing me luck on my journey, and my family photograph—my most prized possession.

I stared at it for a long time. I'd kept it hidden while at the center, and I'd have to hide it now. The Kellys had taken me in believing I didn't have a "background"—that I probably had a family somewhere, but that I wasn't revealing who they were, and that nobody had been able to locate them. I'd been labeled as "lost." A "minor" who would be in the foster care system "indefinitely." But even though I couldn't talk about them, I wasn't ready to let my family go.

"Hi, Mama," I muttered, touching my mother's photograph face. "I'm right here." I wished she could know I was still alive and making the last of my days count. Surely in her wildest dreams she wouldn't picture me in this nice house, with nice folks (at least, folks who seemed nice) taking care of me. I wished I could tell her. I wished I could lean on her shoulder and tell her how lost I felt inside, how lost in the world I was without her and Daddy and the rest. I wished, but for all the force of the wishing, I knew it wouldn't change a thing.

CHAPTER TWO

I woke to the aroma of bacon and eggs.

The smell reminded me so much of home, I thought maybe if I just believed in it enough, I would open my eyes, and there would be the bedside window with a view of the barnyard. Mama would be downstairs, cooking; Daddy would be standing with his back to the counter, his big hands propped behind him. I held my breath in concentration, keeping this all in my mind—expecting it or trying to—and parted my eyelids.

The light coming through the open window in front of me was pale, and a cold draft made me scrunch down into the covers. That and disappointment. I was in the Kellys' house, in the pink room that once belonged to their daughter.

I rolled out of bed and stuck my head out the window. It was still early in the morning. Most of the neighborhood looked to be sleeping, except for a robin redbreast that was hopping across the yard out front happily, picking up bugs. For a silly second I wished I was him. I wished I was anyone but me.

Yanking on a pullover and finger combing my hair, which was tangled full of snarls, I opened the bedroom door. I was feeling shy, but I couldn't exactly stay up here all day hiding. And there was the bacon and eggs—one of my favorite meals.

I padded downstairs with my heart in my throat, nervous about my first full day with these strangers who were now my foster "parents." Through the doorway to the kitchen I could see Mrs. Kelly standing over the stove with a spatula. "Good morning, Glory!" she crooned. Something told me she'd been waiting quite a while for me to come down.

"Good morning, Mrs. Kelly. Good morning, Mr. Kelly, sir." Mr. Kelly was sitting at the kitchen table, reading something that lay flat against the table. He glanced up, said good morning pleasantly enough, but then went back to reading. I took the seat opposite him, trying to focus my sleepy eyes. I never was good at getting up early. And though Mr. Kelly had a cup of coffee in front of him, nobody offered me any.

"Jim, dear, put that newspaper away and be sociable, won't you?" Mrs. Kelly arrived at the table with a platter full of scrambled eggs and bacon dripping with fat. My heart sped up—but not at the sight of the food. I focused my eyes, finally, on what Mr. Kelly was reading. *A newspaper.* A Boston city newspaper.

Mr. Kelly let out a resigned sigh, picked up the messy sheaves of paper in front of him, and put them on the chair beside him as Mrs. Kelly laid down plates and silver. I waited for her to sit, though it was torture, the newspaper being so agonizingly close. If I could just get one thing on my list done today, I would feel so much better.

"You two go ahead," she said, noticing my stillness. "I've been picking all morning." Then she headed back toward the sink.

Mr. Kelly had already started to fill up his plate, and as soon as he was done, he passed the big serving spoon to me. I shoveled eggs onto my plate in as mannerly a fashion as I could while he shoveled them into his mouth. And then I dug in.

The food tasted as divine as it smelled. I kept stealing glances at the paper between forkfuls, wondering when the right time would be to ask if I could take a look. If only it had been Mrs. Kelly reading it. I already felt I was a nuisance to Mr. Kelly as it was, without even asking him for anything.

"It's another lovely day," Mrs. Kelly said, looking out the window over the washbasin. "I—" The sound of the telephone ringing interrupted her. As she picked it up, I thanked heaven that I'd already lived through figuring out a few modern gadgets. A couple of months ago the ringing would have startled me senseless. Living with the Aidens, it had always been a challenge trying to hide what I didn't know about the telephone, the television, the electric clothes dryer . . . all the conveniences we didn't have back home. Luckily the Aiden kids had just found my ignorant behavior something to laugh about. I doubted it would tickle the Kellys' funny bones in quite the same way. They were so much older and probably took things more seriously, like the older people I'd known back in Dogwood.

While Mrs. Kelly talked to whoever was calling, her husband and I both focused on our food. He seemed perfectly fine with sitting in silence, but it made me nervous. I kept on sneaking glances at him. Once in a while our eyes met, but mostly it was just me looking at the top of his head, which was bald in the middle. What was it about balding heads that made them so shiny?

When Mr. Kelly looked up, I looked down again. And that was how it went until we were both done and he had pulled his newspaper back onto the table beside his empty plate.

The paper seemed to be batched up in sections, each one covered in lots of writing and a few colored photographs: a man shaking a woman's hand and smiling, another man dressed up in a green-and-white outfit with a number on the back of it, jumping with an orange ball in his hand. Mr. Kelly skimmed through one pile after another, putting each aside as he finished.

"You want a section?" He was looking at me now, as if my desire was written all over my face.

"Yes, sir!" I reached across the table for the batch on top of the pile. The one with the man with the ball. "Thank you." The words *Magic Take Celtics 101-96* were scrolled near the top of the page in deep black ink. I started reading the tiny words underneath.

There were some words I didn't know, but even the words I did were put together in such a way that I couldn't make a lick of sense out of most of them. There was stuff about "shots" and "overtime" and lots of people's names. The whole section seemed to be called Sports, but besides knowing what that meant from watching the Aidens' television, I couldn't figure out what the point of most of the sports was. Still, I was determined to keep at it, so I read on until I noticed that Mr. Kelly was watching me.

"You like the sports page, huh?" he asked, his eyebrows tilted up with curiosity.

"Um, yes," I replied, shrugging.

"You a basketball fan?"

"Mm-hmm." What was I getting myself into? I didn't know anything about sports or much of anything else, for that matter. I recalled being questioned by the Aidens' friend Levi Bushfield, who'd turned out to be some kind of police person. I didn't have to fear getting caught by Child Welfare anymore, but still, I didn't want to show how backward I was or give away anything that would lead someone to know I was from an isolated town like Dogwood and try to force the village to take me back.

Instead of pressing any further, though, Mr. Kelly just nodded pleasantly and returned to his own reading.

When I finished the Sports section (boring as it was, I read it word for word), I started on one called Arts & Leisure. That was what I'd been hoping for—what Katie and I had imagined. It was very sophisticated and smart and interesting. And best of all, it talked about the city and all the things you could do there for fun. One piece even talked about a restaurant that had a movie screen inside for people to watch while they ate (I'd never been to a movie in the first place).

"Gol . . ." I breathed. The stuff in this paper really stirred my blood. In my time living on the streets, I'd come to doubt Boston as a place full of interesting things to do and see and be a part of. But this showed a whole other world than the Boston I'd known so far, which was mostly loneliness and hunger and wondering where to sleep. The dream Boston was still out there—so close. This proved it.

My toes started to dance against the kitchen floor.

And here I was, missing it all. It filled me with an achy kind of energy, and I felt my duty to Katie pressing harder.

I sighed, overwhelmed. I'd just gotten here, and I had a lot of settling in and figuring out to do—not just about getting into Boston, but also about how to live with the Kellys in the meantime and survive a big modern school. But of course, none of that was *living*. Living would be when I got to do those things Katie and I had talked about. It felt so urgent but so far away.

For now, at least, I could read the newspaper. It was *something*. It was the first thing I'd done since leaving home that brought me one step closer to making amends. It was one check mark on my list. *Finally, Katie, finally.*

"You must have a nice long attention span to do all that reading," Mrs. Kelly said, hunching slightly over the wheel of the car. We were on our way to go shopping at a shopping mall, which should have gotten me pretty excited, but my mind was somewhere else: I was still thinking of the newspaper.

I'd spent almost four hours sitting in the morning room, reading every single page. And even though Mr. and Mrs. Kelly had remarked on it enough to make me feel it wasn't normal to do it that way, I still felt satisfied and full to the brim with thoughts.

I'd seen the news on television while I was at the Aidens', but it had been different . . . and I hadn't liked it. It was all about this or that sad thing happening. It had made me feel that the world was just like Reverend Clifton had said—sinful and sad and corrupt. But the news*paper* was different. It had lots of sad stuff for sure, things that made my heart ache, like people fighting with scary weapons and going hungry and such. But it also talked about leaders around the world and what things were like in different countries that, to me, had always seemed as far away as the moon. It showed a world you couldn't put your finger on. It had started me thinking that the truth was, you couldn't say the world was this way or that like the Reverend had. The world was too many things—some good, some bad. *That* seemed a lot fairer. It seemed like the truth.

I also felt proud. I had finally accomplished one thing on my list: I had read a newspaper from one end to the other. I didn't know anyone back home, minus Daddy, who'd read a newspaper. Well, and maybe Mr. Johansen. He was always making trips outside Dogwood, on town business, to organize shipments and stuff. That's how he'd met Mrs. Johansen. And of course Mrs. Johansen and her stories were how come Katie and I had picked Boston as our dream city in the first place.

"Let me just make sure I have my credit card," Mrs. Kelly said.

We had pulled to a stop in a great big lot filled with cars. Mrs. Kelly zipped open her purse and fumbled around in it, knocking a couple of things out and onto the floor of the car.

"Here you go." I picked them up and handed them to her. She took them absently, her forehead creased with worry. It dawned on me just then that she was as old as old Mrs. White back home. I'd always thought of Mrs. White as ancient and toughened by all those years. But Mrs. Kelly, I had to remember, hadn't grown up doing hard farmwork like Mrs. White, and she seemed too delicate to do all this running around with me.

"Here it is. In the front pocket, where I always put it. Silly." She tapped her forehead lightly to show she was talking about herself, then began to climb out of the car.

From a distance, the building looked like a city unto itself. I gazed at it wide-eyed as we walked closer and closer, finally feeling excited. *My first shopping mall.* The entrance was made of six sparkling glass doors. Mrs. Kelly tried to push one open herself, but I eagerly jumped in to help her at the last minute. And then there we were, inside.

Needless to say, it was a sight. I'd had a taste of shops in

Shadow Tree, but nothing so . . . indoors . . . and big. It really was like a city under one roof. There was even a fountain up ahead, like the one on Main Street in Shadow Tree, tinkling and echoing off the glossy floors. And shops. So many shops, I didn't know which way to look first.

Mrs. Kelly didn't pay any mind to them as we passed. She just made a beeline down the long hallway, and I reluctantly tagged along. It was a slow, shuffling kind of beeline, though, so I had time to swivel my attention this way and that, catching glimpses of books, clothes, a shop with CDs like the kind Amelia Aiden had piled up in her room. All things I would have loved to look at up close. But we didn't stop till we were in a store called Filene's.

"Excuse me, where is the young ladies' section?" Mrs. Kelly asked, leaning toward a brown-skinned lady in a dark brown dress. She was very pretty and unlike anybody I'd ever seen at home. The woman pointed us to the right and smiled.

"Oh, dear."

"Ma'am?" I asked. We were standing in what I guessed was the "young ladies'" section, but Mrs. Kelly looked confused.

"It's just I didn't remember it being so big. But then, I was here a long time ago."

"You haven't been back in a while?" I asked dumbly.

"No, no, not a long while. I don't shop much for myself. . . ."

She met my gaze and turned up the corners of her lips, but her eyes looked sad. She'd probably come here with her daughter, I guessed. Maybe she was going to say something about her. But all she did was sigh. "Anyway, let's just start here. . . ."

We made our way through the racks upon racks full of clothes—brand-new ones, not the hand-me-downs I was used to. Occasionally Mrs. Kelly picked something up and showed it to me. First it was a dusk blue frock with buttons down the front. It looked kind of ugly to me, not at all flowy and soft like Becky's clothes, which I'd always tried to imitate back in Shadow Tree. And mostly I don't like dresses. But I nodded and smiled, anyway. Mrs. Kelly probably had fragile feelings, and also, I wanted her to see how agreeable and sensible I was. She held it up to my body, frowned slightly, and then tucked it under her arm. "You're awfully skinny," she said, her eyes roving the racks. "We're going to change that." Then she picked up a dress similar to the first one, in gray. And then a pair of slacks. They were crisscrossed in black and blue lines that made the fabric seem to vibrate, and they looked itchy. Ick.

I nodded again, but I guess my dismay made its way onto my face because Mrs. Kelly suddenly paused in her tracks and put the slacks back, catching me by surprise. Then she unloaded the two dresses, too. "Oh, I just don't know what kids wear these days. You'll have to do your own picking, dear. Just make sure you get enough to last you for a while."

I tried to protest, but she gave me a smile and said she'd

just have a seat near the register and wait. I slunk away, deeper and deeper into the rows of clothing, feeling guilty but also not believing my luck. I could just pick out whatever I wanted?

Already I'd locked eyes on something. It was nothing like anything Becky wore, but it was the prettiest sweater I'd ever seen, with broad, bright stripes every color of the rainbow. I pulled it off the rack, then kept moving. I picked up two short-sleeved shirts—purple and orange. Then a patchwork-style pair of pants, not so different from something I would have seen at home. Then another sweater—a thick, fuzzy one, with buttons. Finally I went back and grabbed the first frock Mrs. Kelly had showed me, just so she wouldn't feel like such a bad picker. By the time I walked over to her, I had six items in all.

"Oh, you'll need more than that." She had on glasses and was eyeing me over the top of a book she'd pulled out of her purse. "You need some summer things because it's going to get warm soon. And maybe a bathing suit. And oh, look, dear." She picked up two articles and held them next to each other. "This one's extra small, and this is large. We need to figure out your size. And what about trying things on?" She closed her book, looking pleased for some reason. "Maybe I'm not so useless after all." She held out her hand and took my fingers into hers, not seeming to notice how bashful it made me.

"Come on," she said. "This will be fun."

It was all I could do to carry everything back to the car. We had five big bags in all, full of everything a person could ever want to wear, or so it seemed to me. I hadn't owned this many garments in all my thirteen years put together.

"Thank goodness," Mrs. Kelly breathed, settling into the driver's seat after we'd loaded everything up. "Half the time when I go out, I can't even find my car. These big lots. Are shopping malls this big down south?"

I tensed up, looking for an answer, but Mrs. Kelly jumped in.

"I suppose it's the same everywhere." She turned the key and pulled a lever. "Do you mind if we do the school-supply shopping tomorrow?" she asked then, tentatively. "I'm a bit exhausted."

"All right, Mrs. Kelly." Disappointed, I couldn't help but think of Becky. She would have had the energy to go to ten malls and would have talked about interesting things like music while dragging me from place to place.

"Good," Mrs. Kelly said, and smiled. As if she'd been worried about me saying no. Still, it was nice that she'd asked if I minded. And it had been nice of her to take me in the first place. She was no Becky, but I was grateful.

The final and most wonderful thing of the day was the bubble bath I took when we got home. After a day of reading and absorbing and then being out with Mrs. Kelly, it was a blessing to be in the bathroom with just me and my own thoughts . . .

and a tub full of fluffy, white, divine-smelling bubbles just like the ones I used to have back at the Aidens'.

Blessing. It was a funny word. Now that I wasn't sure about God anymore, I wasn't sure about blessings, either. Could there still be blessings if there wasn't a God looking out for me like I'd always been taught? And after all the curses I'd come under (even if I *had* brought them on myself), could I believe that I could be blessed at all?

I lifted one leg out of the water and onto the cool side of the bathtub. I lounged my head back, my ponytail flopping over the edge, feeling the water creep up to the lowest hairs on the back of my neck.

No, despite how nice this was, despite how kind the Kellys seemed and the moments of happiness I had felt from time to time since leaving home, I was cursed much, much more than I was blessed. By Katie's being gone, by it being my fault, by being cast out of my home, and by the curse on my body—the poison that was eating it away.

I hadn't been sick in a few weeks, ever since coming to Boston. But I well knew the sickness would come back. It seemed that every time I felt fine, it meant another, more serious batch of illness was coming soon.

Once, after watching a terrible snowstorm for hours through our back window, my big brother, Theo, and I saw the oddest thing. Suddenly the whirling flakes had stopped, just like that—no tempering off. And having spent hours bundled up by the fire with the rest of the family, restless, we charged out into the calm. We were out long enough to feel the eeriness of it, that it wasn't truly as peaceful as it seemed. And then the wind had started blowing again, and the snow suddenly came back even harder than before, and we ran inside. My daddy had called it "the eye of the storm."

That was how it felt to be fine for now: calm and peaceful, but eerie. I knew it wouldn't last.

"Glory, dear? Are you okay in there?"

I straightened up with a splash. "Yes, ma'am."

"You should probably get out soon. You're going to get wrinkles." Her voice was tentative, worried.

"Thank you, ma'am, I'm fine. I don't mind wrinkles."

Mrs. Kelly didn't say anything more, but I could tell she was still standing by the door. Finally her feet shuffled away. Her and Mr. Kelly's room was to the back of mine, and I heard her door close and faint noises coming from inside.

Knowing she was gone, I lay back again. What would I tell the Kellys when I really started getting sick? Would they try to take me to a doctor? I couldn't exactly tell them that the laws of Dogwood reject modern medicine. How would it—the sickness, everything—affect them?

I let my head sink under the surface as I blew bubbles through my nose. The water surrounded me, warm and quiet and still. I would think of something else. There were plenty of other worrisome things to think about.

Like school. Gosh, I dreaded school. I wished I could stay in the bathtub forever.

I'd always been good at school back home, when I wasn't cutting up or forgetting to do things or getting the Reverend sore at me. But my school had been full of youngsters I'd known since I was born. And there were lots of things I didn't know that most modern folks took for granted, on account of growing up in an isolated place where there was no news from the outside world and no electricity for televisions and radios. I had no idea how I'd manage in a modern school.

So absorbed was I in my thoughts that it didn't occur to me till after I got out that maybe Mrs. Kelly had been worried about something other than wrinkles. I didn't know quite what, but it had to be odd for them to have a strange girl in their house, who wouldn't talk about where she came from or who she really was. They probably wondered a lot about me—and about my past. Maybe that was why Mrs. Kelly seemed so nervous. Maybe she didn't want me to spend so much time locked away on my own.

I should've just gotten out when she asked. I didn't want to ruin my chance with the Kellys. I didn't want to give them reasons to ask questions, especially when I didn't want to answer most questions.

I'd have to be more thoughtful from now on.

CHAPTER
THREE

Oh my heck.

Speaking of the eye of the storm, maybe the sickness had come back. I felt like a million tiny pins were stabbing my insides.

But maybe it was just the big, yellow *thing* rumbling toward me. It said SCHOOL BUS across the front in black letters. It looked like a great bee come to swallow me up. Except for the hands and elbows and faces showing through the windows, dot dot dot, like ducklings in a row.

The bus squeaked to a stop in front of where I stood waiting on the corner. The big front doors whooshed open all on their own, revealing two black steps. Ever so slowly I hefted my knapsack over my shoulder and climbed up them.

"Good morning, ma'am," I said to the driver. She didn't seem to hear me over the din that was coming from inside. She simply nodded at me and pulled a lever that slammed the door shut behind me. *Ugh.* It was like being caught in a rabbit trap.

I swiveled to face the rest of the bus. It was filled to the brim with kids, some maybe younger than me, some who seemed older. There must have been thirty or so total. It was hard to tell, considering the whole lot was in chaos.

The seats were all deep green and benchlike, and kids overflowed them in all sorts of ways, leaning over the backs to talk to the people in front of them, sitting with their knees splayed out into the aisle and shouting and laughing. There was even a pair of legs up front that blocked the aisle completely. Many pairs of eyes were trained squarely on me.

I could feel my face going beet red. My knees trembled as I tugged at my nice new rainbow sweater. And I realized the driver was waiting for me to pick a seat before she drove on. Trying to look less flustered than I was, I found that the seat directly to my right was, blessedly, empty. I ducked into it fast as I could.

Squeezing up against the window, I felt my bottom lip trembling. This was horrible. "Katie," I whispered to myself. "Katie, Katie." I had to remember this was all for her, just in a roundabout way.

I lifted my knapsack onto my lap and unzipped the top, hoping to look busy. I fiddled with the supplies Mrs. Kelly had taken me to buy yesterday: a dictionary full of words and their meanings, pens, and pencils. Even the blank notebooks she'd bought were intimidating. What kinds of modern ideas would I be filling them up with, and how much of it would I understand?

Amelia Aiden had loved school, I reminded myself. And I was as smart as her, wasn't I? Only she'd liked it mostly because she liked the kids. And I didn't care a fig about making friends with any of the other kids. I just didn't want to look dumb, and mostly, I didn't want to be noticed.

The bus wheels churned underfoot just like the wheels of the bus I'd taken to Boston. But they weren't comforting like they'd been then. Occasionally we'd stop to let someone else on, and I'd stare out my window to avoid eye contact.

Snatches of conversation drifted up to me from the back, and I was shocked to hear a couple of cusswords. Someone was eating, and the smell of eggs filled the air. A girl squealed, and a boy laughed hard and loud. It was a nightmare.

But still, when the bus squeaked to a halt in front of what I guessed was the school, all I wanted to do was crawl under one of the seats and stay on the bus till it was time to go home.

I waited for all the other kids to trickle off, feeling some of their eyes on me as they passed. Nobody bothered to say hello. Finally I followed the last person out and joined the flow of kids who were making their way up a set of steps and in through a pair of double doors.

Oh my heck, I thought again.

There were people everywhere. I couldn't believe how different everyone looked. They were all shapes and shades and sizes. Some girls looked downright womanly, with makeup on their faces and curvy figures. Some boys were dressed like the homeless folks I'd met in the city. Mostly the whole place was like a smaller version of Boston—crowded full of people with all different kinds of clothes and looks. And the noise. People were talking, laughing, yelling. I heard some more cusswords. There were even some boys and girls who were holding hands with each other. I gulped. Already I knew I hadn't half guessed how different this place was going to be. Already I felt swallowed up by it.

Main office. Main office. I was supposed to go there straightaway. I scanned through the crowds, searching. Luckily I spotted it right there near the entrance—the words on a big engraved plate beside the door.

The office was brightly lit and filled with the buzz of talk and the sound of a telephone ringing. I leaned my arms onto a large counter where a woman was sitting, working on a computer. "Yes?" she asked, not looking up.

"Um, my name is Glory Mason, ma'am. This is my first day here." I shifted from foot to foot as she smiled absently—still looking at the screen. Somewhere a loud bell rang, making me jump, but the lady didn't seem to notice.

Tap tap tap. "Mason. Yep. Mrs. Carlotta is your guidance counselor. I'll get your books."

In a flash she was up from her seat and disappearing into a doorway behind her. In another minute she emerged with a pile of books in her arms and another woman by her side. Mrs. Carlotta, who stuck out her hand for me to shake.

"Nice to meet you, Glory." She smiled, pulled her hand out

of my grasp, and swept up some papers on a nearby desk. "I'm sorry it's so hectic. We'll have to rush a little. Here." She handed me one of the papers. It said *Glory Mason—7th Grade* across the top. The other woman had laid the pile of books on the counter, and now Mrs. Carlotta nodded to them. "You can grab these and put them in your bag, and then I'll show you around."

I rushed to load the books into my knapsack, one after another, and my head spun as I scanned the titles: *Elementary Algebra, American Literature I, Life Science II, Social Studies—Past and Present, World Geography, Student Handbook and Directory . . .* But before I could even absorb the confusion of these titles, Mrs. Carlotta was leading me out into the hallway. "We call this the Breezeway," she said, her brown wavy hair actually kind of blowing back in the breeze she created by walking so fast. I tried to keep up, hefting my heavy load tighter against my back. I was surprised and worried to notice that all the kids I'd seen when I'd come in had disappeared. "Lockers are off to the right. We ask that you keep all your books in them and not in the classrooms. Your locker number and your combo are on your schedule." Combo—what was a combo? I looked down at the sheet I was holding, which was full of all sorts of numbers next to the words *locker* and *combination* and also my list of "subjects"—English, life science, social studies, lunch, elementary algebra, geography, arts —then stared off down the long hall where she had pointed.

"The cafeteria is up here on the left." We had turned down another hallway, and now she nodded to a pair of double doors. "And all classrooms except for photography, art, gym, and music are down this way." Art, music? You actually learned those kind of things in school?

". . . electives. For now you'll probably have a bit of catching up to do."

Pay attention, Glory, I told myself. Only it was too much to take in. I could hardly breathe.

Finally Mrs. Carlotta came to a stop and turned toward me. With a jolt, I realized we had somehow come back around to the front of the main office. We'd been walking for about five minutes.

"We know you have a lot of adjustments to handle right now," she said, her voice lowering a notch. "As far as the center goes, we'll be in contact with them about your grades, et cetera. They'll be checking in from time to time. But beyond me and a few other people in the office, your personal situation is completely confidential. We don't reveal it to students or teachers—we leave that decision to you."

I felt myself blushing. How did these people know so much about me? Mrs. Carlotta put a hand on my arm.

"Please contact me if you need anything or have any questions. Okay?"

"Yes, ma'am."

We stood there for a moment longer, then Mrs. Carlotta took my paper and looked at it.

"English is your first class. I'll take you. Obviously they've already started." I followed Mrs. Carlotta back down the first hall.

My first class. I wished I had a moment to catch my breath beforehand. I wished I wasn't being asked to soak in years of learning in minutes. I'd never heard of a locker. I didn't know classes could be in all different rooms. I had no idea what electives were. Back at home, we had sat in one room all day and learned very few subjects, and mostly we had done a lot of praying and studying the Bible. Mrs. Carlotta had not said one thing about God this whole time, and prayer wasn't on my schedule. What would school be like, without prayers and Bible study taking up most of the time? How would I ever make it through this day, feeling more ignorant than I ever had?

Mrs. Carlotta came to a stop in front of a door and rapped on it lightly. Then, without waiting, she opened it and I followed her inside.

The room was bigger than our whole school in Dogwood put together. About twenty-five students sat in desks all lined up in neat rows, listening to a woman at the front of the room. The woman stopped what she was saying as Mrs. Carlotta whispered in her ear. Then, with a quick little nod, my guidance counselor was gone.

"Class, we have a new student. Glory Mason. Hi, Glory, I'm Mrs. Blackburn."

"Pleased to meet you, ma'am," I muttered, bowing my head slightly. A low titter came from the back of the room, and I looked up. Blushing and tugging at my sweater again, I wondered if it was directed at me.

"You can sit back there," she said, pointing toward a desk three seats down from the front on the right-hand side.

I made my way back to the desk and ducked into it, laying my knapsack beside me. Glancing around, I noticed a few kids were looking at me. "Pleased to meet you," I offered again. A boy directly to my left replied with a half smile, but behind me, another titter arose. This time I knew I was the reason for it.

Blushing, I snapped my head around to see who it was that had laughed. The girl directly behind me wore a mirthful, careless grin, her head tilted pertly to one side and her mouth turned up at the corners. Her straw-colored hair was pulled back in a sleek ponytail, neat and perfect. She was the vision of a nice young lady, like the kind Daddy had always said I should be—all clean and pressed and pretty. Except maybe for the nice part. I couldn't imagine why someone would be rude enough to laugh at me for no good reason. But then, even though I'd come to know a few, I hadn't really figured out the first thing about strangers. In any case, I couldn't help but scowl at the girl before turning back around.

"Glory, we're just in the middle of discussing *A Separate*

Peace. Have you read it?" Mrs. Blackburn stared at me from under her long bangs, her fluffy red hair cascading down the sides of her face in winglike tufts.

"No, ma'am." No snickering this time. I fidgeted, but Mrs. Blackburn didn't seem to notice. She just smiled pleasantly.

"That's fine. You can catch up for tomorrow. We're only on chapter four. Feel free to jump into the discussion, anyway. Now"—she cast her gaze about the room—"what is the significance of Finny wearing the school tie as a belt in chapter two?"

Significance? For one horrifying moment I thought Mrs. Blackburn was going to call on me for an answer after all. She was looking right at me and nodding.

"Stacy?" *Phew.* A voice rose up from just behind me. That girl's.

"Finny's breaking the rules and getting away with it, something Gene could never do. So even though he doesn't admit it yet, Gene resents Finny. He's envious."

Mrs. Blackburn nodded. "That's right, Stacy. Thank you."

I hunkered down farther in my seat. How come they were talking about significance, as if the characters in a book were real? And how could Stacy figure that out about the tie? I didn't get it. My guts sank with the sureness that this was all too smart and too complicated for me.

I showed up late to my second class, too—all thanks to getting lost in the maze of hallways, looking for the row of lockers

Mrs. Carlotta had pointed out, and then not being able to get the darn thing open when I got there. There was a padlock—of all things—on it, with numbers lining the edges of a dial. And though I was smart enough to figure out the numbers must have something to do with the numbers on my schedule next to the word *combination,* I still had no idea what to do with that knowledge. Finally I gave up hope of lightening my heavy load and rushed off through the empty halls to find room 301B.

The class was called life science, and the teacher, Mr. Tydings, wasn't as understanding as Mrs. Blackburn about my tardiness. He just gave me an annoyed look, glanced at my schedule to make sure I was in the right spot, and pointed me to a desk in the back.

Queasy, I tried to listen to his talk—he was in the middle of saying something about some islands somewhere—but I couldn't concentrate. I took a secretive survey of the room. There were many of the same kids from my last class, but a lot that were different. (Lord, how many kids were in this school, anyway?) Except for a few girls, they mostly looked younger than me. I studied the boy in the desk next to mine. He had short, short glossy dark hair. His eyebrow—the one I could see—cut a dark brown slash across tan skin. Yep, I'd say he was a year younger, at least.

As I stared at him, his face started to do something. His lips pulled back slowly in a smile, his head tilted slightly, and then both his eyes, without warning, darted to mine.

Snap. I quickly turned my face back to the front of the room, my cheeks burning up. I don't know why, but after a few seconds I dared to look over again. He was facing the front now, but he still wore an amused grin. My heart sank. Was he laughing at me, too? In all the time I'd been in Shadow Tree and Boston, I'd always dreaded folks seeing at first glance that I was out of place. Now that I'd stopped worrying about that so much, was it happening at this school on my very first day?

As if things weren't bad enough, my gaze was pulled ever so slightly over the boy's shoulder, to the desk just past him.

There was that girl Stacy again. *What luck.* Well, these kids weren't going to get any more "pleased to meet yous" out of me, that was for sure.

Don't worry about them, I told myself, setting my jaw. I was already caught and in foster care. I didn't have to worry about sticking out anymore. So if people thought I was funny, they could go on and laugh their guts out for all I cared.

Still, I was whistling another tune when I walked into the giant room that was the cafeteria and realized it was just a collection of tables crowded with kid upon kid upon kid. Where would I sit? I tried to back up immediately, to maybe head outside, but a teacher stopped me at the door and asked me where I thought I was going.

"Um, I was just going to go sit outside, maybe . . ." I said timidly.

The man gave me a knowing smirk, as if this was some private joke between us but one that was annoying to him. "You know lunch in the cafeteria is mandatory." He gave a nod meant to shoo me inside.

Figuring *mandatory* meant something you had to do, I slunk past him.

On top of buying me all those supplies, Mrs. Kelly had given me lunch money for a week. I'd considered keeping it all for going into Boston, but I was famished, and anyway, I didn't know where else to go but into the line. By and by, as I waited my turn to choose something to eat, I spotted a group of adults sitting together, with the other half of their table empty. I chose the cheapest thing I could find that still looked familiar—a cheese sandwich. Then I paid and headed in that direction. The adults, for some reason, didn't seem half as scary as the kids.

I spotted Mrs. Blackburn among the group as I passed, and I nodded a greeting to her, which she returned with a smile of recognition. Then I plunked myself at the far end of the table, away from everyone.

Keeping my eyes down, I wished that I could disappear or sink into the floor. The best I could do was swallow my food in three bites. It would be okay, I told myself as my stomach churned. I would be okay. All of this . . . it didn't really matter.

*   *   *

Minutes later, I was locked in a little private room inside the bathroom (Becky had told me they were called stalls, back when I first saw them in a big store in Shadow Tree), sick as sick could be. My stomach was pitching around inside me and my body was racked with chills, my knees pressed against the tile floor and my hands clutched to my middle. Finally I vomited and then knelt back against the door, relieved that I was alone in here. I still hadn't gotten used to the idea of using the facilities with other people right next door to me.

Here it was, what I'd been dreading. The poison creeping up and down my insides and turning me into pure misery. I knew it wasn't from the food, like what had happened when I cooked for the Aidens, because that had taken much longer to make us all sick. No, this was the Dogwood poison at work. I fought back the lump that formed in my throat. No sense feeling sorry for myself. I just needed to get through this, just for now. And then I'd be better about getting to Boston, *soon.*

I longed for my mama with my whole body. I wished she was there to comfort me and hold me and tell me I'd feel better. Or to put me in my bed and rest a cold cloth on my forehead. Just having her beside me, listening to her breathe, even, had always helped somehow with any ailment.

Mama. Daddy.

For what seemed to be half an hour or more, I knelt there and swallowed my tears, and tried to breathe and wait for the feelings to pass. Finally the sweat on my skin began to feel cold and soothing. My insides felt like everything was settling back in the right place. I sighed, standing up slowly and brushing the dust off my knees. I pulled my knapsack over my shoulders, leaned over the sink, and splashed cold water on my face. Then I headed back into the hall.

Of course, I was already late again. I'd heard the bell ring long ago, announcing the beginning of classes. That's what the bells are for, you know.

The afternoon looked like it would be at least a little better than the morning. I scanned my "schedule" carefully and found my way to the right classes—elementary algebra and then geography. And though I was late to the first one, the teacher didn't make a big deal of it. She only checked a little notebook on her desk and directed me to a seat. And neither teacher called on me. Some kids still stared, and I could swear someone whispered, "Nice sweater," to someone else. But I was already learning to close myself into a shell, and it was enough of a time just understanding a smidgen of what either teacher was talking about.

Then came art, and that was actually almost . . . enjoyable. I had to sit at a common table with a bunch of other students, which worried me at first because everyone chattered to each other for the first few minutes while I just sat there and bit my lip. But then Mrs. Sullivan, the teacher, got everyone to quiet down.

She introduced me quickly but then launched right into a project that involved making things out of these wire clothes hangers. It was almost . . . fun. I couldn't believe it was part of school.

It was when the final bell rang that things got even worse than I'd thought they could be. At first I didn't realize it *was* the final bell I was hearing, and I scanned my schedule for what should come next. But there was such a commotion in the hall—accompanied by the sounds of the main doors opening and closing—that I realized it was time to go home, and I drifted with the last of the crowd outside. That's when I saw several buses lined up, side by side, in the parking lot. Each one had a number sitting on display in the front window: *#1, #3, #8* . . .

A lump knotted up in my throat. Which one? Which one was mine?

The crowd was thinning out to almost nothing as I stood and stared and wondered what to do. Minutes went by and I stood there dumbly. And then the buses started to move. *Oh, no.*

Swallowing my pride, knowing that I would probably be drawing attention to myself, I did what I had to do. I started running. First to the bus nearest me. Just as I got to the door, it roared forward. I tried to keep up as it slowly pulled out, peering in the doors to see if I recognized the driver. Nope. This one was a man.

I backtracked, rushing to the bus that was now moving, too, following the first one, and almost fell over as I tried to push up against the door, peering in through the glass. *Nope.*

I headed for the third one. I was nearly crying. I caught a glimpse of the faces in all the windows. Several of them were staring out at me. I didn't care.

I got up to the doors and looked inside, and there, thank goodness, she was: the driver from this morning.

Beyond feeling shy anymore, I pounded on the glass to get her attention. But she just kept facing straight forward. Finally she tilted her head back to yell something to the kids, over her shoulder. Our eyes met. The bus squeaked to a halt, and I climbed on, panting, spent.

"Thank you," I breathed as I brushed past the driver. My seat from this morning was open. I sank into it like lead.

I ignored the urge to look back to see if anybody had noticed the whole ordeal.

"Are you all right?"

The voice was coming from directly behind me, and I turned around sheepishly. The girl who'd spoken had curly, brassy hair, and on her face were the hugest spectacles I'd ever seen. They took up half of her face, and the glass magnified her eyes so that they looked buglike. She seemed bashful and worried, and on my word, I wanted to say something that would reassure her. It was kind of her to ask, after all.

But to tell the truth, I was too mortified to say a thing.

That night at dinner Mrs. Kelly was eager to hear about my day.

"Did you make any new friends?" she asked, putting a hand on my shoulder as she laid down a plate piled high with steaming baked potatoes and then sat. She seemed so hopeful—perched there with a concerned, expectant smile on her face. I sighed. I didn't want to let her down. I wanted her to be pleased with me, even though I was dying to tell *someone* how truly rotten and perplexing and crazy the whole day had been. I wanted Mrs. Kelly to see how normal and adjusted I was so she'd like me and trust me. Because when that happened, she'd let me go to Boston.

"Um, I guess," I said, moving a piece of steak on my plate back and forth with the tip of my fork. Mr. Kelly had cooked it on something he called a grill, and it looked delicious, but I was still feeling a little too queasy to dig right in. "You didn't have to cook for me, Mr. Kelly," I ventured. He muttered something about it being no problem, and as he sat there chewing and staring off into space, I wondered if he meant it. Then I looked back at Mrs. Kelly, who was still waiting for me to finish answering her question. "I mean, I guess I made a few."

She clasped her hands together with pleasure. "That's wonderful. What are their names?"

"Um . . ." I sawed harder at my steak, thinking. "Um, Stacy . . . and—"

"Stacy. Is she in one of your classes?"

"Um, yes, ma'am. She's in two of them."

"Oh, isn't that nice of them. And she's a nice girl?"

"Well . . ." I thought of how rude Stacy had seemed. "Yes. She's smart and . . . nice," I finished.

"It's important, in a big school like that, to make *nice* friends. Isn't it, dear?"

She looked across to her husband.

"It's important she make *nice* friends. Isn't that right, Jim?"

"Yep." Mr. Kelly nodded and shrugged—humoring her, I guessed. Mrs. Kelly frowned.

I had a whole other idea of what was important. I decided to take my chance. "Mrs. Kelly, ma'am," I said, addressing her since so far she seemed to be the one in charge and giving her my most charming smile. "Do you think maybe I could go into Boston this weekend? To go sight-seeing?" I'd heard someone in school use the word today about a weekend trip and figured out it meant seeing all the exciting things in a new place— exactly what I needed to do in Boston!

But Mrs. Kelly frowned again, deeper.

"Dear, who would go with you? You can't go by yourself."

I thought for a second. "Um, well, maybe you could go with me, ma'am? I want to go on the swan boats and . . . see some things. We could have the whole day together and get to know each other better. . . ." I thought this last part would help.

"Oh, that does sound nice, but I'm afraid"—she smiled

apologetically—"I have so much gardening to do this time of year, and then it's getting hot and I don't handle the heat very well. I can go with you as soon as it cools down again, in the fall. How's that?"

I held in a sigh of frustration. Of course, the fall was no good.

"Well, how about if I went by myself?"

Mrs. Kelly darted a glance at her husband.

"It's probably not a good idea," Mr. Kelly replied.

I looked down at my steak, then up again.

"I'll be good, if that's what you're worried about." I cleared my throat. "I'll come back."

Now both the Kellys made such a show of shaking their heads and chuffing at my words that I knew I had hit the mark. They were worried about me going alone, at least partly because they were worried about what I might do. Like run away. I could have told them not to worry, that living on the streets would make things even harder than they already were. But then I'd have to explain a whole lot. And the Kellys seemed to have made a pact—maybe with Sherry, even—to let me keep the explanations to myself.

"Maybe . . ." Mrs. Kelly had her fork paused before her mouth as she spoke in a smoothing-things-over voice. She'd cut her steak into teeny-tiny pieces and trimmed off every bit of the fat, so that each bite she took was only a smidgen. ". . . you can go with a friend. Maybe this Stacy you told us about.

Perhaps one of her parents would take you one weekend. They could drive, or the T stops right near here. We'd have to meet them, of course, but"—she grinned—"wouldn't *that* be nice?"

My heart sank down into my knees. No, it wouldn't be nice. It would never happen. But I managed a grateful, friendly grin. "Yes, that would be nice. Thank you, Mrs. Kelly."

In the silence I turned over the problem in my mind. I couldn't go back to being homeless; it wouldn't solve anything. I'd just have to keep trying to win Mrs. Kelly's trust and friendship. I'd just have to be so good, she couldn't say no.

Mrs. Kelly reached her hand across the table as if to put it on top of mine but stopped about halfway. "Anyway, I don't think this weekend would be a good idea. You look like you're coming down with something."

I swallowed.

Coming down with something. As in a cold. As if what I was "coming down" with could be as simple as that. It was kind of funny. But not really.

In fact, I just wanted to cry.

CHAPTER
FOUR

"On page fifty-two, after Finny falls, why does Gene say that his fear of jumping out of the tree is forgotten?"

It was almost the end of my second English class. *Almost.* At least I had found my way to class before the bell rang. Now I was just waiting for it to be over—it and the rest of the day.

Mrs. Blackburn surveyed the room, her eyes meeting mine briefly before flitting away. *Phew.* I'd realized as soon as I stepped into the classroom that I'd forgotten to read the chapters she'd told me about. *Fool, Glory.* I clung to the hope that she wouldn't make me "join in the discussion." Relief flooded me as I felt a *whoosh* of air behind me and knew Stacy James had raised her hand.

Mrs. Blackburn looked over my shoulder, but she didn't call on Stacy. Instead she looked at me again. "Glory? Don't be shy. There are no wrong answers here. What do you think?"

I squirmed. "Um. Um . . ."

"Did you have time to read the assignment?"

"Yes, ma'am." I hung my head, thinking, *Some things never change.* I remembered Reverend Clifton back home saying I'd forget my head if my body wasn't attached. "I just forgot to."

Mrs. Blackburn looked disappointed for a moment. But then, instead of scolding me like the Reverend would have done, she simply shrugged.

"That's okay. I know you're probably overwhelmed. Can somebody *besides* Stacy . . ." I felt another whoosh as Stacy pulled her hand down. I guess she usually answered a lot of questions. ". . . tell me why Gene feels the way he does about jumping out of the tree?"

I slumped in my seat, relieved once again. But this time it was mixed with something else. Disappointment.

I wished I had known the answer. I really did.

I didn't bother going to my locker after class, determined to make it on time to life science. I took the seat the teacher had pointed out the day before, unsure whether it was supposed to be my seat forever, and kept myself busy when the boy from yesterday who'd sort of laughed at me walked in, talking with another boy and that girl Stacy. He moved with the kind of ease I'd never seen on the few boys I'd known back home. I pretended to fiddle with my pen as he slid into his desk. I'd never owned my very own pen before, and now I had a packet of five.

"Is your pen broken?"

He was talking to me. I should've known there's only so much fiddling you can do with a pen before you draw attention to yourself.

I tried to look indifferent as I replied, "No, it's fine, thank you." I waited for him to laugh or at least smirk at my accent, but he didn't. Still, I turned my head away real quick so he wouldn't say anything else. Mr. Tydings walked in then, and that put an end to it. Or so I thought.

"Textbooks away." The teacher held up his own book as if to demonstrate and laid it down on the desk by his side. "We're going to do another partner exercise today. We're going to fill in this diagram of a flower. Here are the dittos."

Mr. Tydings picked up a pile of papers and began passing a stack of them to the first person in each row of desks. Then those people took one sheet each and passed them back. I sat, bewildered. What was a ditto?

"I'm going to let you *pick* your partners today." A low cheer went up from the class. My heart started pounding with dread. "But people, people . . . that doesn't mean this is a social gathering."

It was no use. The last words were buried amidst loud voices as kids rushed toward each other, moving their desks closer together. I'd never seen such a thing—partnering up in school. But I understood what it meant. My ears started ringing with embarrassment. Of course, nobody was going to pick me.

A high-pitched squeak brought my attention to the desk of the boy next to me. It was *right* next to me. He had pulled it within a few inches of mine.

"Do you mind if we're partners?" he asked, leaning close so I could hear him. I stared blankly, searching his face for a hint of mockery, but could find none. Still, why would he want me for a partner? He obviously had friends. In fact, Stacy was looking our way, crestfallen. I felt a bitter happiness about that.

I tried not to show my other feelings—the painful, shy ones. "Okay," I said, half shrugging.

I turned my attention to the sheet of paper, the "ditto," and made a big show of studying it. It was a flower. At least, it looked like a flower. Only there were all these extra bits drawn in and blank lines pointing to each of the parts. I started biting my thumbnail, fearful and confused.

"Where are you from?"

In a daze, I looked back to the boy next to me. It took me a second to realize he was even talking to me. I'd only been here a day, but already I'd decided I was somehow invisible. Well, maybe not invisible, but certainly unapproachable.

The boy's brown eyes studied me, openly curious. He'd flung his arm across the back of his chair carelessly.

"Oh, I'm Joe, by the way."

"I'm Glory," I muttered.

"I know. The teacher said, remember?" He grinned. I could feel my cheeks going crimson. Why had it been so much easier to talk to Becky, and even to Jake, than to this boy?

"How old are you?" he asked.

"Thirteen."

"You're from the South, huh?"

I didn't reply. He stared at me for another few seconds,

waiting, I guess. Finally his eyes sparkled with mirth.

"You want me to guess where you're from?"

"Um." Was he making fun of me? My jaw clenched. "No."

He studied me another second.

"Well, I'm not from here, either. We moved last year from California. Believe me, I know how you feel."

For all my nervousness, I almost actually snorted at this last bit. California was far away, I knew that much. But unless he came from a part of California where there was no electricity, no one had cars, and they didn't believe in the government, he could have no idea how truly strange this place was to me. It was the most I could do to nod politely.

Still, Joe seemed to realize that I wasn't feeling very kindly disposed to him because he didn't ask anything else. We just turned our attention to the "diagrams" in front of us. Which was maybe even worse because we were supposed to discuss how to *label* them.

And I'd never *seen* a diagram in the first place.

"May I sit down?"

I looked up from my cheese sandwich to find Mrs. Blackburn hovering above me, tray of food in hand. I'd just been thinking how grateful I was that I hadn't needed to throw up yet today, but now my stomach gave a little gurgle.

"Yes, ma'am," I responded, scooting over slightly even though there was plenty of room. Inadvertently I got a big glimpse of the room as I did so and spotted that boy Joe at a table across the way. I quickly looked back at my sandwich.

The teacher laid her tray right next to mine and climbed over the bench. I glanced quickly at the other teachers, wondering why she wasn't with them.

"It must be hard, being new," she said, unwrapping a clear bowl filled with lettuce and tomatoes and onions. "I went to the same school all the way through eighth grade. Then half of us went to the same high school."

I swallowed, and we sat in silence for a few moments. I tugged at the crust of my sandwich.

"So I guess I'm not one to talk. But sometimes, you know, you've just got to take the plunge. They're not so bad, these kids. They're probably as shy of you as you are of them."

Oh. She'd come over here on a mission. Well, I didn't want her pity. I rolled the dough I'd torn off up into a little ball, and nodded, as if I was really learning from the advice.

Finally she just came right out and said it. "Why don't you try sitting with some of the other kids? I'm sure they'd be glad to have you."

I stopped then and looked at her earnestly. "Ma'am . . . is it *mandatory?*" I asked.

Unbelievably, Mrs. Blackburn threw her head back and laughed. For someone so proper and kind looking, she laughed kind of wildly.

"No, no, no. Are you kidding? No."

I smiled. It didn't bother me that she was laughing. It kind of made me laugh a little, too, though I didn't know why.

"Anyway, it's nice to have a chance to talk. I'm always happy to have a new student. What are your interests, Glory?"

"Interests? Um, what do you mean?"

"Well, what do you like to do?"

"Um." I thought of what I'd liked to do back home and the things I'd liked to do since. In Dogwood, I'd liked wading on the edges of the lake with my dungarees rolled up, fishing. I'd liked spending time with Katie. I didn't feel like I could talk about either of these things—anything involving home, really. I didn't know what, exactly, I *could* talk about. "I like making jewelry," I tried, thinking of Becky and her shop, and all the fun we'd had piecing together necklaces and bracelets and listening to Bob Dylan on the tape player. "And I like reading." Then I added apologetically, "Even though I forgot to do those chapters."

Mrs. Blackburn waved away the apology with one limp hand. "What's your favorite book?"

I thought back to the last book I'd read, back in Shadow Tree. I wasn't sure it was a good answer. I knew the Reverend, at least, would have flipped his top if he knew I'd read it, especially since it didn't hardly say a word about God. Still, I felt somehow it was okay to tell Mrs. Blackburn. "I like *Gone with the Wind*."

My teacher's eyes widened so much, I thought her eyeballs

might pop out. "Really? You've read the whole thing?"

I nodded.

"And you liked it?"

I nodded again.

"Glory, that's quite advanced for a girl your age. What did you like about it?"

"Um . . ." I thought for a second, losing myself in the memory of what I'd read. "Most of all I like that Scarlett does all these bad things and has all these ornery thoughts but that you still like her, anyway. I like that you don't have to think she's a bad person just because she's not perfect."

Mrs. Blackburn tilted her chin thoughtfully. "I agree. I think that's the very reason Scarlett is such a great character."

I felt a smile flash across my face. Mrs. Blackburn *agreed*.

"I identify with her, don't you?"

"Identify?"

"Well, I can understand because I'm not perfect, either. You know?"

My smile faded. Yes, I could understand.

Mrs. Blackburn didn't seem to notice my sudden thoughtfulness and went on talking about characters and books and such, but mostly just about ideas. Like that even smart writers had made mistakes in their books—like how, in *Gone with the Wind*, the writer tried to make slavery look like a good thing when any fool could tell you it was plain evil. Slavery had never happened in Dogwood—I guess it was around that time that our town founders had separated themselves from "society." But in our town history they talked about slavery and called it sinful (along with lots of other things "society" did).

The leaders of Dogwood had strong opinions on just about everything: taxes and *true* Christianity and such. That was why I feared ever being sent back there—because folks back home would do anything before they'd break their own laws by taking an outcast back. It was also the reason why Mrs. Blackburn's talk seemed so strange to me. It was open to discussion. It was like there were no right or wrong answers.

With the Reverend, back home, you always *had* to be right or wrong (and I was usually wrong). But Mrs. Blackburn talked as if learning was about just about thinking and pondering. Even in my other classes yesterday, I'd noticed kids raised their hands and said when they were confused or asked questions that back in our school in Dogwood would have been called impudent. How could human beings and their beliefs be so, so different?

The lunch hour seemed to pass in about five minutes as I listened and sometimes added my own thoughts to our talk. It was only when Mrs. Blackburn started gathering up her things to leave that the dread of school returned.

Still, I went into the afternoon feeling much better. And even though I had lots more classes and countless more strange kids to face, that made it all a little more bearable.

CHAPTER
FIVE

I'd made it. Well, at least through the first week.

Saturday I stretched out in bed, basking in the late morning sun through the window, grateful as I could possibly be that it was the *weekend*. It seemed funny to have started looking forward to that word and what it meant, like the Aiden kids had back in Shadow Tree. No school. No kids to feel shy of. Just me and the Kellys.

Granted, I didn't know if I would ever be at ease with the Kellys, either. But still, at least they were nice to me. Except for that one boy, Joe, the kids at school this week had mostly either darted stares at me or not noticed me at all. And the Kellys didn't throw words at me like *significance* and *dittos* and expect me to understand what they meant.

Yawning, I sat up and stretched. A little pang of nausea rose up in my belly, but then in a moment it was gone. I decided to ignore it.

I reached into the bedside drawer and pulled out a wad of bills—the money I had saved this week by just buying cheese sandwiches. Ten dollars. It wasn't a whole lot, but it was better than nothing. It might buy me a ride on a swan boat, at least, once I got back into the city. Once I found out how. Lazy as it may sound, I was too exhausted to worry about that right now, especially when I had no plan.

I pulled on a cotton robe Mrs. Kelly had bought for me at that Filene's place and then headed to the bathroom to rinse my face. Looking in the mirror, I smoothed back my hair. It had grown longer in the past few months than it had ever been. I suppose it would have been pretty had it not been so brittle and dry looking. Mama had always said my brown hair was glossy as a pearl, but if that had been true once, it wasn't now—though it *was* striking, next to how pale my face had gotten.

I stared into the glass, and the longer I looked, the more it seemed I was looking at someone else and not myself. It wasn't that I looked *awful*, I thought, just *less*. Less of myself than I was before Katie died and everything fell apart.

I padded out into the hall and down the stairs, bracing myself like I did every morning to greet the Kellys, who were always up and about long before I was. But they weren't in the kitchen or the morning room, and they weren't in the parlor, either. In fact, after a few minutes looking around, I realized they weren't anywhere in the house.

Hmmm. I had not spent a minute in the house, so far, without one of them being here. It was strange. It all felt so empty and forbidden.

I wandered back into the parlor and stood in the middle of the room for a second, kind of excited. Curiosity was getting the better of me. I knew it was my chance to have a good look around.

Not that the Kellys kept anything off-limits to me that I knew of. But I'd felt too awkward so far to stick my nose all over the place in their presence. Now I went straight to the parlor shelves and picked up a small brass box with a little key poking out of the front, one doodad I'd been eyeing with curiosity. I turned the key and pulled up the lid. *Huh.* Nothing. There was just a velvet-lined space inside, but it was empty.

I set the box down and picked up a photograph next to it. A man and a woman, in grainy, fuzzy black and white, were standing next to a lake of some sort, their arms wrapped tightly around each other as they smiled at the camera. With a start, I realized the couple was Mr. and Mrs. Kelly. They looked like they were both laughing at some wonderful joke—maybe even like their lives were one long wonderful joke. Their smiles were that joyful. They looked so . . . *young.* It was hard to connect them to the people I knew now. I put the photo down and looked around. Then I made my way over to the big piano in the corner.

There was a bench in front of it, and I maneuvered myself around and sat down. There was a sort of cover with hinges that I pulled up, revealing a row of shining white, and smaller black, keys underneath. I placed my forefinger on one of the ones directly in front of me and pressed it gently.

Ding. Whew! I jolted at the loudness of the sound and pulled my finger away, then put it back. I pressed again. *Ding ding ding.*

A huge smile spread across my face. How lovely! It sounded off, like the notes weren't quite right, but still . . . so nice.

Now I placed both hands on the shining white bars and pressed, over and over again, once with all my fingers, once with just a few.

I bobbed my head a little as I made my own rhythm and plucked out a little tune.

"What are you doing?"

A shock raced up my spine, and I turned toward the voice. Mrs. Kelly was standing in the archway, wearing gloves, a big straw hat, and her own look of surprise. She'd been gardening. She must have been gardening out back the whole time. *Stupid Glory.*

I made to stand from the bench, but before I could, she was across the room and pushing the cover back over the keys.

"We don't play this piano, dear. It's an antique."

"Yes, m'—" My voice cracked. I swallowed and tried again. "Yes, ma'am."

Mrs. Kelly didn't say anything for a few seconds. She cleared her throat. Slowly I backed around behind the bench.

"I'm sorry," I said. I meant it with all my heart. I didn't want Mrs. Kelly to be annoyed with me. What if she decided I wasn't trustworthy?

She put her hand over her heart, and her face softened.

"No, *I'm* sorry," she replied abruptly. "You didn't know."

We both stood in silence. I stared at my feet. "It's just . . ." Mrs. Kelly continued, her face full of an apology. "It's just it was our daughter's, handed down from Jim's family. She was taking lessons when she died." She nodded to the photograph that sat on top of the piano, the one I had seen from behind the first day but hadn't even glanced at in my excitement of a few minutes ago. "We just don't play it."

The photograph was in black and white. *Oh. Oh, gosh.* It was a girl with long blond hair parted straight down the middle, silky pigtails hanging forward over each shoulder, her hands folded on her lap. She looked almost exactly my age.

"I suppose it doesn't make sense, the piano going to waste. We're just set in our ways, I guess."

Mrs. Kelly stared at the photograph with a strange, calm smile on her face. Her daughter had died. It truly made sense to me now, for the first time. With her little hands and her powdery white skin and all her politeness, Mrs. Kelly had lived through that. How she must have suffered. How my own parents must be suffering.

Had Mrs. Kelly back then looked as lost as my mama had at the church that night? Had Mr. Kelly been as angry as Mr. Johansen had been when he'd sent pure hate at me from his eyes and said he wanted me gone forever? Had the Kellys had somebody to blame like Katie's mama and daddy had? I didn't dare ask.

I just nodded, trying to show her in that nod that I understood, better than she'd ever know. If I were going to live to be Mrs. Kelly's age, I knew that I would keep Katie's memory tucked away and precious and unchanged as the piano. I bet that was just what Katie's mama and daddy would do, long after I was gone. It was so unfair that daughters could die before their parents.

Facing Mrs. Kelly now, I suddenly found it possible to imagine her as that young woman in the picture. I felt awful for up to now only noticing the way she cut her meat and how strange and old she seemed. Once she'd had all these dreams of happiness ahead of her that hadn't quite worked out. I almost wished I wasn't here to get in her way. I almost wished I was back with the Aidens. Maybe leaving them had been a mistake.

I spent most of Saturday and Sunday just catching up for school since I could do nothing about Katie's list. Most of my homework made me want to cry with frustration—it was so confusing and difficult. But I read everything I was supposed to, even when the words made no sense at all. I didn't want to look dumb. I didn't want to *be* dumb, either.

A Separate Peace was a different story. Even though we were only supposed to read up to chapter nine, I finished the whole thing, reading late into the night on Sunday.

I couldn't put it down. It reminded me so much of my own life. In *Gone with the Wind* and other books I'd read, I'd seen little pieces of the characters that were just like me. But this book was so similar to my life, it was shocking. It was about this boy, Gene, who hurts his best friend, Finny. And then he feels terrible, but he can't take it back. And then later Finny dies. And Gene's whole life changes because of it.

Of course, I hadn't hurt Katie out of jealousy like Gene hurts Finny; it had been an accident. But just like Gene, I'd always felt Katie was a better person than me. Just like Gene, I had done her harm, even though I hadn't meant to. As with him, it was all my fault.

I'd finished the book with tears in my eyes, sad to see my pain mirrored in so many places—Mrs. Kelly, this book. It just went further to prove that God was really messing things up, if he was up there at all.

Monday morning, I found my locker and got it open, as I'd finally figured out how to do, with no problem. I gathered my supplies like a normal student who knew her p's and q's and headed toward class. I felt confident today. Partly because I was starting to get used to being here. I was realizing that in a place like this, I was just a drop in the well, and as long as I kept to myself, people would leave me alone. Only Joe made a point of saying hello to me in class every day. And the only student who seemed to dislike me was that Stacy, who, whenever I caught her eye, gave me a cold look. Maybe she was jealous over Joe being my partner before. Maybe they were in love or something. Didn't matter. Stacy James could go suck an egg for all I cared.

Mrs. Blackburn walked into the classroom, greeted us, and opened her book, talking about what had happened in the chapters and asking questions. The kids around me raised their hands but, even though I had lots of thoughts about everything she said, I was too shy to raise mine.

"How does Gene feel when Finny comes back to school after the accident?" she asked about fifteen minutes into the class.

Scared, I thought. *Scared and sad because it reminds him of how he hurt him.* A boy in the front of the room answered almost exactly the same way, and Mrs. Blackburn nodded and agreed.

"And why do you think Gene goes along with Finny's plan to train him for the Olympics?"

I felt a *whoosh* of air behind me.

"Stacy?"

"So he can be a successful athlete, like Finny used to be before he broke his leg." She sounded satisfied with her answer, but Mrs. Blackburn wrinkled her forehead, looking thoughtful. "Yes, *partly.* And?" She looked around the room, but all hands were down. "Glory?"

Uh-oh. I sat straight up. "Um . . ." Mrs. Blackburn stared at me very calmly, like I had all the time in the world to answer the question. But there was a lump in my throat. For a second my thoughts about Gene and Finny just blacked out. "Um . . ."

Then, blessedly, they came back to me. "He wants to be an athlete because Finny can't anymore."

Mrs. Blackburn nodded, urging me onward.

"Gene is trying to make it up to him." I paused, forgetting about my nervousness and remembering things that I understood all too well. "It isn't enough, of course. It's not the same as taking things back, but he just *can't* take things back, ever. So he makes it up to Finny the only way he can. By doing the things Finny would have wanted to do if he still could."

I swallowed. Mrs. Blackburn didn't say anything for a second, and I had a momentary vision of her telling me that was the silliest, wrongest answer she ever heard. Which would be all the worse for my feeling that I was somehow opening my heart for the whole class to see. But finally she smiled. "Very good, Glory. Very, very good."

Very, very good. It was the best compliment I'd ever gotten from a teacher. Well, especially since Reverend Clifton was the only one not related to me by blood I'd ever had before last week. He'd never said, "Very good, Glory," in my life. Much less, "Very, *very* good."

I flushed with pride. And raised my hand to answer three more questions before class was through.

I ended up walking behind Stacy James to science class, just because she happened to walk in front of me. It was funny, thinking how in the Kellys' minds, Stacy and I were fast friends. Mrs. Kelly had asked me about her several times, though by the weekend, at least, she seemed to be giving up. As anybody would when all they got for an answer was "Stacy? Oh, she's fine."

As we reached the classroom door, Stacy turned, noticed I was there, and gave me an undeniably snooty look. I just tilted up my chin and brushed past her and toward my desk. Even the classrooms were starting to seem familiar to me, and I'd created a routine: Go straight to the desk, sit down, and don't make eye contact.

Joe was in his usual place, talking and laughing with some of the other kids. I barely replied to his greeting as I slid into my seat and hoped for the lecture to go by fast.

Not surprisingly, it didn't. Mr. Tydings was giving some talk about a kind of bird I'd never heard of showing up on these islands he'd been talking about last week called the Galápagos. Now, I like hearing about faraway places, but somehow he was managing to make it terribly boring. Because he wasn't talking about the beautiful parts of the islands or what they were really like. He was talking about something complicated called a theory, which was basically an idea. I wished I was back in English class, absorbed in Gene and Finny.

"Can someone define *evolution* for me again?" he asked, his eyes roaming our desks.

Several hands went up, and Mr. Tydings pointed to a girl with short ginger-colored hair to the right.

"It means we came from apes, and apes came from other less-developed animals, and on and on to the smallest organisms."

Before I could take this in, Mr. Tydings bobbed his head from side to side. "Well, more or less. And where does natural selection fit into evolution? Glory?" *Oh, no.* "We haven't heard from you yet."

"Um." I went over the ginger-haired girl's words to help me think, but I knew I couldn't have heard her right. I'd thought she'd said, "We came from apes." I'd read a lot of confusing stuff over the weekend about apes and even remembered seeing the words *natural selection,* but it hadn't made a lick of sense to me.

"I'll give you a hint," Mr. Tydings continued, looking tired. "How exactly did man evolve? How did he come to be stronger, smarter than, say, a lizard or a monkey?"

I sighed. *All right.* This I knew. Or at least, I'd been told the answer, even if I wasn't sure I believed it.

"Um, God made it that way. Sir."

A roar burst out from all around me, and it took me a second or two to notice it was laughter. My heart sank into my feet.

Only two people in the whole class didn't seem to be in on the joke. Joe, to my left, was staring down at his hands seriously. And Mr. Tydings was frowning at me.

"This isn't a philosophical debate, Glory. Clearly I was speaking in scientific terms." Clearly? Clearly? He was looking at me like I'd meant to cause trouble (I knew that look well), but I had no idea what he was talking about. "Now, can you tell me the *scientific* definition of natural selection?"

"Um." I cast my mind back to the reading again. The remaining titters died around me as I struggled for an answer that simply wasn't in my brain. "Um . . ."

Riiiiiiiiiiiiiiiiiiiiiiiiiiiiiiiing! The bell. *Whew.* My shoulders collapsed as everyone jumped out of their seats and gathered their books. As I stood up, I kept my red face turned toward my notebook so nobody would see.

"You poor thing."

I looked up. Stacy James was walking beside me, eyeing me coolly.

"You're kind of slow, huh?"

"What?" I asked. I couldn't understand what she was saying.

"Well, I heard you saying you were thirteen, right?"

I nodded, confused. Why was Stacy talking to me? What did she mean, *slow?*

"And they held you back to the seventh grade? Maybe they didn't hold you back far enough. Maybe, you know, they should drop you down again, to sixth grade instead."

The smirk on her lips made my flesh crawl for some reason, and then the words sank in. *Oh. Oh.* It only took a second or two, but suddenly everything was in place. Why the kids in my classes seemed younger than me. Why Sherry had sounded sorry when she'd told me what grade I was going to be in. I wasn't supposed to be in this grade. I was too old for this grade. And I was still, by the looks of it, too dumb for this grade. It was all I could do to keep afloat in it.

Hurt and disappointment and embarrassment all roiled inside me. But I had enough control not to show that to Stacy. I met her eyes straight on. I'd never seen anybody be so mean while looking so calm. I opened my mouth to tell her . . . to tell her what? All I wanted to do was run and hide.

"Stacy, why do you have to be such a jerk?"

We both snapped around at the same instant to see Joe, walking a few inches behind us.

"You're just threatened by the pretty new girl. Last year it was Jess Schneider."

"Whatever, Joe. I am *not threatened* by her," Stacy replied as we stepped into the hall. She rolled her eyes, but underneath she looked wildly surprised and hurt. My own eyes swiveled back and forth between the two as I let myself be swept along at their pace. I couldn't believe they were arguing about me— Glory, the mostly invisible. It made my already frayed up nerves feel even more frayed.

"Stacy, I'm just saying, don't bother yourself over this one. Leave her alone. Just because she got held back . . ."

Don't *bother* yourself over *this one*? Held back? I clenched my teeth tight. Who did he think he was? Who did she think *she* was? Both of them talking about me as if I wasn't even standing here, as if I needed anybody to talk *for* me.

The two were already deep into a long stream of bickering when I thrust my hands between them and, unbelievably, shoved my palms against their shoulders. "Don't you—I mean *either* of you—*bother* yourselves over me. Just leave me alone!"

With that, I turned on my heel. If I hurried, I could make it to the bathroom before I burst into tears.

"Glory." It was Joe. He'd grabbed my elbow and was pulling me back to say something else.

I don't know what came over me at that moment. I don't remember planning to hurt Joe. Somewhere between the time he grabbed me and the time I'd turned around fully, I had my right foot cocked way back behind me. And then, before I could stop myself, I'd brought it forward—hard—against his left shin. The blow had all the force of the embarrassment and hurt and anger that were swirling inside me.

Seconds later I was at the far end of the hall at the main doors, heading away—from class, from school. As the doors crashed open against my weight into the spring sunshine, I didn't turn back to see if anybody wanted to stop me. I didn't turn back even to see if Joe was okay.

By the sound of his howls echoing down the hall, I figured that at least I already knew the right answer to *that* one.

That afternoon on the bus ride home, I was dread itself. As I sat in my usual seat, keeping to myself in my usual way, I watched the different neighborhoods roll by, watched the kids get off at stop after stop, and didn't find any comfort in the fact that at least this daily ride was becoming routine.

All I could think about, besides my guilt over kicking Joe, was having to face the Kellys. The school had probably called by now, and that meant I was already in big trouble. I'd hurt a student, and then I'd skipped all my afternoon classes and sat in a deserted corner of the school yard for hours, breaking apart twigs and leaves and waiting for the buses to come.

As I walked from the bus stop to the front door, I just kept on thinking, *She'll be so disappointed.* I'd already been feeling awkward with Mrs. Kelly ever since what happened with the piano. And the last thing I wanted was to talk now, about *this*. How could she ever allow me to go into Boston on my own if this was the Glory I let her see? A hot-tempered, mean-spirited one. What if she sent me away? I *was* a foster child, after all. That meant temporary, Sherry had explained at the center. The Kellys could get rid of me anytime they wanted, and Mrs. Kelly, surely, was the one in charge of that decision.

But when she came out of the morning room just as I entered, she didn't look disappointed at all. She was wearing her gardening gloves. Her straw hat sat askew over her white hair. She was bedraggled but smiling, and she looked kind of . . . cute. "Glory, can you come here for a second?"

I froze, dropping my bag by the stairs. *Uh-oh.*

"Yes, ma'am." I followed her back to the morning room, past Mr. Kelly. Surprisingly, he looked up from his reading and greeted me kindly. "Hey, Glory," he said, smiling what I could have sworn was a sympathetic smile.

"Um, hi, Mr. Kelly," I replied.

We wove through the kitchen, then out into the backyard. She finally stopped at a batch of rosebushes.

I'd never actually stood in the backyard before, though I'd seen it through the kitchen windows. It was small, filled with all sorts of lovely flowers, but I hadn't, up to now, felt comfortable coming out and exploring it.

Mrs. Kelly unraveled a magazine that, I noticed, she'd had rolled up under her arm.

"I'm just trying to pick out colors, dear, and I thought you might have an opinion."

Opinion?

"Now," she said, holding out the magazine before me. The pages she displayed were covered in photographs of roses—there were yellow, pink, and light purple—with tiny words scrolled beside them. "You can see I already have the red. They're called Don Juans. And the white ones are John F. Kennedys. Now, I'm wondering if I should get these"—she pointed to the picture of the lavender—"or these"—she pointed to the pink. "Which do you think would go better?"

"You mean, you're going to buy some from this?" I sputtered.

Mrs. Kelly looked confused. "Yes, to order. From the catalog."

"Oh. Well, um," I stalled, trying to let the idea sink in. "But Mrs. Kelly?"

"Hmmm?" She seemed distracted, peering down at the pages. I was tempted to let her stay that way, uninterested. But I couldn't. She'd find out sooner or later, and it was better if I told her right out. "I have to tell you something."

"Yes?" She turned her full attention on me now. I bit my lip. "Today . . . at school—"

"I know," she broke in gently, "the school called." I gazed at her, wide-eyed. She wasn't grinning anymore, but then, she didn't seem mad.

"Aren't you sore at me?"

She pursed her lips, looking torn, then shook her head slightly. "No," she said, though it seemed to me more that she was just afraid to admit she was. "Not that I want you to do it again," she added quickly. "You'll never do it again, will you?"

Amazed, I nodded eagerly. No, I'd never, ever do it again, no matter what.

"That's what I thought. I know you're a good girl." The smile smoothed its way back onto her face. "Now, how about these flowers?"

That was it? That was all?

"It was just that it was a bad day," I offered. I don't know why.

Mrs. Kelly met my eyes again. "Yes, I thought so. Actually, I was a little ruffled at first, I have to admit. But Jim said it must be something like that. We both feel for you, you know. It must be hard, adjusting. . . ."

Wow. Had he really? Was that why Mr. Kelly had made such a point of greeting me so nicely—because he "felt" for me? We stood there a few seconds more, and it seemed like Mrs. Kelly was waiting for me to continue. Instead it was I who now turned my attention to the "catalog."

"Surely you'd rather decide yourself on these flowers. I mean, it's *your* garden and all."

Mrs. Kelly lowered the magazine, or catalog, to her waist. "Tara's garden," she said with a soft smile. "My daughter picked out these flowers."

"Oh." I looked at my feet.

"It's okay. I know I overreacted the other day, with the piano. And I'm sorry about that. We can talk about her. You don't have to feel bad."

I felt myself blush at the mention of the piano incident, but I noticed she was still smiling. I couldn't imagine why, when it was all so unfair. I imagined her as a young woman. I'd been imagining that a lot lately, since seeing that photo. It made her seem more like a real person. And it made me feel worse and worse for her. "I just thought, well, it'd be nice to have some new life given to this garden. Life has to go on, you know."

I didn't know what to say. I didn't see how she could be so

calm and peaceful about something so horrible. I did know one thing. Life *wouldn't* go on much further. At least not for me. And I could never act that way about losing Katie. Even if I lived to be a hundred.

Still, I wanted to do what Mrs. Kelly wanted. Without a word, I gently took the catalog from her hands and surveyed the flowers she had pointed out. The pink photo had a line of type beside it proclaiming its name—Diana. How strange to have these kind of names for flowers. The lavender one was called Blue Girl.

I stared and stared, distracted. Funny, but I didn't feel completely relieved about not being in trouble.

You know how sometimes you have a bad thought, and it makes you feel all dark inside, and then you forget what the thought was, but you still can't shake that feeling something is *wrong?*

That's what I felt right then, about the Kellys being so kind and understanding. And truly, I had no idea why.

Maybe it was just the general sadness of Mrs. Kelly's daughter and my broken-up life and the image of running away from Joe this afternoon.

"Well, I guess this one," I said, pointing to the lavender. Blue Girl. Whenever Mrs. Johansen wasn't feeling well, she would tell me she was just a little "blue" that day. Like how I felt all the time now.

It seemed only right.

CHAPTER
SIX

I walked into school with a slab of ice in my stomach, hoping I wouldn't see Joe in the halls but also wishing I would. I hoped that if I did see him, he'd give me that same quick smile he gave me every morning and let me know he'd forgiven me for what happened yesterday. But as I scanned the halls before English class, I didn't spot him at all. I'd have to live with this nervousness through at least another hour.

All night I'd lain awake with these visions of how our conversation would go. We'd both be in class before everybody else, so there'd be time to talk in private. I'd say how sorry I was for kicking him, how I'd got carried away. And I'd say very graciously that even though I didn't need him to fight my battles, I would forgive him if he would forgive me.

Then I'd decided to change that part. I'd imagined just saying, "I'm sorry," very quiet and dignified, looking him right in the eyes. And he would say it was no problem, and then he would congratulate me in that joking manner of his on being such a good kicker (even though he'd say it didn't hurt). And he'd ask me if I'd want to play kick ball sometime—this game some of the kids played in the field out back of the school. Then after that he would say something about me being pretty. The visions went on and on and kept me awake for hours.

But as I walked into life science, which was already crowded and noisy, and saw him sitting there and staring at his desk, I realized how foolish I had been. I wasn't even going to be able to look him in the eye, much less say something dignified. I was hardly going to be able to say hello.

I didn't glance in his direction as I sank into my seat. When I finally did, he was looking straight ahead. Had he even noticed me come in? Did he care? I waited and waited, but I couldn't get up the nerve to say his name and get his attention. Finally Mr. Tydings walked in and began his lecture.

The class was agony. I picked at the skin on my fingers. I wiggled my toes, restless. Not once did I sense Joe looking in my direction, though I looked in his about twenty times. When the bell finally rang, he started talking to another boy and shuffled toward the door, with me shuffling behind him. Finally the boy went on ahead, and I caught up to Joe in the hallway just outside the door.

At that moment he turned slightly and met my eyes—just for a second. And I knew it. He had not even the hint of a smile on his face. He hated me.

I had my mouth open, but my voice just caught in my throat. Joe looked away and kept walking on without me. He'd definitely seen me. He'd definitely noticed me standing there, trying to talk.

That's okay, I told myself, my eyes glued to his back as he walked away and my throat tightening up. He wasn't worth getting upset about. I didn't even know him.

It was a good thing I didn't care about stuff like this.

It was a good thing it didn't matter.

Over the next few weeks I threw myself into my school-work. I tried to get better in the classes I was bad at (life science, social studies, geography, elementary algebra) and do well in the ones I was already okay in (English, art).

It wasn't that I cared so much about getting the good grades everybody was always carrying on about, considering I was never going to need them for things like college (which did sound nice) and the future. And especially considering school wasn't the reason I was here—my Katie list was.

But I did want to at least pass the seventh grade, especially now that I knew I'd been put in a young class and that other kids like Stacy, and probably Joe, thought I was dumb. Since I had no choice but to go to school, anyway, and I hadn't yet convinced the Kellys to let me go into the city, I figured I might as well make the effort to prove Joe and Stacy and the others wrong.

If Joe still knew I existed, though, he didn't show it. In the days after I kicked him, I tried again to apologize lots of times, but either I'd lose my nerve or he'd turn away before I had the chance. He never again looked at me from his desk and smiled. He didn't offer me a pen when I made a big show of fiddling with mine or offer to be partners again. And though I felt terribly guilty, it didn't take long for me to give up trying to make it up. I was never very good at apologies.

Like I'd told myself before, it didn't really matter. But still, I felt this little kernel of sadness whenever I saw him. I guess a small part of me missed his friendliness. Now more than ever, it seemed a boon compared to all the indifference surrounding me.

People in general appeared to have stopped noticing me altogether. Kids who had tossed me half smiles or a few words during my first few days—like the redheaded girl on the bus, for instance—hardly looked my way anymore. Students who'd chuckled at me and my accent forgot to find me funny.

It was like I'd managed to make a soap bubble around myself. And I guess that was a relief; it was exactly what I'd wanted to do. But it hurt a little, too. I couldn't shake the feeling I was losing. Like when you are upstairs in bed and the grown-ups are downstairs, laughing over something you can't hear. The kids at school talked and joked and even argued with each other, but I could tell they had all forgotten to see *me* anymore at all.

Everybody except Stacy, that is. The kind of attention she had given me before, I now realized, had been nothing but her normal rude old personality. Now, after what had happened with Joe, she acted mean as a cat. She started giving me nasty looks in the hallways. She whispered to her friends about me to make them chuckle, and they all flaunted the fact that they were chuckling about me.

That would never have happened in school back home. No grown-up would ever have stood for young folks being so awful to each other. And no young person would have bothered with such a grudge since we all had to see each other every day of our lives. But this school was so big, nobody seemed to notice.

It was especially bad in English class. Stacy raised her hand to argue against everything I ever said. If I mentioned that I liked a certain character, she argued why that same character wasn't worth spit (well, not in those words). If I said a certain paragraph was hard to understand, she said it was easy and then explained the whole thing like I was a big mush-for-brains. And when Mrs. Blackburn paid me a compliment, she stewed and steamed and muttered little insults at my back.

One morning Mrs. Blackburn asked us both to stay after class, along with another boy who was always raising his hand. I bubbled with bitter triumph. Was Stacy gonna be punished for being so mean? I'd been thinking Mrs. Blackburn hadn't caught on. Of course she had.

"Glory, Stacy, Julian . . ." Mrs. Blackburn opened her shoulder bag and pulled out three identical books. "Since you three are so especially enthusiastic, I thought you might be open to doing some special reading. This would be on top of what you already do for class." She handed us each a book, and I examined the cover. It said *The Old Man and the Sea.*

Stacy was beaming, and I couldn't understand why. Were we being punished?

"Ma'am," I ventured, at the risk of looking ignorant—but I had to know. "Are we in trouble?"

Before Mrs. Blackburn could answer, Stacy hooked a thumb at me. "Are you sure you want *Glory* to do this? Don't you think maybe it's a bit . . . well, um . . . advanced for her?"

Mrs. Blackburn frowned, annoyed. "No, Stacy, I don't think it's too advanced for her. Glory," she continued, turning her attention to me, "it's not a punishment. It means I think you're doing very well and that you can handle doing more. I won't be testing you on the books for special reading. I'd just like for us to discuss them." She swiveled her eyes from me to Julian to Stacy. "Are you all right with that?"

"Yes, Mrs. Blackburn," they both said.

"Good. And Stacy," she said, turning to her directly, "let's not get carried away with debate, all right? I do appreciate your enthusiasm, but remember, we're all friends here."

Stacy turned a shade of pink and nodded. "Okay, Mrs. Blackburn."

*   *   *

I was over the moon on the bus ride home. I sat dazed, staring out the window and playing stories over and over in my head. I imagined Stacy and Mrs. Blackburn and that boy Julian and me having our own little discussion about our special advanced book, and Stacy making some really dumb answer and then getting really embarrassed when I gave a good one. I imagined Mrs. Blackburn announcing to the class that I was her star reader and giving me a prize, like a cake she'd made or a special bookmark.

When the bus pulled up at the corner of Baker Street, I bounced out and almost ran up the block to the Kellys'. I couldn't wait to tell Mrs. Kelly. If this didn't convince her I was an upstanding foster daughter, I didn't know what would.

On my way in through the front door, I stooped toward the little stone troll that stood in the garden and patted him on the head.

Mrs. Kelly's voice was coming from the kitchen—she was on the phone. I hurried into the morning room, slid into a seat, and dumped my knapsack. I watched her standing there, her thin hands resting on the counter, her fluffy white head pressing the phone against her ear.

"That was Sherry," she finally said, putting down the receiver with a *click*. "Just checking in. She's going to stop by and see us on Sunday. I told her how you've been helping me with the garden. And how we're getting to be such good friends and how I hope you'll be with us for a good long time."

She reached forward and patted my cheek. Surprised by this little act and her words, I stayed perfectly still.

"Do you have some good news, dear?" she asked, sensing my unease and pulling her hand away but smiling. She backed up and picked up a pitcher of lemonade, pouring me a glass and setting it on the table. "You certainly came in here like a whirling dervish."

I tried to reply—to summon up the energy I'd had just seconds before—but my voice caught in my throat. *Good friends. Here for a good long time.* I saw the way she was looking at me, all trusting and hopeful. Exactly how I wanted and needed her to be. And I saw everything else with perfect clearness.

Here I was, intent on winning her over so that she'd give me what I wanted—permission to go off on my own into the city. And here *she* was, only wanting me to be happy, with nothing in it for her. And I was going to die on her.

"Yes, ma'am. I mean, well . . ." I closed both hands around the lemonade but didn't take a drink. I just stared into the cloudy yellow liquid while something dark and murky and thick and heavy gnawed at my guts.

"No." I said it in a flat tone and watched her deflate before my eyes. "Nothing to tell." I couldn't bring myself to drink the lemonade she had poured. "Sorry, I'm not thirsty. Thank you." Stiff as a board, I stood up and grabbed my knapsack. Then I turned and headed for the stairs.

* * *

Up in my room, I went straight for the window. I swiveled the lock and pushed it open, then leaned forward and looked around to make sure the street was empty. Then I hoisted one leg over the sill, followed by the other. I held on to the wooden frame as I scooped the rest of my body forward and stood up on the landing that was actually the roof of the parlor below. *Phew.* It was higher than I'd expected. I felt breathless and dizzy.

My room was shaped so that part of it curved back a little on either side. Now I scrooched out to the side where I'd be most hidden from view, to a nook where I could look out the window at the tilting roof of their house. Gosh, it was high. My heart was racing. I felt a moment of fear that Mrs. Kelly would come upstairs and find me here, but then, she'd never come in my room without knocking. I'd listen for her.

Relieved by this notion, I settled into my spot and did what I'd come here to do. Think.

My joy over being picked for the special reading group had all but vanished. I'd gotten Mrs. Kelly to care for me, had been *working* at it constantly. And all that time I'd known. I'd known how wrong it was. I was going to leave the Kellys, just like their daughter had. Up till now, I hadn't really thought about what that meant. Hadn't *let* myself think was more like it. I hadn't let myself think that they didn't deserve the hurt, much less that they'd been hurt too much already. I'd been so, so selfish. And this when I was thinking I was being selfless for Katie.

It wasn't that I thought the Kellys loved me or anything like that. But before the Aidens, I would have thought that was impossible, and now I wasn't so sure. My mind flashed back to a few minutes ago and the pleased look on Mrs. Kelly's face when she noticed I had good news.

The fact was, as much as I needed them to shelter and feed me and needed to prove I was worthy of their trust where Boston was concerned, I couldn't rightly make myself a place in the Kellys' hearts. It wasn't fair. It wasn't right. I'd have to stop letting it happen.

I'd had my face buried in my hands for the past few minutes, and now I looked up, disoriented. I'd almost forgotten I was still on the roof, so absorbed was I in thought. I sighed and leaned back till I was lying flat and facing the sky.

I used to feel like looking at the sky was looking at God. But the only thing I saw up there now was the clouds.

Floating by, they didn't seem to notice me.

CHAPTER SEVEN

What I am about to tell you is the full, honest-to-goodness truth. It's about how everything changed between me and Joe. But first things first. If I'm gonna talk about the day it happened, I've also got to tell you what it was like going to my first modern doctor.

That Sunday, Sherry came and went, asking me a whole mess of questions. It wasn't the same as before. She felt strange to me now, having been out of my life for so long, though she was as nice as could be. She stayed a half hour or so, asked me—in private—if I was happy with the Kellys and what I was learning in school. I gave her a bunch of normal answers—said that I liked the kids and that my classes were hard, but I was doing okay—and that seemed to satisfy her. Then she left.

The only big thing that came of her visit was that afterward, Mrs. Kelly started talking to Mr. Kelly about taking me to the doctor for a "checkup." Mr. Kelly was his usual easygoing self about it, which meant either he didn't *care* or he didn't *mind.* That was pretty much as far as I'd ever been able to pin him down, anyhow. Living with him longer and longer didn't make him any easier to read.

I don't know if the two had anything to do with each other—if Sherry and the Kellys had talked about my health. But despite my reassuring her that I felt fine and didn't need to see a doctor, off we went that Friday morning for my appointment, missing my first couple of classes.

I fretted about it at first, remembering Reverend Clifton's last words to me after I drank the poison. He'd said I wasn't supposed to seek help from modern doctors. He'd said they wouldn't be able to help even if I did.

But when I considered it, Dogwood and its rules were miles and miles away. And it wasn't me who was doing the seeking, it was Mrs. Kelly, so I didn't have much choice. And then, really, what could they do to punish me any more than they had already?

Of course, that didn't make me any less nervous as we drove to the doctor's office that morning.

Mrs. Kelly and I waited in a small room until a lady came out and got us. She led us through a couple of doors, into a smaller room with a shiny metal table to one side, and handed me a bundle of papery cloth.

"Just change into this," she said. "With the opening in the front. You can keep your underwear on. The doctor will be in to see you in a few minutes."

When she closed the door behind her, I shook out the bundle and saw it was a kind of robe. Then I looked at Mrs. Kelly.

"I'll wait outside, dear."

She shuffled through the door and closed it behind her, leaving me standing stiffly, the robe draped in my arms.

I sighed, then started undressing. In the white lights of the room my body looked even paler. I glanced down at my naked, sticklike arms, my knobby knees. Then I quickly yanked the robe around me and pulled the edges tightly together and tied them. I blushed at the thought of the doctor seeing my body. Not that I had anything to be modest about—I was as straight and flat as a boy. But back home, we'd never had to undress for a doctor's visit.

I could hear voices outside the door and recognized one of them as Mrs. Kelly's. In another moment the door opened. A woman entered and shut it behind her.

"Hi, Glory, I'm Dr. Filkin. How are you feeling today?"

"Fine," I muttered. A woman doctor? She had a file folder in her arms, and now she laid it on the counter beside her.

"Good. Well, let's get started here."

She pulled a gadget down around her neck, sticking parts of it in her ears, and put one hand on my back. With the other she slid a metal circle onto my chest, just inside the crack in my robe. I shivered, partly because the metal was cold and partly because of how nervous I was having someone touching me in such a private place.

"Sorry about that," she said, staring off as she moved the gadget around against my skin, concentrating. When she was finished, she squinted at me. "Glory, are you a little anxious right now?"

I gulped, then nodded.

"Yes, your heart's beating pretty quickly," she said. "But otherwise everything sounds fine."

I blinked, wondering what that meant. What had she heard inside me? She'd actually been able to listen to my *heart* beat? I couldn't help wondering if somehow that tool could also let her hear the poison flowing around my body. But no, she'd said it all "sounds fine."

She asked me some more questions then, about what I ate, and if I got tired a lot, and even if I was happy. She mentioned my foster mother was worried about my weight and my "energy levels." She made me stand on some contraption that told her how many pounds I weighed, then stuck something in my ear, which she said was measuring my temperature, even though it looked nothing like the thermometer Dr. Venable had back home, which he always put in our mouths.

I kept telling her that I felt fine, that I was fine, although deep down a part of me longed for her to discover otherwise. To find the poison and then know how to cure it.

"Okay, well, I'm going to have Patti take some blood to screen you for a few different things," she finally said, picking up her notebook and scribbling something with a pen. "You may be anemic. But other than that, I don't think there's anything wrong with you. Though you should probably start taking multivitamins."

I guess she saw the puzzlement on my face because she added, "It's your iron levels—you need a certain amount of iron in your blood to be healthy. I'll write it down for your foster mother. And really, you probably need to eat a little better, a little more. All right, Glory?"

I nodded, and I meant to take her advice. It was nice to be fussed over by someone who seemed to know so much about being healthy, even though I knew it wouldn't do much good. She hadn't found the poison, and it wouldn't show up in my blood, either. That wasn't how it worked. I was going to die, and this kind, smart doctor would never have any idea why.

As Mrs. Kelly and I zoomed along from the doctor's office to the school, I pondered over my visit. Before we left, the nurse, Patti, had put a needle in my arm and sucked out a few glass vials of blood right before my eyes. I wondered how they planned to use that blood to tell what was going on inside me. I wondered if the Reverend knew they could use blood like that. It seemed that if modern doctors could look at your blood and tell what was ailing you, they'd be powerful enough to fix whatever it was. Maybe the folks at home just didn't know about it. Maybe Dr. Filkin could help me after all.

That's what was on my mind when I walked into the cafeteria

at lunch—the possibility of hoping that I might not die and what that would mean. But then I reasoned with myself, The poison inside me was something so old, handed down from our ancestors and made from Lord knows what. How would modern doctors even recognize it? Would I even want to live if I could? It wasn't worth thinking about. I told myself I was just getting worked up for no reason. It wasn't going to happen. I wasn't going to be cured.

The lunchroom was louder than ever. Monday was going to be a day off, and the excitement over it was making everyone extra rambunctious.

On June 18, still more than a month away—though you couldn't tell by all the talk about it—school would let out, which for most kids meant a break until next year, when they'd start again. For me it meant that school might be over forever. And while that sounded heavenly to me, I didn't like to see things end. It made me see how quickly time was barreling past. And it made me feel like everything was good-byes—good-bye, classroom, good-bye, locker. But even though it all made me miserable, it meant I was still alive.

I'd decided to treat myself to a full lunch to celebrate getting through the doctor's visit. Anyway, I had lots of money and nothing to do with it since I'd had no luck getting into Boston yet. If it didn't happen soon, like by the end of school, maybe I'd have to run away. Maybe that'd be better for everyone, anyway.

I filled my tray with food—a hamburger, french fries, soda pop. Even something called lemon meringue pie. I paid the man at the register eagerly (I was starving) and headed toward the teachers' table, where I still sat every day.

As I walked, I looked out of the corner of my eye at Joe's table. He was sitting with his regular bunch of friends. Three girls, including Stacy James, were gathered behind the boys; Stacy was leaning over the shoulder of the one next to Joe, laughing. I picked up my pace. It was so annoying the way they all talked and laughed like that all the time.

I guess I didn't realize I was staring, but suddenly I was surprised to see Joe looking back at me with an expression of curiosity. I jerked my eyes away and . . .

Whoosh! All at once my left foot went sliding forward on something slick and wet. My body pitched sideways, then forward, trying to right itself. And it did . . . but the tray was another story. It went teetering, then tumbled. It happened in a split second, but I could see it so clearly, slipping off my fingertips, tumbling so that it was upside down as it hurtled the last inches to the floor.

The first sound was a *sploosh.* I guessed that was the pie. And then a thunder of laughter. Laughter so loud, I couldn't tell at first what it was. I was too occupied, anyway, by the feeling of cold wetness across my chest—the pop. It had fallen backward, onto me, and I looked down to see a big wet patch on my nice white shirt.

It seemed every single person in the cafeteria had seen it happen, even though I knew that was impossible. I couldn't move. I just gazed at the laughing faces, stunned. I'd never known a feeling quite so cold and burning hot at the same time. And then it sank in.

I was never coming back here. Never, ever, ever. This . . . this was too much. Too humiliating. The last straw. Tears trembled on my eyelids. *Please, please don't let me cry. Not now.*

I hardly noticed that someone had come up next to me until he spoke.

"I hate the food, too," he said loudly. He was holding a tray, still full of his half-eaten lunch—which included an untouched lemon meringue pie. "This stuff's disgusting."

What happened then was so odd that I truly did not believe my eyes. With both arms, Joe held his tray out at arm's length in front of him. Then, cool as you please, he tipped it right over. The laughter around us went still. The tray upended in the air and landed beside mine.

With everyone in the cafeteria suddenly silent, this *sploosh* sounded extra loud.

"Don't worry," Joe whispered. We were standing in the principal's office. I figured that was somebody you went to see when you were being punished. I pictured a person like the Reverend—all angry and sour looking and with a mole, and hair coming out of his ears. So you can imagine how surprised I was when—before I could answer or even look at Joe—a tall, skinny, very calm woman came out and introduced herself.

"I'm Ms. Delaney. Hello, Joe. Nice to meet you, Glory. Though it's too bad it's under these circumstances."

"Nice to meet you, ma'am," I muttered. I felt guilty, and I didn't know why. She looked back at me sternly.

"Glory, can you explain what happened in the lunchroom? You two seem to have caused quite a stir."

I gulped. What *had* happened? I searched for the words, but before I could find them, Joe blurted:

"It wasn't Glory's fault. She just had an accident. But then I got carried away and—"

"No, that's not—" I went to interrupt, but Joe continued. I swallowed my voice, not knowing what I wanted to say, anyway.

"I thought it was funny. I guess I was just trying to make a joke. You know, about the food. You know?"

No. No. I *knew* that wasn't true. One minute I'd been so embarrassed and ashamed and feeling terrible. And the next minute I'd forgotten all about it. And so had everybody else. Because of Joe.

"Ma'am, it wasn't like that. You see, I think Joe was—"

"Yes, it was like that." Joe gave me a look that said, Be quiet.

"No, it wasn't." I squinted at him.

He squinted back. "Yes, it *was*." Gosh, he was being annoying.

Did he think I couldn't tell my own story? Did he think I needed him to get in trouble for me?

"Listen . . ." I began, clenching my fists.

"Enough!" Principal Delaney held one hand up toward Joe in a "stop" motion. "Joe, let Glory finish. I asked *her* the question, not you."

I cast a triumphant look in Joe's direction. "Ma'am, it was my fault. I . . . I *made* Joe do it." Do what? I just didn't want him to get in trouble. But the truth—at least, what I thought was the truth—was so strange and far-fetched that I . . .

But now it was my turn to get Principal Delaney's "stop" hand.

"I get it," she said calmly. "You're trying to protect each other. Fine. But it gives me no choice but to punish you both. Detention for three afternoons, after school, starting Tuesday. I'll have the office put in a call to your parents. . . ."

Detention? What *was* detention? It sounded terrible. I hoped it didn't involve getting whupped. And then the other words sank in. Call my parents? Meaning my foster parents? Meaning the folks whose trust I was trying so hard to win so I could finish the list for Katie?

I'd explain to them. They'd have to believe me. They'd have to.

After Ms. Delaney gave us a few more parting words that were very stern, Joe and I made our way out into the hall in silence. There were still a few minutes before the bell rang, so we dragged our feet. Finally we both spoke at the same time.

"Why—"

"Sor—"

Joe closed his mouth to let me speak.

"Why did you . . . ?" I asked.

Joe shrugged, stuck his hands in his pockets. He looked uneasy. "I dunno. I just, well, I didn't think she'd believe. . . ."

I nodded, even though that hadn't been the "why" I was asking.

"I'm sorry, Glory," Joe continued. "I didn't mean to get you in trouble, too. I guess I should just give up, huh?"

I swallowed. "Give up what?"

Joe gave me a long look. "On us being friends. Seems I just get you more and more ticked off."

"No," I exhaled without meaning to. He'd said "friends." "No," I continued, more sure. "*I'm* sorry. I mean, thank you. I mean"—I looked him straight in the face now—"I'm real, real sorry I kicked you."

Joe shrugged again, thoughtfully. His dark hair glinted in the lights of the hall. "Yeah, I was mad at you. But I guess I'm over it. I guess I can understand."

"What do you mean, understand?" I asked. "I kicked you. Hard. It was so . . . mean."

Joe stopped and smiled. "I told you. I know what it's like to be new. I guess I understand why you feel so . . . prickly."

I let out a little apologetic laugh. *Prickly* was maybe a good way to put it, like a porcupine. "Yeah."

We didn't say another word until we'd made it to the locker hall. All sorts of thoughts and questions swirled around in my head, fighting to be said. But one rose above all the others.

"Joe, um . . . why are you being so nice to me?"

It wasn't the first time I'd asked the question. Since I'd come to the outside, there'd been people who'd been much nicer than they needed to be. And there'd been some who'd been much meaner, too. I was starting to learn it was just a big, mixed-up world and there was no telling who'd do what. But still, I wanted to know *why*.

Joe surprised me by laughing. He looked shy for a minute, which seemed out of place on him somehow, like a shirt that didn't fit. Then finally he spoke up. "I think you're interesting. And like I said before, you're the pretty new girl."

I sucked in air as he chucked me on the arm, like we were old pals, then turned on his heel and headed down the hall. "See ya," he threw back over his shoulder.

It was good he didn't turn around, because my face must have been crimson. Had I heard him right? Was he teasing?

Shaking my head, I turned and headed for my locker. It didn't even matter if I was pretty or not. He'd said he wanted to be friends. *Friends.*

I decided to ignore the fact that I'd already decided I didn't want any of those.

CHAPTER EIGHT

Riiing.

I glanced up at the sound of the phone, then heard footsteps tapping along through the kitchen.

"Glory," came Mr. Kelly's voice, floating up the stairs. "It's for you."

I'd been lying on my bed, reading *Watership Down* for our second book discussion next week. The first one hadn't gone quite as I'd pictured, with me the star of the group. But it had gone well—we all pitched in ideas at lunchtime, and Mrs. Blackburn gave us her thoughts. Stacy had been as snooty as usual, but I hadn't let her bother me, and I was looking forward to the second meeting.

Now I hurried to my door and cracked it open.

"For me?"

"Yep."

Mr. Kelly sounded unconcerned, but you could have knocked *me* over with a feather. Who on earth was calling me?

"Are you sure?" I said, stepping out onto the landing and taking a couple of steps down the stairs. But apparently Mr. Kelly hadn't heard because there was no answer.

I walked down into the hall, feeling out of sorts. I'd gotten used to people talking on the phone. I'd even gotten all right with doing it myself when customers called The Rock Shop when I'd worked for Becky. But a call *for me?*

As I padded through the kitchen, I noticed Mr. Kelly was rumpled and a little dirty. He'd been out cutting the lawn with a big machine called a lawn mower.

He was standing there, holding the phone out to me. I was relieved to see he wasn't wearing an angry expression. He and Mrs. Kelly had been pretty upset when they'd heard about the detention. They hadn't yelled or anything, but they'd said they were awfully disappointed. Still, we'd talked about it. I'd even told them what had happened—very logically, not in a way to win them over or anything. And Mr. Kelly had actually—believe it or not—broken out into a chuckle at the part where Joe said the food was disgusting.

"It's a boy," he now murmured, letting out a little amused smile. My heart stood still. It couldn't be. It couldn't.

I walked the last few feet into the kitchen and took the telephone from him, then waited till he walked back outside. "Hello?"

"Glory." It was. It was Joe.

"How . . . ?" I couldn't finish.

"Got your number from the office. I hope you don't mind."

"No," I managed to blurt. "I don't mind." I was getting that hot-and-cold feeling again.

"Well, my mom said it was the proper thing to do—to call, I mean. I wanted to know if you wanted to hang out Monday, to celebrate the day off. My mom said I should call you at home and ask so you can ask your parents."

"Hang out?"

"Yeah, you know. I thought we could do something fun for the day off. And you said we could be friends, remember?"

I detected the teasing note in Joe's voice, and it made this embarrassed smile jump to my lips. I didn't think I'd said anything of the kind.

"We could meet up with my friends at the park and play Frisbee. We could get some people together over at my house—"

Finally I gathered my brains up enough to think clearly. My nerves tingled with urgency. And before Joe could finish his suggestion, I interrupted. I tried to sound careless.

"Well. Um. If we, um . . . *hang out* . . . could it be in the city? Could we hang out in Boston?"

There were lots of rules. Joe's mom had to talk to the Kellys first. Joe had to come over so the Kellys could meet him. (Of course, he looked a bit taken aback when he saw them, but he didn't ask any questions.) He must have apologized twenty times for getting me into detention, swearing up and down it was all his fault and sounding like a true gentleman the whole time. Somebody had to drive us (Mr. Kelly actually offered, surprising me, but

Mrs. Trew—Joe's mama—worked in Boston and had to go in for a morning meeting, so it was easier for her). But we managed it all. And before I knew it, I was in Mrs. Trew's car, with ten extra dollars that Mrs. Kelly had slipped to me at the last minute (on top of what I already had, that was twenty dollars), and headed back into the city. Feeling a little dizzy and tired but all the more determined for that. Today I was going to get things done.

We pulled into a parking spot inside a building just for cars, and Mrs. Trew began leading us toward an elevator. She was a tall, slender woman. Her dark hair, glossy like her son's, was pulled into a tight knot at the back of her head, and she wore dark purplish lipstick. I wondered if Daddy would have called her a Jezebel because of that. I hoped not. From my point of view, she was lovely. The way she held her head up high, the way she walked—like she was important. I wished I could be like her.

"Here's my building," she said, pointing to a set of metal doors. I'd seen the type before—at the shopping mall and other places—but didn't know what they were all about. "We have an entrance directly from the garage. There's the exit to the street." She pressed a button beside the door as she nodded toward a wide arch that led outside. "Do you two want to come up for a few minutes?"

"You wanna see where she works, Glory?" Joe asked. For some reason, looking at him made me feel blushy inside. I wondered if I looked nice enough. I was wearing slacks and a short-sleeved white shirt. I'd let my hair down loose for once.

"Um, all right." I thought about all the things I wanted to get done today. I knew we didn't have much time. But a few minutes couldn't hurt, right?

Suddenly the metal doors slid open with a hiss. I tried not to show my alarm as Joe and his mom stepped into the tiny, windowless room and waited for me to follow. When we were all in, the doors closed behind us.

Whoosh. My stomach fell to my feet as suddenly I could tell we were moving up, up, up. Oh, my. We were on an elevator.

A moment later we jarred to a stop. The doors hissed open again.

We stepped out into a hallway filled with bright lights and lots of people dressed extra nice. A few of them waved to us or said hello as we followed Mrs. Trew down to the end, turned right, then turned left through a doorway. *Joanna Trew,* a little plate said beside the door. And then, oh my gosh.

The window stretched from the floor to the ceiling. I ran to it, past a desk that took up most of the room. Oh my gosh. Oh my gosh.

The ground seemed to be a mile below us. People scurried to and fro, but they didn't even look real. The buildings, the ones that were much lower, looked like houses for dolls.

"We're in a . . ." I breathed. "A . . ."

Joe had come up beside me and was eyeing me curiously.

". . . skyscraper?"

Joe laughed. "Seventy-third floor. Cool, huh?"

My eyes stayed glued on the view. "Cool," I repeated.

"You've never been in a skyscraper, Glory?" Mrs. Trew piped up from behind us over the sound of shuffling papers. I turned.

"No, ma'am." That was an okay answer, right? Skyscrapers were only in cities, so lots of people had probably never been in one.

"What part of the South are you from?"

I shuffled my feet, not sure what to say. Joe, too, was looking at me expectantly.

"Just a tiny town," I said truthfully. "I'm sure you haven't heard of it."

"Well, it takes a little getting used to, working up this high. But now I don't even notice it." Then she added, smiling, "Actually, I still notice the sunsets. They're beautiful."

Sunsets. Gosh, they must be. I stood for a few more seconds, staring out into the unbelievable world while Mrs. Trew picked up her telephone and tapped at the buttons. More than ever before—more, even, than the moment I'd arrived on the bus— I suddenly felt like I was truly in Boston. The city was all laid out here, at my feet, the way it should have always been. I thrilled at the knowledge that I could mentally check off the skyscraper part of my list. I tried to imagine Katie here beside me, enjoying it, too. But I was distracted by Joe's breathing, which was forming a circle of white mist on the window right next to me.

I tried to focus. *Katie. Katie, I'm doing it. For real this time. Aren't you happy?* Joe drew a smiley face on the clouded glass.

We made our way out of the office, back onto the elevator, and down to the bottom floor, which let us out onto the street.

"What's your mama's job?" I asked, curious about how important she'd sounded talking on the phone and all the important-looking stuff on her desk.

"Um, she's kind of an executive. She's the boss of a bunch of people," he said matter-of-factly. "They're financial analysts."

Financial. Analysts. It was gobbledygook to me, except for the boss-of-a-lot-of-people part. "She . . . is she the boss of men and women both?" I asked.

"Sure." Joe shrugged indifferently.

Gosh. And I'd thought Becky had been amazing with her own shop. I'd never heard of a woman bossing men. At home, it was always understood that men were the bosses (even if sometimes the women secretly ran things). I had never imagined a woman being quite as powerful as Mrs. Trew seemed to be. With her very own office in the sky and men she could boss.

"So, where to?" Joe asked. "It's your day." We'd stepped out onto the concrete walkway in front of the building. I leaned my head back and looked up, wondering what window we'd been standing in. Then I looked at Joe. Even if it hadn't been my day, I would have made it so.

"Which floor were we on?" I asked him.

He grinned. "The top," he replied. "The seventy-third floor."

Wow, it really was my day. I'd done it—I'd gone to the top of a skyscraper! "The swan boats," I said, bubbling over with excitement. "Let's go ride the swan boats."

Joe grinned. "Sounds good to me. Since you're the new girl"— he raised his chin in exaggerated pride—"I'll lead the way."

The whole city appeared to have changed in some invisible way. The streets seemed more inviting and familiar. The people seemed less foreign. Everything was more comfortable. It was so different, having spent those first days here by myself, sleeping in a train yard, to be walking through the city, a girl with a house to go to at night and a . . . friend . . . walking by her side. I did see a couple of people who I now recognized were "homeless," like Greta and the other folks at the train yard, and I wondered if I'd see Greta herself. But I knew it wasn't likely in a place as huge as this.

I focused instead on all of the beautiful things to see around me. Spring was in full bloom—and summer was coming fast. Folks were in short pants and dark glasses that shaded their eyes from the sun. I myself was sweating, and I felt relief as we walked onto the green grass of the park where the swan boats were. It looked so cool and inviting.

There was a line for the boats, and as we waited, I fingered the money in my pocket and peered beyond the people in front of me with bated breath.

My Lord, how long had I dreamed of the swan boats? When Mrs. Johansen had talked about them when Katie and I were just little girls, they had sounded like something out of a fairy story. I'd pictured real live swans reined to boats full of doll-size people, even though I knew that couldn't be real.

Katie had had a more practical notion—more like what was actually in front of me. I'd always known she was right (like usual), but still, looking at them now, I wished they could have been a bit more . . . majestic. The boats—shaped like swans, sure—didn't look half as magical as I'd pictured.

Now that we were stopped, I thought I should make some kind of talk with Joe, but I didn't know what to say. He didn't seem bothered. He had his eye on some tot and was making goofy faces at her, sending her into cute little giggling fits, which made my heart ache for Marie. Gosh, he was an interesting boy. I compared him to the boys close to his age that I had known. Bo Aiden, who had slunk around all the time and not said hardly a word. Jake had been kind like Joe, but more countrified and reserved. Thomas Johansen, Katie's brother, who'd tried to kiss me but who I'd never liked back in that way. Theo, who was always tormenting me and trying to get me riled.

Joe was different. He was sophisticated. He seemed to stand tall, and I don't mean heightwise (though he was about as tall as me, and that's tall). He seemed to have lots of things figured out. I wondered if his mama had taught him that.

"So," Joe said, catching me studying him, "those aren't your parents, are they?"

I knew he was referring to the Kellys. He and his mama had been very polite to them but hadn't asked any deep questions. It was pretty obvious the Kellys and I weren't a parent-daughter fit.

"Yeah," I said. "I mean, no, they aren't."

"You wouldn't want to tell me how you ended up with them, would you?" We scooted up in line as he said this. "Are they your grandparents?"

"Um . . ."

I thought about lying and saying yes. But I didn't.

"They're my foster parents," I said. The term felt weird in my mouth.

"Oh."

It wasn't an *oh* like Oh my gosh, how strange. Or *Oh,* I wish I knew more. It was just a very content *oh.* Like it didn't matter one way or the other.

Finally we were at the front of the line. I pulled out my money. The ride, it said, was two dollars. Cheap! I handed over two bills, then Joe did the same. And then we were on the boat.

I'd always figured that if I ever got to ride the swan boats in Boston, I'd be the happiest, most excited girl in the world. It wasn't quite like I'd planned it. And it wasn't just that Katie wasn't there (though I tried to remind myself she was there in spirit). The man who sat next to me kept talking really loud how his car's transmission had gone out, whatever that meant. On my other side, Joe's leg was pressing against mine, and it made me feel distracted and nervous.

And the boat itself. Well, I'd never been on a boat, so I reckon that was pretty exciting. But while from the shore the swan boats had still looked kind of swanny (even if they weren't so magical), from the inside, this boat didn't really remind me of a swan at all.

Before I knew it, the ride was over and we were making our way across the grass again.

I felt my forehead wrinkling as I watched my feet push down little patches of green. It was strange, that's all. I hadn't hardly thought of Katie the whole time I was riding, on account of so many other things going through my head. And now that it was over, I figured I should have felt excited because I could check another thing off my list. But I didn't. I just felt . . . blah.

Well, I told myself, *it'll be different when you've got the list finished. Then you'll feel like you've really done it.* Then I'd know it was all worthwhile. There was still the church and the restaurant with the real waiter to go. And the taxi to ride in. I was getting close, at least. Though I wasn't quite sure how I'd ever manage the "Be happy" part at the end—not without Katie at my side.

We were supposed to meet Mrs. Trew at lunchtime and eat with her in the company cafeteria, and Joe said we didn't have time to go far.

I wasn't surprised, but I was disappointed. I would've liked to look for the church, but who knew how long that would take. Anyway, so far I hadn't seen any part of Boston that fit Mrs. Johansen's picture. The church in her photograph had looked perfect and peaceful. What I could see of the street had looked clean and lovely and somehow quiet. The parts of Boston we'd been walking in so far were kind of crowded and a bit dirty.

It had to be in some very different part of the city.

"Have you been to the pier yet?" Joe asked.

I shook my head no.

"Well, we've got to go, then. It's not far from my mom's building."

I didn't protest, though I didn't really care about seeing any "pier." All I did was suggest we take a taxi there.

The ride was short. Joe had said that we shouldn't do it at all—the pier was only a short walk away—but I'd insisted, saying truthfully that I'd never ridden in a taxi. When we got out, I made sure I paid like a modern girl is supposed to do, though the ride itself didn't seem worth the $3.70. Still, it was worth anything if I could check it off my list.

When we got out, Joe gently took my elbow. I was so busy

thinking of his fingers on the inside of my arm that I didn't notice the edge of the walk until we were right up close.

All the water—it was breathtaking! It just seemed to stretch forever and ever.

"Boston Harbor," Joe explained, seeming to enjoy my surprise. "It leads all the way out to the Atlantic Ocean." *Lord, the Atlantic Ocean. So much world.* We stood there for a long while, taking it all in. Unlike during the swan boat or the taxi ride, I couldn't stop smiling.

On our way back to the office, Joe and I talked and laughed, mostly about school and our teachers. He did an imitation of Mr. Tydings that made my stomach ache with laughing. He talked about his first few weeks at the school. He'd moved here from San Francisco in California and had hated it right off the bat. He said he'd missed his old friends and thought the people here were *lame.* But then he'd gotten used to it. And actually gotten to like it.

"And," he continued, "you just have to weed out the people you want to be friends with. You find who you like, you just start to notice the signs. That's how I knew about you. I knew I'd like you. I could just tell."

I felt myself blushing again.

"That sounds conceited, doesn't it?" he said. "I mean, I'm not saying I assumed you'd like me, too, or anything. For a friend. I just . . . hoped you would."

We both kept walking, uncomfortable. Of course I liked Joe. What wasn't to like? I just felt strange *saying* it.

Before I could say *anything,* Joe pointed over my shoulder to the store window behind me. "Postcards. I'm gonna get some."

He hurried into the store, and I followed him in, gazing around the shop, then watching as he chose carefully from a rack full of photographs. Curious, I picked one up. It was a picture of some tall buildings, with *Boston* written across the bottom in tilted yellow letters. On the other side was a lot of blank space and a little square with these words inside: *Place stamp here.* Stamp. You were supposed to mail these.

"These are so corny. That's why I like them. I'll send some back to my friends in Cali," he said.

"Yeah," I agreed. *Corny?*

The important people of Dogwood—Daddy and Mr. Johansen, mostly—used to get a few bits of mail with shipments from the outside. I wasn't supposed to know about it, but Mrs. Johansen had even received some from her sister up north and read parts of them to us once when I spent the night, me and Katie tucked up tight in Katie's big bed, all ears. Up till coming to Shadow Tree, though, I hadn't even known what a stamp was. Or that I could think of sending mail myself. And then it hadn't ever occurred to me to do it.

Now, even if I could send mail, I couldn't send any home. In the first place, how would I? Just address it to Dogwood,

West Virginia, with a wish and a prayer that it would get there?

Ding. It was the cash register. Joe was behind me now, paying for his cards. I gnawed at my lip.

And I had no right writing home, anyhow. I was dead to them. What if it got there and Mama and Daddy refused to read it? What if they didn't want to hear from me and I only made them sad again by breaking another rule?

Still, they probably thought I really was dead. And I would've liked to let them know I wasn't.

I wouldn't send it. I couldn't send it.

But I could buy it.

I grabbed the prettiest card that caught my eye and carried it over to the counter. It was only twenty-five cents.

It was worth just buying out of a wish and nothing else.

CHAPTER NINE

Sometimes I like to imagine I have my own photograph album, like the kind Amelia Aiden had. Only mine is full of all the pictures in my head. I can open up to any page and see the town garden full of cabbages, a certain curve in the main path to the church, Teresa braiding my hair while I sit on the slate stoop behind the house. All these images would be clear as they are in my mind—all frozen, all saved forever and ever.

If I were to show you the pages that covered those weeks after my trip back into Boston, they'd look something like this: me and Joe sitting in detention, him rolling his eyes and me with my feet tapping on the floor restlessly; me reading or studying on my bed with my hair in a sweat-sticky bun and my feet in sandals; me standing over the sink from time to time, pale and splashing water on my face as a sick spell came and went; me laughing at Joe while he cut up in science class, one hand over my mouth; me and Joe lollygagging down the hall after the last bell.

What I'm saying is, life became all about Joe and schoolwork and books while I waited to tackle my Boston list again. And also maybe about the Kellys—though in my album *they* would have been too fuzzy to make out. They stood in the background, Mrs. Kelly fretting, checking up on me, Mr. Kelly calm and removed, watching me and his wife like he was watching a baseball game on television—all the action happening without him. Meanwhile I was well behaved and polite, but I also kept my promise to myself to keep my distance from the Kellys. I didn't tell them my feelings or talk about my life at school. And when the call came in from the doctor's office the week after we'd gone for my checkup, saying my blood tests showed nothing out of the ordinary, I didn't let Mrs. Kelly see my disappointment.

Most of school was still a struggle, but it got better. I still felt knocked over by all the things there were to learn about geography and math and science, things I'd had no inkling of at home. But by studying and memorizing all the time, I at least kept from failing. I almost felt disappointed that I probably wouldn't be able to come back after the summer—that I wouldn't have the time to catch up and show everyone I was smarter than I seemed.

English and art were the only subjects I was really satisfied with. Mrs. Blackburn made me feel that even when I didn't know a certain fact (like an author's name or a book title), I had lots of other ideas to offer. Like, I was good at imagining things. And I could read fast—fast enough to zoom through the extra books she assigned on top of the regular class reading. And I could figure out why certain characters did the things they did. I stopped feeling bothered when Stacy acted rude or gave an answer that was better than mine during our book discussions. I matched every one of her good answers with one of my own, and besides, what did I care about her when Mrs. Blackburn was always saying, "Glory, you're very perceptive," and "Well done, Glory"? And also, when I had a friend like Joe?

"Nice, Glory."

I smiled up at Mrs. Sullivan, then stared down at the table in front of me. It *was* kind of nice, I had to admit.

We'd been learning to make something called "found art." Which was basically bringing in little knickknacks from home, anything we could find that we were allowed to use, and pasting them on a piece of canvas in some sort of design or with some special idea in mind—like maybe, all green objects.

Of course, I hadn't had any of my own things to bring—nothing I would spare, anyway. And I'd felt strange about asking the Kellys. So I'd gone to the bus stop early and gathered stuff along the way. A handful of grass, the regular kind and the tall bushy kind. Some tiny pebbles, a pinecone. I'd picked a couple of flowers, too, for color.

Mrs. Sullivan had looked disappointed at first when she'd seen my materials. She said she'd hoped I'd do something that would last.

But now, looking over the finished product, she gave me a satisfied nod and a pat on the shoulder.

I surveyed my work again. It *had* turned out like I'd hoped it would.

Thinking of the Appalachian hills of home, I'd layered the bits of grass so that they rose across the canvas, like a mountain, pasting them with the special glue we'd been given. Then I'd pulled all of the kernels out of my pinecone and stuck them here and there so that, to me, they looked like tree trunks peeking out through the greenery. Finally I'd plucked the petals out of my flowers and created a rainbow-colored burst above the slope. In my mind, it looked like a sun, exploding with all this color and beauty.

The girl next to me, Denise, leaned over to peek and nodded agreement with the teacher, and then a gaggle of students gathered around to look and mutter admiringly. One, a boy with white blond hair that stood up on end, said, "That's *so* cool."

I thought of Becky, how she'd told me I was creative and artistic. Even then it had made me smile—even after Katie dying and me leaving home.

It was still nice to be praised. I smiled and shrugged and even muttered a "thanks" to whoever could hear.

When I walked out of the art room, Joe was standing in the hall, waiting for me. Before I could say a word, he held out his hand to give me something, and when I reached forward, he dropped a folded piece of paper into my palm.

"I was gonna put it in your locker," he said. "But then I got out of class early. I guess I could still say it instead, but . . . nah. . . ."

I smiled at Joe as I unfolded the paper. "You weirdo," I

said, using one of his favorite words, and read the note.

Glory, wanna ask if you can go to the movies with us tonight?

I looked at Joe, beaming, and nodded. And before I could even say, "Thanks for asking me," he gave me a solid pat on the shoulder and rushed off.

The bus ride home passed slow as molasses, and during that time it dawned on me that Joe had said "us," as in other people besides him and me. I wondered who he meant among all the people he always seemed to be talking to. In all our time together during classes, I'd managed to avoid meeting any of his friends.

But things sped up once I got home, and I forgot to wonder. Mrs. Kelly seemed thrilled about the idea of my going to the movies with Joe (who she called "a fine boy") and his friends, and despite my protests, helped me pick out a nice outfit. Then she insisted on curling my hair. Not knowing how to say no, I let her.

"When I was a girl, your hair had to be perfect before you went anywhere. At least, that's the way it was in my house." She stood behind me, meeting my eyes in the mirror. I just nodded politely. "Of course, if we wanted to curl our hair, we had to sleep in curlers." She laughed then, her white cheeks wrinkling more than usual, like folded-up dough. "Can you believe that? Those darn things were so uncomfortable. Times have certainly changed."

I sniffed. Times hadn't changed all that much in Dogwood. My mama *still* slept in curlers from time to time, though it was considered a luxury to do something so vain. *Mama.*

I'd also never had my hair anywhere near a contraption like the one Mrs. Kelly was holding in her hand. Every time she tugged at another piece of hair and wound it around the hot metal rod, I cringed, worried that I was gonna get burned. Finally I just closed my eyes altogether.

A few squirts of spray to keep the hairs in place and we were done. Mrs. Kelly encouraged me to open my eyes and look in the mirror.

Oh. My hair cascaded around my shoulders in wild ringlets. It puffed out around my ears. I didn't look like myself at all. I looked ridiculous.

"It's . . . nice," I squeaked. "Thank you." Mrs. Kelly nodded at my reflection. *Oh, Lord. How can I face Joe and his friends like this?*

"Are you feeling all right, Glory?" she asked, putting her hands lightly on my shoulders. "You haven't seemed yourself." She surveyed me up and down. "I sure wish we could fatten you up."

I nodded guilty. "I'm fine, Mrs. Kelly. I'm just skinny, that's all." Poor Mrs. Kelly. I had tried to get some more meat on my bones, but no matter how much I ate, I seemed to get skinnier. And as far as being myself, well, I was stuck between a rock and a hard place because being more outgoing around her would hurt her more in the end. This was the best I could do.

The doorbell rang a few minutes later. Joe, wearing short pants and a T-shirt, was standing on the porch when I opened the door. His eyes darted right away to my hair, then to Mrs. Kelly, who was standing behind me, beaming. "Hello." He nodded to her.

"Hello, Joe."

"Um . . ." I muttered, searching for some way to explain why my head looked like a big ball of dark cotton wool without insulting Mrs. Kelly.

"Cool hair," he said, cutting off my chance. There was laughter in his eyes, but not the mean kind. It was like we were in on the same private joke. Like somehow he knew this was all Mrs. Kelly's doing, and he thought it was sweet and funny. I don't know how I got all that from just his look, but I did, and I was relieved.

Joe's daddy was driving, and two other kids I recognized from school were already in the car. Joe introduced them to me (and to Mrs. Kelly, who hurried along behind us and poked her head into the car) as Sadie and Neil. Sadie wore pink glossy lip color and a stretchy blue-collared shirt. She looked like a grown woman, all curvy and sophisticated. I thought of my own self, skinny and straight—except for my crazy hair.

"I've seen you in the caf," Sadie said. "You always sit with the teachers, right?" We were on our way now, Mr. Trew having promised Mrs. Kelly to have me back before such and such a time.

"Um . . ."

"Glory's too mature for us kids," Joe teased. Both Sadie and Neil smiled good-naturedly at the joke.

"Which reminds me, how's your *mature* reading group going?"

"Good," I murmured shyly. "We're doing *Watership Down*."

"Well, anyway, I'm glad I'm getting to meet you," Sadie said matter-of-factly. "You're intriguing."

Intriguing. I knew what the word meant, and that made it all the more confusing. My gosh, I was the least intriguing person at the whole school. Sadie, with her green eyes and wavy ginger hair and grown-up curves, was *intriguing*. I was the opposite. Wasn't I?

Still, I was relieved that she was being nice. I'd been worried about finding things to talk about with Joe's friends, and most of all I'd worried that they wouldn't like me, but Sadie and Neil and Joe jabbered the whole way as if they'd known and liked me forever. They talked to me as if I was in on the jokes about teachers at school (I was in on some) and characters on television (I hadn't gotten to watch much since leaving the Aidens). And they didn't seem to think anything of my hairdo.

By the time we got to the theater, which turned out to be at the same shopping mall where Mrs. Kelly had taken me, I'd stopped feeling bashful and started looking forward to the movie. I didn't even know which one we were seeing. But of course, it didn't matter. I'd never even heard about movies until living with the Aidens.

Two other boys—ones I'd seen sitting at Joe's table at lunch—were waiting for us at the front of the theater doors. We all bought tickets (eight dollars apiece!! Fortunately Mrs. Kelly had given me another ten-dollar bill before I left) and stepped inside. Joe and Sadie went to a glass counter where all sorts of sweets were on sale and bought two huge tubs of popcorn, which was always one of my favorite treats back home. They giggled about something as they walked back, leaning toward each other. Strangely, it sent a little pain racing through me. Maybe they liked each other. I figured I should be happy if they did. Joe was my friend. And modern kids seemed to like being couples. And they seemed to go so well together, both so confident and funny and handsome.

Anyway, gosh, who would have thought I'd ever be eating popcorn in a movie theater with a bunch of strangers? It wasn't even something Katie and I had ever talked about. It certainly wasn't on my list.

It almost made me queasy just to think about my list now. For one, because I hadn't found Mrs. Johansen's church yet and had no idea how I would. And second, because the list just . . . well . . . it wasn't going exactly as I'd planned. Riding in the taxi, on the swan boats, even standing in the skyscraper—beautiful as it was—felt . . . *shallow.* I felt guilty for being at the movies and even for spending so much time with Joe. Maybe I wasn't being as dedicated as I should.

But Katie would understand, right? She'd want me to have some fun, wouldn't she? She'd want me to enjoy myself a little. And it wasn't like Sadie was gonna be my new best friend, like I could ever be close to any girl like I was to Katie. I was just being . . . a little . . . happy. Yes, happy, that was okay—that was even on my list. I was being happy for Katie.

We entered a room full of rows and rows of seats, with a big white rectangle at the front for the movie to show on. There were lots of electric lights along the walls of the room and curtains on either side of the big rectangle. Soon after we sat in the cushioned seats—Joe to my left side and Sadie and Neil to his—the electric lights began to dim. I had a second to notice Joe's elbow pressing against mine, which made me feel strange and embarrassed. And then lights and colors appeared on the screen, and music came from all around us, and I forgot about everything in the world.

At first I got very confused as bits and pieces of things seemed to flash in front of me, unlike the shows I'd watched on television. But then Joe nudged me and whispered something about how he couldn't wait until "that one" came out, and I started to understand that these were little glimpses—like commercials—of other movies that would also play in this theater. Finally I saw the words *Feature Presentation* on the screen. I settled back in my seat, trying to relax, and watched as the movie began.

Have you ever been so wrapped up in a story that you forget you are in your own life? That's how it felt. I can't imagine anybody not feeling that way, sitting in a big movie theater, all those colors and those big people and big stories passing before their eyes.

I don't even know what the movie was about. I mean, I know kind of that it was about some guy who is traveling a long way with his friend, and they both do all this really funny stuff along the way, and one of them falls in love with a girl they meet. But I didn't really grasp a lot of it. Still, it was two hours of pure bliss. And for that little amount of time, with my friend Joe sitting next to me, I felt as lucky as a girl could be.

We went to Boston twice after that. Once with Neil and one of the other boys and once just me and Joe (Sadie didn't come either time). The Kellys loosened up the rules a bit, letting us take the T into town as long as we promised to be back by four o'clock. So that's what we did, two Saturdays in a row.

The first time I was feeling too sick to eat, so I didn't even suggest we go to a restaurant. When the boys bought pizza, I just said I wasn't hungry. I watched them gulp it down and thought about them knowing they'd have a million other times to eat pizza in the sunshine. Feeling sick always gave me thoughts like that.

The second time, when just Joe and I went, we did the restaurant. Joe didn't object when I suggested it. He said he never ate in restaurants and it would be a nice treat as long as we only got something cheap. We walked around for an hour or more, with me looking for the perfect place (and also keeping an eye out for Mrs. Johansen's church). "How about this one?" he kept asking. "What about this?"

"No, it's gotta be perfect," I said. "It's gotta be just right."

"What, are you going to propose to me or something?" he asked, bumping against my shoulder with his own. He was pretty strong, and I stumbled to the side a little.

"You mean for marriage?" I asked, blushing, and also feeling a little thrill. He shrugged a maybe.

"Well, Joe Trew, that's the most fool thing I ever heard," I said seriously.

Joe laughed, throwing up his hands, palms facing me. "Relax. Just a joke."

"Well, um . . . there," I said suddenly, pointing to a place on the corner with a giant yellow sign and big windows through which I could see lots of tables. "That's the one."

It didn't look perfect; it wasn't even close—and we'd passed many better ones already. Only I was getting frustrated with looking, and I needed to change the subject.

"We walked all around town so we could eat at *Denny's*?" Joe said. "Glory, you are the strangest, most mysterious girl I have ever met."

I scowled, even more embarrassed now. "Yes, Denny's. That's where I want to go. What's so strange about that?" So what if it wasn't his first choice? Or that it didn't look as pretty and fancy and glittery as the one I'd imagined? It would do.

It all happened so fast. Our waiter, who turned out to be a girl waiter with puffy black hair, wanted us to order before we'd hardly sat down. I'd always pictured leisurely looking over the menu and picking something very sophisticated, but I felt pressured and chose the first familiar dish I saw—a hamburger. Then it took about ten minutes for our food to arrive and ten to eat it. It didn't taste any better than anything my own mama could cook. Finally a sheet of paper arrived, telling us how much we had to pay. And that was it. No feeling elegant and fancy. No sparkling glasses and fine plates and sophisticated people coming and going by.

When we stood up, I felt like I was going to cry. A lump was stuck in my gullet as I thought about Katie and how nothing I did seemed right. Why had I been so impatient and picked Denny's in the first place?

Joe gave me a little friendly shake. "Hey, what's wrong?"

"Nothing," I replied. "I'm fine." But it wasn't true. My stomach churned—it seemed to be feeling worse than it had in a long while. And some dark mood was bubbling inside me. I was missing something. It had been more fun going to the movies than being in a restaurant like I'd planned. Truthfully, it had been more fun than the swan boats and the taxi—than anything I'd done from my list.

And that was strange. Because what about Katie? She was the one important thing. The reason I was there. But somehow, something deep inside told me I was failing her still.

CHAPTER TEN

We found the church on a Sunday. It was a week before school let out for the summer. Classes had become slower and easier. In English, we didn't do hardly anything anymore. Mrs. Blackburn had made her class even more laid back than usual.

It was refreshing to have the schedule loosened up and to feel that the year was really ending. It was also a little frightening. I didn't want to say good-bye to Mrs. Blackburn. I didn't want to lose all that time I got to spend with Joe.

I hadn't been looking for the church, specifically, that day. Maybe some part of me didn't want to find it—maybe I had known, better than I realized, what it would mean. Or maybe some part of me had secretly given up. Boston was big, much bigger than I'd ever expected, and while our weekend trips to the city had become a habit, I'd seen enough to know that it was possible I'd *never* find it. Ever. And so maybe I tried to forget it was important, or used to be.

But then, all unexpected, there it was. We were talking about fall, and how it was both of our favorite season. Joe had never seen the leaves turn color till he'd moved to Boston. I was telling him he had missed out—that lying under a pile of leaves when you are little is one of the best things you can ever do. And he was trying to make me promise to bury him in some in the fall so he could "get the full experience."

"Mmm," I said, trying to sound casual. "Maybe you'll have to bury *yourself.*" I'd gotten good at sounding casual about things like that. "Or maybe Sadie or Neil will do it for you."

Joe frowned. "But I want *you* to," he said. "I can tell just by looking at you that you are a leaf pile expert."

I rolled my eyes. "You are so corny," I said, using another of his favorite words.

"Yeah, but you love it." He grasped my wrist and waggled my arm a little teasingly. As usual, his touch made me feel all warm and flushed. Especially when, this time, he didn't let go.

We were turning a corner, around a small brick building, and it seemed Joe was about to hold my hand. My heart was racing because his fingers had made their way to the top of my palm. Did he know what he was doing?

And then, before I knew what I was reacting to, my body froze and my mind started spinning. Joe, not realizing I had stopped, stepped ahead, so that his hand pulled away from mine. Then he turned.

The church. It was just like in Mrs. Johansen's picture—brick, with steps out front and a cross above the door. I could have made that part out anywhere, so many times had I seen it in my imagination. A vision came back of me sitting in the Johansens' kitchen, staring at the photo of this place and imagining the world beyond its the edges. And then Katie's feet pattering down the stairs, ready to leave with me, to go to my house and help me with my day's worth of chores, and me putting down the picture but storing all of the things it seemed to promise in my head. I remembered perfectly—so perfectly, I ached with longing to go back in time and be there inside that day.

It was the reality of the promise that made my head spin, trying to place the view in front of me. I gazed around, confused.

It was just a normal street. Like so many other streets I'd seen in Boston. There was a plastic drinking cup lying crushed on the sidewalk right in front, cars passing, houses crowded against each other on either side. I pictured Katie's mama as a girl, standing there, beaming at the camera, and her grandmother holding her hand, both of them in their Sunday finest under a blue sky. It seemed times had changed. Everybody who passed was wearing short pants and sunglasses, caps, and flip-flops.

Most shocking of all, it wasn't in some different part of Boston where things were exactly as I'd expected them to be, all welcoming and simple and perfect. This was just another city street, like so many I'd seen—a bit dirty, untidy, full of regular houses and people who were just getting through life like everybody else—not dazzlingly happy like I'd pictured. I realized now, with a sudden jolt, that there mustn't be any place like the one I'd imagined. This was proof.

The Boston that photograph had promised was all in my head.

"Glory, are you okay?" Joe was eyeing me with worry. "You look like you've seen a ghost."

"Yeah," I muttered.

"Yeah, what?"

"Yeah, um, I mean—I need to be alone," I said flatly, to the air in front of me.

Before he could answer, I left a bewildered Joe behind and made my way to the door of the church. It was so cool inside and dark. A few people sat in benches, their heads leaned forward. It felt like my heart was dragging me down into the nearest seat. A big cross stood at the front of the room.

I almost forgot about you, I thought to myself, or rather, to God. I wished I could lean on His shoulder right now, the way I used to when I prayed. I wished he could carry me, because suddenly I felt I couldn't carry myself. Something was taking shape in my head that was too terrible to accept. I couldn't pin it down yet, but I knew it was coming clearer and clearer.

My head fell all the way into my hands, my palms pressed against my eyelids. I wanted to hide my face forever. For so long I'd been filling this hole—this big guilty hole—by checking one thing after another off my list. So now, at the moment the list was done, why did the hole feel bigger and emptier than when I started? I felt sick. I felt really, really sick.

*   *   *

When I emerged from the church several minutes later, Joe was sitting on a bench in the bright sunshine, his brows knitted down low as he met my eyes. My skin crawled with chills. I swallowed.

"I'm gonna, um, stay here for a while," I said. "I mean, I'll talk to you later."

Joe scrunched his forehead up. "You mean, you wanna split up now?"

I nodded, not meeting his eyes. "Yes," I said. "I want to *split up.*"

"But Glory . . . what's wrong? What happened? Did I . . . ?"

"I *said* I want to split up," I said, feeling faint. "I can get home on my own. I'll see you in school tomorrow. Bye."

I turned on my heel and started walking. As soon as my back was to Joe, I winced, feeling terrible for hurting him. But I just couldn't—I couldn't be around him right now.

"Glory!" Joe called. "Glory, wait." I didn't turn around.

What was that bakery called, the one that was supposed to be just around the corner from the church? I was gonna go there and get a fancy pastry just like Mrs. Johansen had talked about. I'd feel better. I needed to eat. I couldn't worry about Joe right now. It didn't matter.

I don't know if he finally stopped calling after me or if I just stopped hearing him, but moments later I'd left Joe behind altogether.

*   *   *

The bakery was easy enough to find; the name, Vincent's—I remembered now—was spelled in big red letters across a white awning. As I got closer, I could see little white tables scattered about the sidewalk there, filled with people eating and talking and laughing. I was so hungry. I imagined I could eat forever and never fill up.

A tiny something prickled at a corner of my brain as I approached. A man's back was to me, facing a woman whose face was tilted down toward her plate. For some reason my eyes were drawn to them. She reminded me of someone. . . .

What kind of pastry would I get? What would Katie have liked? She always loved raisins, anything with raisins, and . . .

I came to a dead stop. He'd turned. The man had turned.

He'd shaved his beard; his hair was neatly trimmed. He was in nicer clothes than I ever knew he had. But he looked thinner than before. Much older. I held his eyes for maybe half a second.

Then I turned and ran. Ran and ran and ran. I don't know if he got up to chase me. It seemed the whole world was silent and frozen and I was just a ball of fear running and running and having no idea where I was running or caring. I only knew that if I died right there on the spot, I'd be happy just to get away from the image of the staring, shocked face of Mr. Johansen.

When I got to the Kellys' door after riding the T home, I took a quick second to smooth myself out before going inside. I wiped at my face with my hand, where a fine mist of sweat had settled all over my skin. The television was on; I could hear it at the end of the hall as I entered. Mrs. Kelly appeared in the hall.

"How was it?" she asked, wiping her hands on a dish towel.

"Fine. I'm just tired. I'm gonna take a nap."

"Okay, dear," she said, her voice sounding worried, resigned.

I turned away from Mrs. Kelly's look and headed up the stairs. The wood creaked under the carpet, and I placed my hands on the last two steps, feeling the fibers of it, treasuring the softness, wanting to sink into it, feeling the creaks echo through my head.

My room was pink and still in the evening light. I locked the door behind me, then lay down on my bed. Maybe if I just rested for a little while, this would pass. I'd be able to gather my thoughts. My stomach would stop doing loop-the-loops inside.

But even with my eyes closed, the pink seemed to be vibrating off the walls, making me feel worse. I tried to lie perfectly still and imagine the room a different color. It was no use. Finally I climbed out of bed and opened my window, then crawled out onto the roof and took refuge in my secret spot for the second time.

I lay back against the rough gray roof tiles. The breeze felt better, but the nausea stayed. It got worse as I went over and over the events of the last few hours. Had I imagined it? Was I that sick? It all seemed like one of those dreams you have when you've got a high fever, where the ground shakes beneath you and nothing makes sense and you can't even tell if you're awake or not.

Had I really just seen Mr. Johansen? I couldn't have, could I? And then, the church. It had made me feel so empty.

I let out a moan.

It's over. Now I saw it all so clearly. It was nothing. It meant nothing.

I rolled over onto my side, curling up. The pang in my belly got worse. I was so sick. The tears started coursing down my cheeks.

I'd done my list. There was no next thing. After months of planning and saving and running and searching, I had done all that I'd set out to do. And the truth was, I hadn't made anything up to Katie. There was no way to do it "right"—there was *no way* of making anything up to Katie. All this time I'd been chasing the idea as if it made any difference. And now I could see that it didn't. Nothing had changed. It was all nothing. It was all for nothing.

"Katie," I choked, low so nobody would hear. "Katie, I'm sorry. I'm so, so sorry. Please forgive me." I choked again. I wiped the sticky tear-wet hair out of my face. I pictured her daddy, his rage that night at the church. I saw his look of surprise at the bakery. Had it been him? I was sure it had. Surer he wished I was dead. I wished it, too. What in the world was I living for?

I couldn't make out where I was when I woke. There was some loud banging in the distance, like a drum, like one of those drums in one of those music bands on television. It sounded bloated and sad.

The lights winking down on me—they were stars. Why stars? How? They looked like little tiny fires, burning and burning.

Bam bam bam.

The drum again. I lifted my head. Maybe the drum was inside my head, because it got louder now. It took all my effort to look left to right; it felt like my skull was full of rocks.

But now I saw. I was on the roof. I lived at the Kellys', and I was on their roof. I stood and wobbled, not bothering to hunch over for balance. I'd just go in through the window. Something told me that when I did that, the drumming would stop.

I went in headfirst, tumbling over and hitting the carpet with a thud. Then I stood up and wobbled toward the door. I realized that it wasn't a drum; it was somebody knocking. Why had I thought it was a drum? It seemed to take forever to get to the door because my legs felt like they were soft melted butter. The knob felt slippery and so cold in my hands, but I managed the lock (why was it locked?).

The door was pushed open before I had a chance to pull it. Mr. Kelly's face loomed out at me from the doorway. Why did he look so upset? I wondered.

Then I was falling away—down, down, down. And then there was nothing but blackness. Maybe I was still under the dark, dark sky.

CHAPTER ELEVEN

Was I dead? Was I a ghost now for real? Because surely I wasn't in heaven. Though it was very cool here. And there was beeping somewhere.

I opened my eyes. Mrs. Kelly was sitting beside me, my fingers clasped in hers. I stared at my hand for a second, like it didn't even belong to me. It was so lifeless and pale. Then I looked around, ever so slowly. *Oh.* Everything was white, and there were all sorts of contraptions next to my bed. I was in a hospital, where they had doctors and beds and things like that.

Mrs. Kelly was beaming at me. "You're up," she said. "How are you feeling?"

I parted my lips, trying to answer, but they felt so dry. Surprisingly, Mrs. Kelly had a cup of ice water at the ready, with a bent white straw poking out. She held it to my lips.

"Thank you," I said, lying back from the effort. The nausea was gone, thank goodness, but I felt so terribly tired.

"You're welcome. I'm glad to see you up. Jim will be, too. He's out in the waiting area."

"Did I . . . ?"

"You fainted. You had a terrible fever. Why didn't you tell me you weren't feeling well? You just went up to your room, do you remember?"

I nodded. I was thinking of Mr. Johansen. And the church.

"And then dinner came around and you hadn't come down, and I came up to get you. And the door was locked. Honey, why did you lock the door?"

I just stared blankly. I didn't know how to answer.

"We were just about to get a screwdriver to take the handle off; we didn't know what on earth . . . but then you opened up."

"And I fainted?"

Mrs. Kelly nodded. "You *collapsed.* I just don't understand; why wouldn't you tell me if you were feeling ill?"

I looked down at the blanket, my long white arms sticking out over the top of it. I didn't know what to say. Every ounce of hope inside me had disappeared sometime between the church and now, and without it I didn't have the energy to speak.

"Glory, I want to ask you something. I need you to tell me the truth. All right?"

Did she know more than I thought? What else could I do but agree? I nodded.

"I know you probably don't think I'd understand, but Glory, you look so skinny, and I know you eat. And with locking yourself in your room and spending so much time alone and . . . I want to know . . . dear . . . are you taking drugs?"

Drugs?

"Drugs?"

"I'm sure you think I don't know about these things, but if you are, you have to be honest. We can get help for you, and—"

"I'm not taking anything, Mrs. Kelly," I said. I had an idea of what she was talking about. Drugs—she meant the kind that are like alcohol—that make you do silly things. Taking drugs was probably considered a terrible sin back home, like drinking, but I'd heard that some kids at school did it sometimes. Personally, I'd never even *seen* a drug.

Mrs. Kelly sighed. "Okay, then." She looked slightly relieved, but not much. "They said they did a blood test for that, anyway. I was just . . . I just wish we knew what was wrong so we could fix it."

"Fix it?"

Mrs. Kelly gave me a sympathetic look. "Honey, we're very worried about you."

She started telling me about the doctors and how they'd said they didn't know what was wrong with me. That they would have said it was just an extreme attack of fever, only my body was malnourished and was low on some of the stuff I should have had inside my blood. I listened absently, not caring. I knew what was wrong, of course.

"We can take you home once you've spoken with the doctors a little," Mrs. Kelly continued. "There's not much else they can do for you now. But Glory, it's very important that you tell them, *us,* everything you can that might help. Maybe it's time for you to open up a little. If it's something genetic . . . well, if you've inherited something from a family member, the doctors can figure it out. Some diseases—not that I'm saying you have one—but some diseases skip a generation or two."

She paused here and fiddled with her necklace. It was the first direct mention she'd ever made to my having a family. I almost wished, for her sake if nothing else, that I could tell her all about the poison and what *was* happening to me. But there was no point, and it wouldn't do any good.

Suddenly I felt an awful dread as something occurred to me. "Mrs. Kelly," I began. "How did your daughter die?" I'd never had the nerve to ask before, but just then I had to know. I had to know if they were going to lose me in the same way they'd lost her.

Mrs. Kelly sighed and gave me a calm, sad smile. "She died in a car accident. She was a little bit older than you. She'd just learned to drive and . . ." Her voice trailed off. "Well. It was an accident."

"I'm sorry," I said to my hands. An accident. So she hadn't been sick, like I was. But an accident was terrible enough—I knew that better than anyone.

"Oh, don't be sorry. Not for me or Mr. Kelly. Tara was a gift. We were lucky to have her as long as we did. We were lucky to know her."

My lip started shaking. My voice came out quivery. "How can you think that way? It's so *unfair.*"

Mrs. Kelly took my hand again. "Oh, Glory. It's so sweet of you to feel that way for us. But you're wrong. Not that I haven't felt the same many times, but . . ." She paused, looking up at the ceiling as if she could find her next words there. "I don't believe you can ever be separated from the people you love."

"Because of heaven?" I stared at her doubtfully. Maybe I had figured out things she hadn't—like about God not really being there for us. Maybe that was why she seemed so *okay* with everything.

"I don't know. I don't know if there is a heaven; there may be. But I don't need to know. I have my daughter in my heart always. And I have a lovely life with my husband. And we have a new gift—you. I'm so glad we have you."

My lip started quivering again, and suddenly tears were coursing down my cheeks.

"But I'm sick," I whispered. "I'm sick, and maybe I'll die on you like your daughter did."

"Oh, Glory." Mrs. Kelly wrapped me in a hug. Her cheek felt good against mine. "There, there. It's all right. You're not going to die." She was rubbing my back like Mama would have done. Her voice felt gravelly through her chest. "Don't worry, at least not on my account. You can never know the future, much as you think you can. Anybody can leave you at any minute. What's important is that you enjoy the time you have."

Forgetting to be strong and keep my distance, I let myself

sink into Mrs. Kelly's embrace. I wished so much that she was right about everything. I wished I could agree with her that having Katie and my mama and daddy and my brother and sisters in my heart alone was enough.

At least she'd managed to make me feel better about one thing. Most of the time I'd known her I'd spent feeling bad for her, with her fragile little body and these sad things in her past. But now I realized how wrong that was. She was a stronger, bigger person than I'd ever be.

I was back in my room two days later, propped up with loads of pillows, the blinds down, and all sorts of snacks and treats on my bedside table. I wasn't hungry, but I nibbled on some crackers. Funny, being sick anywhere—in a big modern house or my own old-fashioned one—felt exactly the same: miserable. At least the walls weren't vibrating anymore.

And in fact, I didn't feel so much sick as empty. I was weak and tired, but not out of nausea, like before. I'd talked to two doctors a whole slew of times in the past couple of days. They'd listened to my heart and poked and prodded me and sent me through these strange machines. And they'd questioned me. But I'd kept quiet about the poison, time after time. I was resolved. I'd take the knowledge with me to my grave.

In the end, they'd said the same things as Dr. Filkin: that I needed to eat better and take iron and other vitamins. They said that none of the tests they'd done had come up positive, which meant that I didn't have any of the diseases they thought I might have, and that for now that was the most they could tell us. It looked like it wasn't the end for me, yet. I guess I should have been relieved.

But I was haunting this world, and that wasn't the same as living. Mostly I wished I was already dead.

And then, I was also haunted. The reality of seeing Mr. Johansen was like a nightmare to me. Of all the people in all the world, I'd had to run into *him*. He knew, more than anyone, how bad a person I was. He had suffered because of me and hated me because of it more than anyone else. And while it wasn't so strange that he'd been in Boston and, I now realized, even that I'd run into him at the bakery (Vincent's was, after all, his wife's favorite—although who was that woman he'd been there with?), it seemed especially unkind of fate to bring the two of us together like it had. Deep down, I feared he was some kind of dark angel come to fill my thoughts in my last days. Reminding me how little I deserved to be here on this earth and be the slightest bit happy, when I had taken so much away from others.

Voices rose up from the parlor below in a low hum. Sherry had come over, and she and the Kellys were talking. I wondered if she was going to take me back to the center now that I had turned out to be such a calamity for everyone. The phone rang, interrupting them, and then I heard Mr. Kelly's heavy footfalls rounding the landing.

On my lap was the postcard I'd bought in Boston. I tucked it under the blanket.

"Glory, it's Joe," Mr. Kelly said. He was standing in my doorway, frowning doubtfully. We had been through this before. "Won't you talk to him?"

"No, thank you, Mr. Kelly," I said, my voice thin.

He nodded. I heard him moving down the stairs and then down the hall, getting back on the telephone. I couldn't hear what he said to Joe, but I knew it was something like "She's sleeping right now, Joe" or "She can't come to the phone." I'd asked the Kellys not to tell Joe I was sick. I didn't want him coming to check up on me.

When the click of Mr. Kelly hanging up the line echoed its way to my room, I bit my lip, trying to ignore the hurt it caused. I'd missed the last week of school. If I kept ignoring him like this, I might never have to see Joe again. Like I'd never see Mrs. Blackburn again. Or the inside of the cafeteria again or the school bus.

I knew, deep down, that I should at least apologize. Joe probably thought I hated him, and that wasn't it at all. But maybe it was for the best. My time with him was over. It seemed like to have friends, you needed to feel alive inside. And like I said, I already felt dead. I couldn't even imagine speaking to him once, so far away did I feel.

I could just tuck him away as a nice memory. I would try.

Gosh, I *missed* so much—my family and Joe and the Aidens

and Mrs. Johansen. I felt angry about being sick, and scared of getting worse, and angry about losing Katie. And then, now that death was coming so close to me, I felt terrified at the fact I'd never see my family again. It had never gotten me so *panicked* before. Now I felt like this big lonely darkness was pressing down on me.

I pulled out the postcard again. A while back I'd addressed it and stuck on a stamp. It said *The Mason Family, Dogwood, West Virginia.* I wished I could send it.

I wished I had the right to be alive to them while I still could be.

When I started getting up and around, it was mostly for the Kellys' sake. They seemed so sad and worried, and I wanted to cheer them up. I started cleaning myself up in the morning, taking walks outside, looking at the birds and flowers and such. It was so hot, it made me think of summers back home.

One morning I sat on the Kellys' front porch, thinking about all the summers I could remember. How Theo would tie a rope to a big old oak tree and a bunch of us kids would take turns swinging over the lake, then letting go. We weren't supposed to—we always did it in secret. Katie would spend those days at home, helping her mama, because except for the night she died, when I convinced her drinking those spirits would be fun, she never broke the rules like me.

I was busy daydreaming about this, almost floating away, when I looked up to see Joe standing before me.

His nose was rosy and peeling a bit from sunburn. It made his dark eyes stand out. His lips were turned down at the corners. Since I'd known him, I hadn't once seen him looking so unsure of himself.

"Hey," he said, sitting down beside me. I didn't feel the thrill, like before, when his knee pressed against mine. I just felt sad.

"Hi," I said back, putting my chin on my hands and staring at my knees.

"Where've you been? I took the bus over. I've tried to call. . . ."

"I've been here," I said. I wished he would leave. It wasn't just that I felt too *empty* to be a friend or too worried that any friend of mine would end up hurt. I also didn't want one. Really, truly this time, I hadn't the faintest desire for one.

"Well, why didn't you call me back?"

I turned to meet his eyes now. He looked so sad and worried. But I managed to level a clear, unfeeling gaze at him. "I didn't feel like it," I said.

Joe winced slightly, as if I'd hit him. His eyes darted away, then looked back at me. "So what do you want me to do? You want me to leave or something?"

I guess he didn't expect me to say yes. Maybe he wanted to argue. I nodded. "Yes, please. I want you to leave."

Joe stood up and backed away slightly. His forehead crinkled up with frustration. "What's *wrong* with you? What happened? What did I do?"

He wasn't going to provoke me. I squeezed my lips together tight. "Nothing's wrong with me. I just didn't feel like calling you. I don't feel like seeing you. You should go away."

I didn't care if I hurt his feelings. In fact, I almost wanted to hurt him as much as I was hurt. I wished for once somebody could know what it was like. I didn't flinch as I stared at him. I wanted him to see I meant it.

Joe trembled slightly, his hands balled up in fists. He took a few more steps backward. "Fine." His voice cracked softly, and he seemed embarrassed and even looked like he might cry. "Fine. You don't want to be friends anymore. Well, maybe I did something stupid, and I'm sorry. Or maybe something else is going on with you. I don't know. But don't bother calling me when you change your mind. If you want me to go now, I'm really going."

I made a show of being bored. I rolled my eyes. I felt mean and evil and I didn't care. "Just go."

Joe gave me one more wounded look and turned on his heel. The birds kept chirping as he pounded away down the sidewalk. They didn't seem to notice how sad it all was.

But I was glad he was gone. It was a clean break, like Dr. Venable said once when Theo broke his arm falling off the rope, before he got out over the water of the lake. We'd never gone swinging again after that.

I made sure Joe had disappeared around the corner before I let myself cry.

CHAPTER TWELVE

I saw this show on television back at the Aidens', about how people are sometimes drawn to look at ugly, horrible things. They talked about how there was this tornado that swept through this small town. Tornadoes can tear up anything in sight.

They were talking about how after this one, people came from miles around just to see where the roofs had been ripped off houses, and nobody could get anywhere on the roads because there were so many folks driving in to have a gander.

Once I was strong again, I was drawn back to Boston in the same way. I didn't want to see Mr. Johansen, but I went back to look for him, almost as if I couldn't help myself. The Kellys didn't dare stop me, though they tried to talk me out of it. In the end I was so set on going that it was either allow me to or upset me by arguing about it, and they were still too worried to do that—if they ever would have done it at all.

I knew it was wrong. But I couldn't help it. Part of me was out of control.

Part of me had also held on to all these possibilities. Like maybe Mr. Johansen had my daddy with him. Or maybe *Mrs.* Johansen.

Maybe I could just see them and know they were okay. Though it scared me that Daddy might be *too* okay—okay without me.

It took me a long while to find Vincent's again; I'd been so shattered when I'd left it the last time. After about two hours of walking around, I saw it. Turned out it wasn't that far from where Joe had first shown me the water. Funny how the city seemed to shrink, and things that had seemed so far away from each other at one time could actually be right around the corner.

Mr. Johansen was nowhere to be seen. I bought myself a coffee and sat at a table for two or three hours, waiting, but nothing. He had probably gone back to Dogwood by now. He never stayed away on his business long.

I reluctantly headed to the T station and then home, where Mrs. Kelly fussed over me as usual. Even Mr. Kelly popped up to my room and asked if I needed anything. I felt a pang of conscience when I heard him climbing the stairs. They were both too old to be worrying about someone like me.

Later he came in with a couple of magazines Mrs. Kelly had sent up. *Bless the Beasts and the Children,* the last book Mrs. Blackburn had assigned back during the group I'd missed when I was sick, sat on my bed stand, untouched. I didn't have the energy to tackle any books that would make me feel anything. So the magazines were a welcome distraction, and they reminded me of Jake, which was a nice memory to have.

"It's a beautiful day out today," Mr. Kelly said, surprising me.

Unlike usual, he didn't leave; instead he sat down on the edge of my bed and took one of the magazines from the pile. We'd never sat together, just the two of us. I wondered what he wanted.

Finally he sighed and turned to me with a shrug. He leaned forward and patted me on the shoulder timidly.

"You're a nice girl."

A nice girl? I didn't reply, not even with a smile. It was too strange—too beyond what I would have expected to happen.

"I know you probably think you're a burden with all of this, but I want you to know I don't regret it."

I scrunched up my forehead, thinking. Mr. Kelly was a man of few words, that I knew. It was hard for him to be talking like this, I could tell. But I couldn't help asking.

"Regret what?"

He raised his hand, palm up, in a gesture that said, Isn't it obvious?

"Convincing Caroline to do this—the whole foster child thing. We needed you—we needed some life around this house, and we needed to do something for someone besides ourselves." He paused. "Of course, she took right over, just like I knew she would." He cleared his throat and shrugged again.

Mr. Kelly. The whole time, it had been his idea to take me in. And I'd thought from the first that he hadn't wanted me at all.

Part of me—a part that wasn't off in outer space, far away and too lost to care—was deeply, deeply comforted.

"You want some company?" Mr. Kelly asked. Changing the subject, I supposed. "I could just sit with you for a while," he added.

"Okay," I muttered.

He let out a deep breath. He opened up the magazine he'd taken. We read in comfortable silence.

I was surprised to hear that in the modern world, summer arrived on a specially picked out day, June 21. Back home, you knew it was summer when you could smell fresh-cut hay in the barn and hear the sound of wheat being threshed, and when you could watch the tomatoes growing—green and not yet ripe—on the vines. In Boston, summer brought a thick smell rising up from the pavement and flowers popping into tiny boxes lining every few window sills. It was hotter here, it seemed, than it had ever been at home, or at least there was less of a breeze. And I basked in it. I had been so cold back in the woods, and the memory of it was still so close, that now I could probably walk on the sun and still not mind the heat.

The smells and sights, as I drifted back to the city again and again for no real reason that I could tell, reached into my heart and gave me these tiny little moments of wanting to be alive that disappeared almost as quickly as they came. It was one of these lighter moments that brought me to stand by the harbor one day, a long, long while, and stare and stare at the water. I'd been at Vincent's that morning. I guess, more than anything now, because it made me feel close to Katie. Now I stood and breathed in the salty air.

It was so lovely. So peaceful. There was a breeze coming off the water that felt extra nice mixed with the hot sunshine.

Finally I gathered myself to leave. I hadn't felt entirely well since being in the hospital. Maybe it was time to head back to the Kellys' and rest. And wait.

I started back, taking the path along the river's edge. How many more times would I see this river before I died? I wouldn't even know when the last time would be. Maybe it was today.

I was crossing under some kind of overhanging road when I heard footsteps behind me. I didn't bother to turn around and look. I'd gotten used to passing strangers in the street. But I did notice the steps seemed to be quickening. Only when they got too close to ignore did I know they were coming for me, and by then it was too late. I caught my breath and turned just in time to see Mr. Johansen's face—and his thin but still muscular body—looming toward me.

He grabbed me roughly, squeezing me so hard that I felt my bones would break. "I knew it was you," he said, his voice coming out deep and enraged. A sickly sweet and familiar smell hit me with force. Where did I remember that smell from? But there was no time to wonder or to think, because my feet were scraping along the walkway behind me, and Mr. Johansen was dragging me away and shoving me into his car.

CHAPTER THIRTEEN

We drove through the back streets of Boston, getting farther and farther from the places I recognized. Amazingly, Mr. Johansen seemed to know them all like his own hand. I realized he must have been here many times before.

As I sat staring straight ahead, unable to talk and too afraid on top of that, a million thoughts went racing through my brain. The one that kept coming back was, Maybe he was here to take me home. Maybe they'd sent him to get me, or maybe he'd spotted me and then decided on his own. This could be the way out of Boston. If only it was nighttime, I could see the stars and know if we were headed south.

What would it be like to pull into town at Mr. Johansen's side? Would my family be happy to see me? Would folks be surprised? And angry? I didn't care; I could handle my father's anger as long as I could see his face again.

A few minutes later Mr. Johansen steered the car around a turn, and then what I saw made my flesh go cold. We were in a vast, deserted yard of some sort. It was along the water, but it was nothing like the place where I'd stood a half hour before. I could see several piers poking out into the water, and giant metal boxes piled up alongside the piers. It was desolate and lonely.

And now a new thought came to the surface. If he wasn't taking me home, where *was* he taking me? And what was he going to do when we got there?

The car squealed to a halt, and I turned to look at Mr. Johansen's profile. His jaw was set, his teeth clenched. He kept his hand on the steering wheel for a moment, then threw open his door and got out. He swayed on his feet a little as he came around to my side and flung my door ajar. I didn't move. My heart flapped around in my chest like a wild bird, trapped, desperate. He swayed again, looking at me, and I dared to turn and meet his eyes.

Oh. Oh, Lord. Now I knew what I smelled on his breath. And why he swayed when he walked and why his eyes were so red and glassy. He was drunk! Mr. Johansen was drunk on spirits!

His arm shot out, his hand digging into my arm as he yanked me from my seat. I tried to pull away, but my whole body felt weak, like I'd run a thousand miles. He practically lifted me as he dragged me toward the bank of the river.

"Please," I cried. "Please, Mr. Johansen!"

He didn't seem to hear. He was saying stuff—something about his Katie and that I had the devil in me.

He got me all the way to the edge of the water, then set me down, holding me tightly by the shoulders. He looked me dead in the eyes and started shaking and shaking and shaking me till I felt I would fall apart.

"Please," I begged, through tears that were falling into my mouth. "I'm so sorry. Please. Don't kill me. I'm gonna die, anyway. The poison . . ."

He didn't seem to hear for the longest time. But then suddenly he stopped shaking me. His glassy eyes widened and came into focus, like a person waking up, who can't believe what he is waking up to.

He looked at me doubtfully for a second, his mouth working but nothing coming out. And then he said, "The poison."

I sputtered. "I—I know, I didn't think I could last this long. But it was for Katie." I paused, waiting for him to interrupt. He didn't. "Because we always wanted to see Boston, and I thought I was doing something for her. That's why I came, and I know it's fool thinking, sir, but I didn't realize, and now . . ." I didn't know if anything coming out of my mouth was making sense. "The Kellys . . . it's just . . . please . . ."

I think I would have crumpled if Mr. Johansen hadn't been keeping me up. I stared up at him. He was studying me look ing me up and down—my skinny arms and legs, the bruises where they'd stuck so many needles in me at the hospital.

His face started bunching up in what looked like a grimace. And then he released me.

I fell backward a step, then managed to right myself in time to see Mr. Johansen himself crumple, his face falling into his hands. He stumbled the few feet toward the car, splayed both hands along one side of the hood, and hung his head.

After a minute or two of standing and watching him, panting and wiping at my face, I took a few wary steps toward him. Maybe I should have run. But all I could think was, I was to blame for this.

"You'll never know what I would give to make it so I died instead of Katie," I dared to warble at his back. "I'm so sorry. I know I'm a bad person."

He raised his head and looked over at me, his eyes dry and not as glassy as before. His jaw was working under his skin, clenching and unclenching. I wanted to say something about his drinking spirits, how I didn't understand how he could do it after the part it had played in Katie's death, and how he was a town leader and all and shouldn't be committing sins. But his look told me I better not. I just stood with my head down awhile.

"You're sick."

I nodded, though I didn't know if it was a question or not. He was studying me again. "You look it."

"I know," I said. "Everybody says that. The doctors say—"

"Doctors?"

"Oh," I said, putting up my hands and waving them. "No, I mean, they made me go. I swear, I didn't say anything about the poison or home or . . . They just . . ."

He didn't make a peep, so I continued.

"They just said they didn't know what was wrong with me. They don't know I'm dying. I didn't tell them."

Mr. Johansen was giving me that look again, that amazed look that I didn't quite understand. I guess he thought I would have died sooner, me being a girl and all.

"But don't you . . . ?" Mr. Johansen stopped. Sighed and searched the sky. "How'd you get here?" he finally asked.

I took the rest of the steps to the car and timidly leaned against it for support. How did I get here?

"I followed the North Star through the woods," I said. "It took days and days. I didn't think I'd make it. But then I found a house. This family lives there, it's a farm, and . . . this boy helped me get to a town, and I worked at a shop there to earn some money, only the money got stolen, and . . . I had to stay longer and earn more, and then I had to get away because Child Welfare can get you, and I took the bus here and . . ." I paused for air. It was amazing to be telling someone my real story. I had never told it before. "And I got caught and put in foster care. But I had this list of things Katie and I talked about doing here. And I did them all, I checked them off. Only . . ."

Here I finally stopped.

"Only?"

"Only, of course, it doesn't matter. I can't make it up to Katie . . . that I . . ." I swallowed. "I can't make up for what I did. I can't do anything for her."

Mr. Johansen was shaking his head. I sniffled, then wiped at my nose. He was still looking at the space between his hands when he began to talk.

"I knew it was you, at Vincent's. I didn't doubt it for a second, even with you looking so different now. I would have come after you, but Laura was sitting right there. . . ." I remembered the lady who I'd seen facing him at the table. Laura, I realized with a jolt—that was Mrs. Johansen's sister. "Sent word home that business was holding me up. Been looking for you since. I don't know what story I'll tell when I get there. I sure won't be telling this."

He seemed to be forgetting he was even talking to me; he seemed to be talking to himself. Still, I hung on every word.

"I was gonna kill you, I guess."

Silence hung in the air after that for a long while.

"But I couldn't kill you," he finally added. He stood back from the car and let his arms hang at his sides. "Not even . . . if I hadn't known . . . Coming here for Katie, even though I guess it doesn't amount to much . . . Still . . ."

He let out another sigh. Then he walked past me and opened the car door. He climbed into the driver's seat, then closed the door on the other side.

He was going to leave me here. Panic, not relief, took over. Not because I was scared of being left. But I was desperate to ask him something before he went, lest I miss my chance forever.

I swallowed deep. "Mr. Johansen . . . sir." I placed my hands on the rim of the open window daringly. "How is my family?"

He put his hands on the wheel and gripped it tight, staring straight ahead. As if this one favor . . . this one answer . . . was too much for him to give me. But then he met my eyes, and his held pity. I nearly jerked back from the shock of it.

"They're okay," he said. "They're fine. . . . They miss you."

He looked at me another long second. "I guess they figured the winter must have killed you. We all did. I didn't . . ." he continued. "I didn't know Katie wanted to see Boston."

He pulled his door closed.

I watched him another moment, then blurted something more. "And *Mrs.* Johansen?" He froze. "Is she, um, is she okay?"

Through the open window, he looked me up and down a final time.

"Godspeed, Glory."

Then he turned back to the steering wheel, twisting the key in its slot. The car rumbled to life, moved beneath my hand, and pulled away. Mesmerized, I stared after it. Mr. Johansen had come and gone. He had been here, for real. He had wished me Godspeed.

I walked into the Kelly home long after dark, spent, exhausted, overwhelmed with thoughts of what had just happened, and hungry.

Mrs. Kelly was sitting in the kitchen by the telephone, her husband rubbing her back. She was doing that twiddly thing with her necklace, but when she saw me, her fingers froze and her eyes widened. For the millionth time in three quarters of a year, I had no earthly idea what to say. Luckily I didn't have to.

"Glory!" Mrs. Kelly breathed, leaping out of her seat with more energy than I would have believed she had in her. She plucked my hands from my sides and pulled them toward her to get a better look at my arms. Now I looked at them, too. Large dots lined the insides of both elbows—four finger marks on each side. Five more circled my left wrist. The bruises were the same color as the veins showing through my skin—deep blue. *Blue Girl.*

"Call the police again," she threw back over her shoulder, moving her hands to my chin and tilting my face from side to side under her gaze. "Glory, who did this to you?"

I continued to let her inspect me, but I shook my head gently in her hands. "No. Please. Please don't call the police. It . . . it won't happen again." My voice came out choked, and I realized I was going to cry. And all I could think was, Mr. Johansen had wished me Godspeed.

"What do you mean, it won't happen again!" She and Mr. Kelly met glances across the room. He held the telephone suspended, hesitating.

"I mean, it won't. I swear. I know it. Please." Tears wobbled on my lower eyelashes, and Mrs. Kelly seemed moved. She held my face another second, then let me go.

"Well, I am at a loss. We thought you'd run away. We

already called the police once tonight." Her face contorted as she spoke, and at first the expression was so foreign to me, I didn't understand what I was seeing. But then, as I focused my mind on the present, I did. Mrs. Kelly was spitting mad.

"You stay out past dark, in the city, alone, and you come back like"—she waved her hand to indicate my whole body—"like this. And you're sick already, and you know more than you're telling us. And I may only be a *foster* parent; maybe you think that doesn't qualify me to care, but I just . . ." She squeezed both hands together in front of her, a hopeless gesture.

She shook her head, her voice cracking. Mr. Kelly rushed to her side, hanging up the telephone behind him. He wrapped his arm around his wife and pulled her against him, giving me a look that was both pitying and angry.

"Why won't you let us help you?" she said, her voice low and hopeless. She turned to her husband. "Why won't she let us help her?"

I stared at the Kellys and their anger. Had I ever seen them in this light before? Had I ever seen this kitchen in quite the same way?

Everything around me felt different, like it had taken on some deeper color. From the moment I had walked in the door, it had felt different, only I hadn't noticed.

And then I realized why. This—the Kellys' fancy old house, the Kellys mad at me and worried, caring . . . this was *life.*

Not tasks. Not waiting to die.

Mr. Johansen had wished me Godspeed, and that was something, since Katie died, I had never wished for myself.

And I wondered now: If there could be mercy, if Mr. Johansen could have pity on me, if the Kellys could care for me and want to help me . . . then didn't I deserve to hope for that? Didn't I deserve to want it, for as long as I had it? I didn't have to forgive myself for what had happened with Katie—I didn't think that was possible. But did that mean I couldn't hope?

"That's . . ." I began, trembling all over. "I want to talk to you about that. I want to tell you." I stopped, swallowed. "I have a lot to tell you. And I want . . ."

The Kellys were frozen—watching me and waiting. I think we all knew that what I was going to say would change everything.

"I'm sick," I said. "I'm dying. And . . . I don't want to die." I looked from one to the other. "Can you help me? Please, I want you to help me get better."

As the words came out, I felt desperate and hurt. But it wasn't like the hurt from knowing my days were numbered or of having nothing to live for. I hurt with hope. With the chance I wanted to take.

EPILOGUE

Mrs. Kelly says I'm a Scorpio. But she says I'm more like a Gemini, because I have two sides—the side I show (stubborn, strong) and the side I don't (scared, weak, lonely). I never thought of it that way; I always thought I was what everybody told me I was. But I guess she's right. I keep a lot hidden, and not just the things I know I'm hiding.

Since telling the Kellys the truth, we've had a lot of talks like that. Getting-to-know-each-other talks. Even talks that show Mrs. Kelly has gotten to know me a lot better than I thought already. It's comforting, I suppose. All that time, I thought nobody was seeing me.

We're sitting on a blanket at the park. It's not the one with the swan boats. It's a different one, bigger, with lots of tall sturdy oak trees. It's very much like the countryside back home—all rolling and green, with birds chirping and squirrels zipping around. It's the perfect place to celebrate Mrs. Kelly's birthday.

I planned the whole thing myself. Can you believe it? It sounds grown up and modern, doesn't it, to plan a party for your foster mother? Well, it's not as fancy as it sounds—it's just the three of us. And the cake didn't turn out all that great. But still, it is something for a birthday. I hope I make it to mine.

And I reckon I am grown up, about as much as any thirteen-year-old could be. More than I want to be. I'm weaker every day—no more "spells"; it's constant now. I worry about this a lot; it bothers me even more than it used to. It hurts to want to live.

I've been back and forth to the doctors. I've told them everything aside from the color of my underwear . . . and what happened to Katie, and where, specifically, Dogwood is. That, I keep to myself.

But I've said everything I could about the poison, about what I've heard it's made of, when and how much of it I drank, how it's made me feel. The doctors just shake their heads. And I get sicker. They say it sounds so bizarre, but I get sicker, and they are no closer to figuring out a way to fix it.

I don't know what will happen. It's anybody's guess. But in the meantime I'm living. Not for Katie or some fool dream I had—like Gene in *A Separate Peace*—not for making things up to someone by living *for* them. I tried, I really did; I would still if I thought it would make a lick of difference. But now I know that all that time, I was lying to my heart. That I can't make things up.

So I've got to live for *myself* now, hard as that is in its own way. It means, despite my guilt over Katie—despite all the sorrys I still say to her over and over in my head and all the anger I still have at myself—wanting things for *myself.* Like Joe. I want Joe back.

He hasn't spoken to me since the last time I saw him. He won't take my telephone calls. He won't let me back into being his friend. But I'm going to try to show him how sorry I am. I'm going to be truly *here* with the Kellys till the end, and I'm going to try to count my blessings and push aside those things that drag my spirit down. I push aside the guilt and count my blessings.

And this is one.

Standing up from the picnic blanket, I lift up my knapsack and fling it over one shoulder.

"I'll be right back," I say. Mr. and Mrs. Kelly are seated in front of a spread of cookies, fried chicken (store-bought, of course), a half-collapsed cake, and lemonade. They look at me nervously for a second, but I grin at them and say it again. "I'll be right back."

Then I head to the corner of the park. A blue mailbox is standing there.

I pull my postcard out of my knapsack—the one with Boston on the front. I press my thumb against the stamp to make sure it's secure. And I reread what I've written, next to the address, on the back.

Dear Mama, Daddy, Theo, Teresa, Marie,
    I want you to know I am okay. I want you to know that
    I love you. I am not lost. I am still your Glory Bee.

I drop the card through the slot in the post box. Then I turn back into the park. And let the breeze lift my hair, up, up, and up.

Read

FORGET ME NOT

the final installment in Glory's gripping drama . . .

It's been nearly a year since Glory was cast out of Dogwood, sent away from her family and the only home she's ever known. With the deadly poison running through her veins, she never thought she would make it this far. But through sheer determination—and devotion to the memory of her best friend Katie—she has somehow found the strength to persevere.

But now her time is running out, and there's one last thing that she needs to do. Somehow, she's got to get back to Dogwood. She's got to make sure that once gone, she won't be forgotten.